THE CHURCH
AND
CONTEMPORARY COSMOLOGY

THE CHURCH
and
CONTEMPORARY COSMOLOGY

Proceedings of a consultation of the
Presbyterian Church (U.S.A.)

Edited by
James B. Miller
Kenneth E. McCall

Carnegie Mellon University Press

Pittsburgh 1990

Library of Congress Catalog Card Number: 89-81311
ISBN 0-88748-101-9 (pbk.)
Copyright © 1990 by the Presbyterian Church, U.S.A.
Printed and bound in the United States of America
First Edition

The drawing by J. Mirachi on page 382 appeared in *The New Yorker*,
15 April 1972. It is being used with the permission of The New Yorker,
Inc.

This volume is dedicated
to the people of Mackinac Presbytery
whose vision outreached their understanding and
whose faithfulness in the midst of uncertainty
has initiated a renewal of the church
and
to the memory of Harold Nebelsick
whose scholarship, spirit of inquiry, academic courage and
commitment to the Reformed faith in the contemporary world
has helped the church understand its mission in a cosmic
context.

PREFACE

In December of 1981 the Presbytery of Mackinac adopted an Overture to the 194th General Assembly of the Presbyterian Church, U.S.A., calling upon it "to initiate a study of the role of cosmology in the Bible and in the traditional doctrinal formulations of the church, the changes in cosmology as the result of the rise of science, and the theological significance of contemporary cosmological positions for traditional doctrinal affirmations." The Assembly referred this Overture to its Advisory Council on Church and Society charging it "to develop a process for initiating such a study and for communicating its contents to the church."

In response the Advisory Council formed the Task Force on Theology and Cosmology in 1983. The primary members of the Task Force were Rev. Kenneth E. McCall, chairman, McCormick Theological Seminary; Rev. Dr. Ian Barbour, Carlton College; Dr. Eric Juengst, Department of Medical Ethics, Pennsylvania State University Medical School; Rev. Dr. James B. Miller, United Campus Ministry of Pittsburgh; Rev. Dr. Harold Nebelsick, Louisville Theological Seminary; and the Rev. Dr. Robert J. Russell, Center for Theology and the Natural Sciences, Graduate Theological Union, Berkeley. Also participating in the Task Force were Dr. Dean Fowler, Marquette University, and Prof. Edward Daub, University of Wisconsin-Madison.

The Task Force sought to fulfill its charge through a variety of initiatives. [See Appendix I: "Final Task Force Report"] It culminated its work by calling a "Consultation on the Church and Contemporary Cosmology" in which the papers in this volume were the focus of discussion. The papers represented the views of their authors and not that of the Presbyterian Church, U.S.A. However, their purpose was to stimulate discussion among the participants and they served this purpose well.

The participants in the consultation were Presbyterians representing a variety of constituencies within the church: scientists, engineers, other church members, local ministers, judicatory staff, theologians, seminary faculty, church-related college faculty, campus ministers. This gathering helped to begin a long term process within the Presbyterian community to once again take seriously the theological relevance and significance of the understanding of nature developed by means of contemporary science.

The editors wish to express their graditude to the participants in the consultation for their lively and energizing response to the issues presented in the following papers, to the former Advisory Council on Church and Society (especially Dean Lewis, its executive director) for permitting the Task Force to engage in a free ranging inquiry, to the Ministry Unit on Theology and Worship of the Presbyterian Church which is carrying on this effort, to Eleanor Crossley who helped manage the organizing of the Consultation and the preparation of its papers, and especially to the members of the Task Force on Theology and Cosmology whose collegiality in the face of diversity and whose commitment to the intellectual integrity of the church have helped make possible the religious renewal of which this volume is a signpost.

J.B.M.
K.E.McC.

CONTENTS

10

The Church and Contemporary Cosmology: Introduction

Kenneth E. McCall

McCormick Theological Seminary
Chicago, Illinois

We are living in a time when there is a wide ranging discussion concerning the rebirth of cosmology, the return to cosmology, the emergence of a new cosmology. This discussion has appeared not only in learned journals, but has been covered extensively in newspapers, magazines and television programs. But what is cosmology? To what are we returning and what is the nature of this new emerging cosmology? More particularly, why should the Christian church and Christian theology be concerned with such questions? That is the focus of the papers in this volume. They arise out of a deliberate effort to challenge the church and theologians to again see cosmology as a central issue for church life and thought.

George Hendry in his book, *Theology of Nature*, asserts that the meaning of God can be understood in three different contexts. They are the world as a whole, the history of salvation and the inner life. These three parameters of theology can be described as the cosmological, the political/historical and the psychological. It will be obvious that we are concerned in this volume with the cosmological, the world as a whole. While there are a variety of ways to formulate the theological question, Hendry suggests that it can be stated as "the place, meaning and purpose of the world of nature in the overall plan of God in creation and redemption."[1]

One of the first difficulties facing us is the simple fact that theology has focused its attention on the political/historical and the psychological parameters for a very long time. Hendry suggests that the cosmological context has been virtually ignored for the past two hundred years. Nature has been dropped from the agenda of theology.[2] So, if we are to grasp the theological significance of the new cosmological thinking in our time, we must first get it back on our agenda. In order to overcome the years of neglect, it will require a major effort to develop our abilities to think in new ways.

The physical and biological sciences, as would be expected, have had nature at the focus of their agenda and during the past two hundred years have developed a picture of the world, including ourselves, that is radically different from that of previous eras. It is not surprising that as theologians and church members confront the new cosmology, this new understanding of nature and the world as a whole, we feel ill-prepared to enter fully into the discussion about its implications. Scientists may have a similar experience as they find more and more the need to see their work in the context of political/historical and psychological parameters. While both the theological and the scientific communities may have much to gain from one another in the new dialogue about the world, the central focus in this volume is to take with utmost seriousness the knowledge gained by the physical and biological sciences in the last two centuries and to ask what meaning this knowledge has for the theological enterprise and for the life and work of the church.

What then is cosmology? For an initial definition, let us turn to that used by Douglas Knight in his paper on ancient Israelite cosmology. For Knight cosmology is a term that

designates a group's comprehensive view of reality and represents the effort to grasp the nature of the whole and thereby also the place of all the parts within it. What this 'reality' is thought to embrace determines for each cosmologist the method to be employed: theological, philosophical, scientific, humanistic. Issues in cosmology range from the origin and order of reality to its meaning and destiny.

Several things need to be said given this initial definition.

First, this volume is from the perspective of a very particular group, namely persons from the West, who are highly steeped in the Western scientific tradition and informed by Western Christianity. In another setting, less dominated by Western science and Western Christianity, a very different cosmological perspective would emerge.

Second, there are a set of methodological questions — theological, philosophical, and scientific — relevant to this discussion which have been the subject of considerable debate in recent decades. In fact these questions have often dominated the discussions of the relation between religion and science. A few of these questions are addressed in the following papers. For example, to what extent are the methodologies of science and theology distinct and separate, compatible or complementary. Much remains unresolved and in need of further discussion.

Yet, there is little question of the pervasive influence of the logical positivists which has led many in our culture to believe the claim that science — objective, impersonal, detached, ahistorical — provides the only reliable method leading to valid knowledge of the world and all that is real. The philosophical challenge to this claim has been growing in strength over the past several decades but the claim remains extremely influential in the present culture.

There is, however, also little doubt that the rise of cosmology as a science in the twentieth century has itself led us to raise the methodological questions we are now addressing. The new physical cosmology developed by science has provided a dramatic, breathtaking, and exciting perspective of the universe which is our home. We are now able to speak of a cosmic evolutionary history in a way that no generation before us could have imagined. We are now able to understand the evolution of the universe over time, and the various parts of it including ourselves, in a way not possible before the twentieth century. The universe has a history and we are a part of that history. History and nature as concepts can no longer be held apart from one another.

Third, philosophy like theology, has not had nature central to its agenda. From the Middle Ages onward, theology, philosophy and science, once allies in shaping a coherent cosmology, grew far apart. But philosophy too is awakening to a need for new dialogue, due in part to extensive work in the philosophy of science. Epistemological, ontological, and even metaphysical questions are emerging again with new force. The dualistic world view is dying. We have begun to sense that there is a common thread that binds all — human, animal, plant, galaxy — in a structure of reality whose detailed form we cannot yet fully grasp or describe. There is a growing recognition of the close kinship between subject and object, between living and non-living matter than we have acknowledged in our recent past. In our culture we are beginning to explore new ways to describe our knowledge such that the whole of our experience can be comprehended thus moving us beyond the claim that all authentic knowledge is limited to physical laws governing the inanimate parts of nature.

Finally, it should be noted that the questions addressed by cosmology, "from the origin and order of reality to its meaning and destiny," are very old yet ever new questions. Robert Wagoner and Donald Goldsmith observe that

> not surprisingly, cosmology is one of the oldest of human intellectual endeavors; it responds to the same questions that led to the development of religion and philosophy. It is a response to such questions as where have we come from and what is our fate? What role do we play in the universe? The search for meaning in our existence is linked to the quest to understand the nature of the cosmos.[3]

What appears clear is that theology, philosophy and scientific cosmology share a common set of questions and a long history of collaborative effort at responding to these questions. However, what is not clear is whether such a collaborative enterprise is possible in the late twentieth century.

There is now a science of cosmology which is focused on the universe as a whole. It is described as all encompassing because it deals with the structure and evolution of the universe and by implication all aspects of the cosmos. Knowledge of the universe comes to us as the result of an investigation of the detailed properties of nature through such particular sciences as physics, chemistry and biology. From this knowledge alone, it is argued by some, we can arrive at a comprehensive picture of the universe including ourselves.

Some of the papers in this volume challenge the notion that a purely scientific cosmology is adequate to create a comprehensive world view. Is it not possible and necessary, they will ask, that theology and philosophy have contributions to make to the formation of a comprehensive world view, to a new cosmology? There is not agreement among all the parties as the the answer to this question. And even among those who give affirmation to it, there is no absolute agreement as to the path which can lead us in a positive direction. Yet, the following observation by Ernan McMullin, a philosopher of science and Roman Catholic priest, provide both words of caution and of encouragement.

> The Christian cannot separate his science from his theology as though they were in principle incapable of interrelation. On the other hand, he has learned to distrust the simpler pathways from one to the other. He has to aim at some sort of coherence on world-view, a coherence to which science and theology, and indeed many other sorts of human constructions like history, politics and literature must contribute. He may, indeed, must strive to make his theology and his cosmology consonant in the contribution they make to the world-view."[4]

So, we arrive at a notion of cosmology in the largest sense described by James Miller in his paper as

> the broad world view which orients our culture. It is those understandings of the world as a whole that inform the language, practices and institutions of a culture. It is the cosmic sense of place, of orientation, which individuals absorb tacitly by simply growing up in a particular culture.

We in the church live precisely at a point of transition in which our own orientation in and tacit understanding of the cosmos is passing, and yet we are not fully aware of the change that is taking place around us and within us. We can, so to speak, taste it and feel it but still cannot determine what it is we are facing.

This current volume is intended to help the church and indeed demand of us that we think about the theological and moral questions and concerns that are raised when we begin to consider what the cosmos is like in a contemporary framework. While it is certainly not necessary to read the papers in this volume in the order in which they appear, it may, however, be useful to know that this particular order is that of their presentation in the consultation for which they were prepared. As such it is the way which the planners of the consultation thought would be fruitful to proceed in addressing the growing wealth of thinking that is available on this subject. Here then is a brief guide to help you select your own path through the remainder of this volume.

The opening paper, by Eric Chaisson, responds to the general question: What is cosmology. He offers a provocative cosmological perspective, focused on his notion of "cosmic evolution," as a new guiding cultural paradigm. It is at once scientific and religious.

The next two papers deal directly with the Bible. Douglas Knight gives us a careful look at ancient Israelite cosmology as a multifaceted phenomenon and suggests that it may yet contain insights which we might want to appropriate for ourselves. Ulrich Mauser illustrates how the concept of "heaven" partakes of elements of an ancient cosmology while retaining its purpose as a theological concept.

Since cosmological reflection has a long history in Western culture, James Miller provides a summary of the development of a succession of cosmological perspectives using the historical typology of pre-modern, modern and post-modern to guide us. Langdon Gilkey offers a critical review of some specific contemporary cosmologies. He suggests that none of the scientists who have proposed these seem conscious of the philosophical problems surrounding them and concludes that science, philosophy and theology need to be seen as three interlocking but distinct forms of inquiry.

The next four papers address four areas of current physical and biological science. Joseph Silk writes of the present state of physical (large-scale) cosmology, concluding that an understanding of galaxy clusters, the formation of galaxies, of stars, of planets is now well within our grasp. In his discussion of some problems of quantum physics James Maher was able to give insight into issues concerning the state of our current knowledge of physical law. He cautions the religious community not to tie its theology too closely to the science of any one generation even the current one. Philip Spieth articulates the present understanding of evolutionary biology, reminding us that we should neither ignore nor overemphasize the biological facts of human behavior. He affirms that the insights to the human of both biology and theology are needed. The new biotechnology is described by Stephen Phillips. He points out that it will have a profound effect on humanity and urges a dialogue among persons from the religious, philosophical and scientific communities on the possibilities provided by this powerful combination of science and technology.

There then follow three theological reflections. The late Harold Nebelsick brings a rich understanding of the twentieth century dialogue between science and theology and reviews some of the historical and substantive aspects of that dialogue. Robert Russell is very skilled in helping us see how contemporary physics and cosmology raise profound theological questions that urgently require our attention. He seeks constructively to address the Doctrine of Creation and the question of how we understand God's action in the world. The implications of contemporary biology for theological thought are considered by Benjamin Reist. He shows that the new dynamic cosmic context which evolutionary biology has helped reveal is the one within which the biblical witness and our confessional traditions must function.

Ian Barbour then offers a summary of the preceding papers using an historical and cultural framework which can help us more generally understand the current opportunities for dialogue between science and theology. He is especially skilled at showing how the authors reflect identifiable perspectives within that framework.

The remaining five papers attempt to show some of the implications of the new cosmological perspective for personal faith and Christian ethics. Ron Cole-Turner wrestles with the question of how we are to be whole persons, living with intellectual integrity and holding a deep personal Christian faith in the face of contemporary cosmology. Current ethical questions surrounding procreation and reproduction are discussed by Abigail Adams in light of what she describes as the techno-centered world view of our culture. Garret Hardin discusses the ethical dilemmas which arise as we struggle with the allocation of scarce resources and challenges us to make difficult choices in an ecologically interdependent world. Carl Mitcham reminds us of the technological character of much contemporary natural science and argues that the tradition of Christian asceticism may be needed to delimit science and technology in the name of higher goods. Finally, Robert Short offers a Calvinist challenge to the uncritical moral confidence engendered by science and technology in the power of human-centered reason and freedom.

The excitement, enthusiasm and commitment of the presenters (as well as the participants) in the consultation who have made this volume possible are evidence of the urgency of the task before us. I believe that the words of Robert

Russell provide a way for us to sense what lies ahead and where we in the Western Christian tradition are called to go.

We are called to rethink and reaffirm our tradition in the context of revolutionary discoveries about the universe, the evolution of life and the nature and destiny of humankind. We cannot ignore science if we are to have any significant voice regarding today's staggering ethical challenges in technology, ecology and human need. We cannot ignore science if we are to make intelligible and compelling once again the story of a man and a cross and eternal life that continues to be offered through that gift to an age in which miracles seem impossible, metaphysics seem meaningless, religion seems irrational, and science offers the sure path to knowledge. The task of theology is to serve the church in faithfully thinking through, without hesitation, everything we affirm in the Sacraments, in liturgy, in Word, in prayer, and in deed. The promise is that our understanding of God's infinite mercy and work in the universe will be enriched a hundredfold, and our joy reborn on the wings of a cosmic vision and setting unparalleled in former times.

Notes

1. George Hendry, *Theology of Nature* (:,), p. 22f.
2. *Ibid.*, p. 11.
3. Robert Wagoner and Donald Goldsmith, *Cosmic Horizons* (San Francisco: W.H. Freeman, 1982), p. 1.
4. Ernan McMullin, ",," in Arthur Peacocke, ed., *Science and Theology in the Twentieth Century* (Notre Dame:Notre Dame University Press,), p. 52.

Our Cosmic Heritage*

Eric J. Chaisson

Space Telescope Science Institute
Johns Hopkins University
Baltimore, Maryland

Abstract

My conclusions are threefold: The subject of cosmic evolution is my religion. The process of change itself (especially developmental change) is my God.   And thirdly, global ethics and a planetary culture, which cosmic evolution mandates, are the key to the survival of technologically competent life forms—here on Earth and perhaps anywhere else in the Universe.

I. Introduction

I am an astrophysicist, which means that I have been trained in physics and that I have adopted the Universe as my laboratory. I feel fortunate to be a space scientist at this stage in human history, for I imagine that when our great-grandchildren gain perspective on the last portion of the twentieth century, they will likely conclude that we now share a golden age of astrophysics. I say this because the number and diversity of discoveries currently being made are— shall I risk it? —astronomical. In particular, we are currently exploring all the remaining parts of the electromagnetic spectrum, thereby granting us some early glimpses of invisible radiation, including radio, infrared, and ultraviolet waves, as well as X and gamma rays. In hardly more than a single generation — not the generation of our parents and not that of our children, but *our* generation — astronomers are now revealing the invisible cosmos much as Galileo first sampled magnified light from visible astronomical objects. The result is unsurpassed intellectual excitement concerning the nature of the Universe as well as of our role in it.

At the same time, I suggest that future historians will probably judge that we also now share a golden age of biochemistry. The rapid pace and penetrating insight of novel breakthroughs in the biological sciences in many ways equal the impressiveness of those of the physical sciences. The unraveling of life's

*A similar article under the same title appears in *ZYGON: Journal of Science and Religion*, Vol. 23, December 1988, pp. 469-479.

code and the advent of genetic engineering, to cite but a couple of advances, herald a renewed vigor within the biochemical community.

Actually, I am doubly fortunate, for in my research and teaching, I have contributed to each of the interdisciplines of astrophysics and biochemistry, and, furthermore, I have recently been attempting to synthesize these two subjects into an even grander transdiscipline that I call cosmic evolution. Simply defined, cosmic evolution is the study of change through time. More specifically, cosmic evolution is the study of the many varied changes in the assembly and composition of energy, matter, and life in the Universe.

Now I realize that a considerable fraction of the world's populace, most notably in the United States, can become emotional, even irate, and occasionally convulsive at mention of the word "evolution." But let me assure even this distinguished audience that evolution implies neither dogmatism nor atheism. Evolution is hardly more than a fancy word for change—especially developmental change. Indeed, it seems that change is the hallmark for the origin, development, and maintenance of all things in the Universe, animate or inanimate. Change has, over the course of all time and throughout all space, brought forth, successfully and successively, galaxies, stars, planets, and life. Thus, we give this process of universal change a more elegant name—cosmic evolution, which for me includes all aspects of evolution: particulate, galactic, stellar, elemental, planetary, chemical, biological, and cultural.

Broadly conceived in this way, cosmic evolution is not confined to those changes within and among astronomical objects. Rather, it encompasses all change, on every spatial and temporal domain—large and small, near and far, past and future. As such, the familiar subject of biological evolution becomes just one subset of a broader evolutionary scheme encompassing much more than mere life on Earth.

Nor is cosmic evolution in my view an attempt to extend the Darwinian principle of natural selection to realms beyond life forms. Rather, it is the search for—let me say pretentiously, perhaps arrogantly—some principle that transcends Darwinian selection; a search for a physical law that conceives, orders, and maintains all structure in the Universe, in short a search for a principle of cosmic selection.

For me, cosmic evolution is an attempt to build a cosmology in which life plays an integral role. It is an attempt to frame a heritage—a cosmic heritage—a sweeping structure of understanding based on events of the past (for as we look out in space we probe back in time), an intellectual road map identified and embraced by humans of the present, indeed a virtual blueprint for survival if adopted by our descendants of the future.

In effect, (though I again acknowledge its implied arrogance, yet it's the most succinct description I can currently offer), with cosmic evolution as the core, we are trying to create a new philosophy—a scientific philosophy. And I hasten to emphasize the adjective "scientific," for, unlike classical philosophy, observation and experimentation are vital features of this new effort. To be sure, I wholeheartedly subscribe to the notion that neither thought alone nor belief alone will ever make the unknown known. Cosmic evolution is designed to address the fundamental and age-old questions that philosophers and theologians have traditionally asked, but to do so using the scientific method and especially the instruments of state-of-the-art technology.

Indeed, the same technology that threatens to doom us now stands ready to probe meaningfully some of the most basic issues: Who are we? Where did we come from? How did everything around us, on Earth and in the heavens, originate? What is the source of order, form, and structure characterizing all things material? How did (and does) order emerge from chaos in light of the second law of thermodynamics which dictates that the Universe becomes increasingly randomized and disordered? Of ultimate import, armed with a renewed and quantified perception of change, physicists now seem poised to explain the origin of the primal energy at creation itself, and thus to tackle the fundamentally fundamental query, to wit, Why is there something rather than nothing?

II. Broadest View of the Biggest Picture

Consider the arrow of time—the archetypical illustration of cosmic evolution. Regardless of its shape or orientation, such an arrow represents an intellectual road map of the sequence of events that have changed systems from simplicity to complexity, from inorganic to organic, from chaos to order. That sequence, as determined from a substantial body of post-Renaissance observations, is galaxies first, then stars, planets, and eventually life forms. In particular, though I seek not to make any grand allusions to time-honored systems of western thought, I have often maintained that we can identify seven major construction phases in the history of the Universe. They are particulate evolution, galactic evolution, stellar, planetary, biochemical, cultural, and future evolution. As such, the modern subject of biological evolution—neo-Darwinism—is just one segment (albeit an important one) of a much broader evolutionary scheme stretching across all of space and all of time. In short, what Darwin once did for plants and animals, cosmic evolution does for all things. And if Darwinism created a veritable revolution in understanding by helping to free us from the anthropocentric belief that humans basically differ from other life forms on our planet, then cosmic evolution is destined to extend that intellectual revolution by in turn releasing us from regarding matter on

Earth and in our bodies any differently from that in the stars and galaxies beyond.

I dare say that we can now trace a thread of understanding linking the evolution of primal energy into elementary particles, the evolution of those particles into atoms, in turn of those atoms into galaxies and stars, the evolution of stars into heavy elements, the evolution of those elements into the molecular building blocks of life, of those molecules into life itself, of advanced life forms into intelligence, and of intelligent life into the cultured and technological civilization that we now share.

By most accounts, the Universe began with the explosion of something hot and dense—hotter than the tens of millions of degrees Celsius in the cores of most stars, denser than the trillions of grams per cubic centimeter in the nucleus of any atom. Precisely what that "something" was, we cannot currently say with much certainty. Perhaps nothing more than a bolt of energy. Or perhaps nothing at all, if some of the latest physics harbors any measure of truth. And why that something exploded, we really don't know. The origin itself resembles the "Here there be dragons" school of ancient cartography. Still, people persist in asking, "What happened before the bang? Frustrated, I often resort to Saint Augustine who long ago reportedly mused, "Before the Universe began, hell was being created for people who worry about such issues."

With time's passage, the Universe changed rapidly. Of foremost importance, it cooled and thinned. Sometime between the first few minutes and the first million years—the nature of the physical process was gradual—the elementary particles of matter became clustered. Electrical forces bound the particles into atoms; the weakened energy could no longer break them apart. In effect, matter had gained some leverage over the previously dominating energy. I regard this change from energy-dominance to matter-dominance as the first of two preeminent events in the history of the Universe.

Once the so-called Matter Era had successfully emerged from what was previously the Energy Era, matter effectively controlled radiation. And, it has dominated radiation ever since, successively forming galaxies, stars, planets, and life. But advanced life is special, and that's not an anthropocentric statement.

We can legitimately reason that technologically competent life differs fundamentally from lower forms of life and from other types of matter scattered throughout the cosmos. We are different because we have learned to tinker not only with matter but also with evolution. Whereas previously the gene (strands of DNA) and the environment (be it stellar, planetary, geological, or cultural) governed evolution, we humans on planet Earth are rather suddenly gaining control of both these agents of change. We are now tampering with matter, diminishing our planet's resources, while constructing the trappings of utility and comfort. And we now stand at the verge of manipulating life itself, potentially altering the genetic makeup of human beings. The physicist unleashes the forces of nature; the biologist experiments with the structure of genes; the psychologist influences behavior with drugs. We are, in fact, forcing a change in the way things change.

The emergence of technologically intelligent life, on Earth and perhaps elsewhere, heralds a whole new era—a Life Era. Why? Because technology, for all its pitfalls, enables life to begin to control matter, such as matter evolved to control radiative energy more than ten billion years ago. As such, matter is now losing its total dominance, at least at those isolated residences of technical competence. This change, from matter-dominance to life-dominance, I claim is the second of two preeminent events in the history of the Universe.

III. A Sense of Ethics

Humanity now stands on an astronomically significant threshold. We have come nearly full cycle. With that remarkable cluster of star-stuff embodied in the human brain, we have become smart enough to reflect back upon the material contents that gave life to us. Life now contemplates life. It contemplates matter. It probes our origin and our destiny. It explores the planetary system we call home. It searches for extraterrestrial life. It quests for new knowledge. But—and oh, this is a big but—shall we survive beyond the dawn of the Life Era? Is there some tool, institution, or attitude to help guide us along the way?

A central point of my essay, indeed an integral part of my personal credo, happens to be the most important implication for the Life Era. It is this: As the dominant species on planet Earth, we must now develop—evolve, if you will, and quickly too—a global culture. We need to identify and embrace a form of planetary ethics that will guide our attitude and behavior toward what is best for all humankind. In short, humans must begin to acknowledge that we are first and foremost citizens of a planet, only secondarily members of nationally sovereign countries with ever-changing boundaries. It is essential that we broaden our outlook in all respects.

Ethics. My dictionary asserts, among other definitions, that ethics means "conduct recognized in respect to a particular class of human actions or a particular group, culture, etc." Formerly the nearly exclusive purview of philosophy and religion, a viable ethic for today's world is in my view no longer provided by either of these venerable institutions. Lest I be misunderstood, in the next few paragraphs I shall attempt to clarify my criticisms of philosophy and religion *as a source of modern ethics*. And lest someone think my panacea is science, I shall also include science in my brief polemic, for it too, alone, will not likely provide the ethics I feel we need to seek.

Recognize that my concern is worldly, earthly. Whereas ethical values have, for the most part, been historically limited in scope (like unquestioned loyalty to some tribe) or even regionally widespread and more sophisticated (like those introduced into human affairs by Christ), today's set of ethics, like the global problems they must check, need to be of a more planetary, even universal, nature. We must redefine ethics to denote "conduct *collectively* recognized with respect to all classes of human actions comprising our *global* culture" (my amended definition), and we must strive to make those ethics a practical reality by simultaneously casting them both broadly enough to apply to Homo sapiens in toto and flexibly enough to incorporate the process of change itself. Appropriately, the heart of the required ethics is change and adaptability, not a set of rigid, immutable rules.

At the risk of alienating a number of good friends, consider philosophy for a moment. Once the symbol and guardian of ethics in human society, philosophy has in my view forfeited the influential position it held throughout much of human endeavor. Mostly dated, abstract, anthropocentric, and astonishingly specialized, traditional philosophy has seemingly lost its compass in providing aims and objectives for human society, which in our day and age is both multinational and technological. Regrettably, the great synthesizer is virtually extinct, the legacy and philosophy *of approach* left by Socrates, Plato and Aristotle, among others, rather thoroughly squandered. Even if we could look to philosophy for worldly guidance, which of the many competing systems of thought should we espouse to the exclusion of all others— rationalism or spiritualism, existentialism or *élan vital*, or even a revival of essentialism, among legions of other philosophies proposed throughout history? In a related vein, which politico-economic doctrine might be most compatible with a global ethics—capitalism, communism, or perhaps a return to theocratic rule, likewise among numerous governmental systems?

As for religion, I deplore its fragmentation. Though we surely now live in a pluralistic society, what are we to make of the fact that our civilization is ministered to by some ten thousand different faiths, each with its own set of beliefs, dogmas, and often insistence that theirs is the "one true faith." How can the institution of religion, given its surprising lack of worldly cohesiveness, guide today's society toward what will surely need to be a coherent framework of understanding for the good of all peoples? And while I welcome diversity and pluralism among humanity, how can we possibly base a planetary outlook regarding any principle, let alone one as subtle as ethics, on even a major theology, whether Buddhism, Catholicism, Hinduism, Islam, Judaism, Protestantism, or Unitarianism? As with the dilemmas just expressed regarding choices of philosophical and ideological systems, I perceive no way to decide which set of beliefs could realistically become the effectively official global religion without inviting active hostility among the thousands of competing faiths not so chosen. Note that I am not claiming such a choice to be difficult, rather that it is unproductive, given religious proclivity to grant dogma precedent over reason. Who among today's eccelesiastics takes the larger view, addressing the present and future and not just the past, while advocating unification that might provide a holistic sense of global well-being? Who among them speaks for planet Earth, as materialistic as that may sound?

Nor will science alone (and even less likely in conjunction with its practical by-product, technology) provide the kind of ethics required to attain the Life Era. Here I mean broader societal ethics, not the highly regarded and remarkable scientific ethics that keep fraudulent science to an absolute minimum. Despite the moral concerns of some scientists and professional societies—witness the 1975 Asilomar conference of biologists questioning the proprieties of genetic engineering, and the moral distress expressed by many physicists associated with the development of the atomic bomb—the great majority of my colleagues are unaware, or at most mindful but inclined toward benign neglect, of the socioethical implications of their work. (Even at Asilomar, the debate concerned public health consequences, not the larger ethical and moral issues, of research in recombinant DNA technology.) Though we seldom admit it, our excessive specialization makes us astonishingly myopic, blinding us to the wider cultural impact of our research—at least while working at the height of our careers. Later in life and often in retirement, when scientists are usually dismissed as "no longer active" or even potentially senile, many of science's most eminent scholars begin examining the broader consequences of their work. Regrettably, often only when their influence has eroded by a sort of career entropy do they discover that some of their earlier research carried global implications. Is it possible that the duties and responsibilities, normally coupled one-for-one in the legal profession with every right and privilege, have not comparably grown in the last decades with the rapid expansion in basic scientific research? Should we not awaken our attention to a formal code of socioethics among scientists as a sort of *quid pro quo* for the right to freedom of research?

All this is by way of encapsulating how in my view neither philosophy nor religion alone, alas not science alone either, is likely able to generate a compelling set of global ethics required to aid humankind at our current turning point. Granted, each of these institutions might think they do, but my claim is that none of them individually can be counted on to provide an ethical standard needed for the human species to endure rapid, global, often self-induced change in our politico-economic and especially technological environments. The twentieth-century philosophical writer, Will Durant, well articulated our growing predicament: "We suffocate with uncoordinated facts; our minds are overwhelmed with sciences breeding and multiplying into specialistic chaos for want of synthetic thought and a unifying philosophy."

If not to one of these established institutions, then where do we turn for guidance, for survivability, at least for a sense of hope? The answer in my view is that we should look to an amalgam of these three, provided we can identify a common denominator or underlying unity to which each of these three institutions can subscribe. Fortunately, we do know of a unifying pattern pervading all; that common basis is evolution. Affecting everything in the Universe, from galaxies to snowflakes, from stars and planets to every aspect of life itself, evolution—developmental change—pertains to all objects, societies, civilizations, and institutions. In particular, the concept of evolution, invented by philosophy and now fully embraced by science, is acceptable to all but the most fundamentalist religions. Its broad approval is why an appreciation and understanding of evolution in its most awesome sense—cosmic evolution, a scientific philosophy capable of applying the tools of technology to the time-honored questions first posed by philosophers and theologians— can provide a map for the future of humanity.

For those who would promptly balk at this proposed synthesis, seeking instead to preserve the status quo by resorting to traditional institutions, let me say this. In my mind, all philosophy and religion seek a static truth—a one true dogma on which everyone can converge. But modern science has now (re)discovered such a fixed reality and bolstered it with observational evidence; it is the process of change itself. In an intriguing apposition of terms befitting the age-old ideas of Heraclitus, change has a genuinely static presence in the Universe. What's more, in the new non-equilibrium thermodynamics, change is the root of all organized stability. Once we have adjusted our thinking to accept this permanence of change, we can proceed, if need be, to change that change in ways that lead to beneficial evolution rather than devolution, entropy, and extinction. Of great import, the process of change and the "big thinking" that cosmic evolution represents can form the essence of an intellectual vehicle needed to develop, indeed to evolve, a worldly set of ethics.

As noted earlier, the seventh great construction phase of the Universe I often label "future evolution." I now tell my students that if our species is to survive to enjoy a future, then we must make synonymous the words "future" and "ethical," thus terming our next grand evolutionary epoch, "ethical evolution."

The Universe does conform, not to a grand design, but to the chancy dictates of evolution, including, presumably, the developmental advances required for technologically intelligent life forms to survive. After all, since we have recently become agents of change on Earth, we must now begin playing an *active* role in the process of evolution. And I maintain that that active role must begin with a collectively recognized set of ethics or principles suited to the preservation of all humankind. Furthermore, like the evolutionary changes that, in turn, originated and developed particles, galaxies, stars, planets, biochemicals, lives, and cultures, transition toward the next step of globally conscious life forms is a universal phenomenon. All technological beings, on any planet, must evolve a planetary ethic, lest they be unprepared to endure the by-products of technoculture. In fact, implicit within our cosmic evolutionary paradigm is a transcendance of the Darwinian principle of cosmic selection: Those technological civilizations (of any type on any planet) that recognize the need for, develop in time, and fully embrace a global (even a galactic, and then a cosmic) ethics will survive, and those that do not will not.

Of course, the possibility always exists that no species on any planet, ourselves included, will be sufficiently intelligent and especially wise to take the next evolutionary leap forward. Though I prefer to think otherwise, the Universe could conceivably be regulated by a natural (or even supernatural) "cosmic principle of self-destruction" dictating that all development abruptly stops roughly within a few decades to a century beyond the time when each civilization begins encountering world-wide problems; if so, then we on Earth have come within this principle's purview only during roughly the last decade. More than just a statement of ordinary biological extinction (for here destruction is self-induced), such a principle could naturally derive from a drive toward complexity that effectively runs out of control. The rate of change might itself change so rapidly that not even technologically intelligent life could keep pace with its accelerating onslaught of global troubles, the result being that eventually all civilizations commit the ultimate devolutionary change—termination. Less of an anthropocentric statement than it initially might seem, this supposed principle of destruction would ostensibly apply to every planet, thus alleging that no one progresses much beyond our level of expertise. According to those who subscribe to it (strangely enough, mostly biologists, aside from the habitually negative sociologists), the Universe remains matter dominated everywhere and forevermore, making no appreciable advance beyond the dawn of the Life Era.

By contrast, there are those, myself included, who prefer to opine that some civilizations—though not necessarily ours on Earth—could become smart enough quickly enough to welcome the needed ethics sufficiently to persist beyond our current level of technological expertise. Though I know nothing of the sociology of galactic aliens, my thesis here is that the way *for us* to wisen rapidly is to adopt cosmic evolution as the guiding paradigm and nouveau scientific philosophy for our time. Mine is a positive view, a synthesizing posture, and, I judge, a realistic attitude despite the onslaught of apocalyptic issues now confronting us on Earth—a vision that decidedly rejects the cosmic principle of self-destruction just noted, to be sure one that offers a more confident, enduring, or at least optimistic prognosis. To employ cosmic evolution as an intellectual as well as practical guide toward the Life Era is to think in dynamic rather than static terms, to forge a link between natural science and human history, to realize the evolutionary roots of human values, to renew a sense of hope.

IV. Summary

I suggest that cosmic evolution is a powerful synthesis to use as perspective—a grand ethos of potentially unprecedented intellectual magnitude—while approaching an uncertain future. Looking backward, we sense that its central feature—the time-honored concept of change—can account for the appearance of matter from the primal energy of the Universe, and in turn for the emergence of life from that matter. Change further seems capable of describing the act of creation itself, thus scientifically accounting for the origin of all energy at the alpha-point of space and time.

But are we Earthlings to survive to learn more about ourselves, our planet, our Universe? Looking forward, shall we achieve some astronomical destiny? Just how wise, quite aside from sheer intelligence, are we? Put bluntly and not insignificantly: From the study of cosmic evolution may well emerge a sense of "big thinking" and with it the global ethics and planetary citizenship needed if our species is to have a future. In the words of Kierkegaard, "Life can only be understood backwards, but it must be lived forwards." Tritely stated though no less true, our future will likely be a measure of our current wisdom.

Ancient Israelite Cosmology: Images and Evaluations*

Douglas A. Knight

Vanderbilt University
Nashville, Tennessee

Among the most severe and inescapable obstacles that the modern world can encounter in the biblical tradition is its cosmology. To be sure, this is not a hindrance to many persons, who, whether for reasons of fundamentalist faith or sheer disinterest in contemporary science, resolutely envision themselves in a three-storied universe shared with deity and demons alike. Even three decades of space-travel or repeated discovery of early fossils and human or pre-human remains have not been sufficient to shake such views for many. But this phenomenon is an exception, however widespread, and has its own etiology and significance, just as does the effort by some religionists to make science legitimate their creationist arguments. Somewhat different are the incidental residues of ancient, pre-scientific cosmologies. Scientists and laity alike are often heard to employ conventions that locate God in space ("up in heaven") and in human categories of time. Is this "merely" a problem of language, of finding expedient forms for communicating ideas?

What is important for us in the present context is the radical and probably irreconcilable disparity between the ancient and the modern cosmological conceptions—a problem which actually cuts both ways. Like many others in what are considered by anthropologists to be "primitive" (i.e., pre-scientific and pre-industrialized) cultures, the biblical people could not have comprehended theories of biological evolution, the relativity of space and time, laws of thermodynamics, or the issue of causality and determinism. Nor could they have fully appreciated what is known now about the immensity of space or the minuteness of the atom. Furthermore, they would not have been inclined to accept many of the perceptions about human nature that are common fare among modern scholars and the general public. Ancient Israel's laws and customs reflect little awareness of the social rootedness of a person's character, the individual's psychological makeup and motivations, the arbitrariness of political systems, the comparable developments among a wide range of cultures, and the intricacies of modern philosophical and theological thought.

*This essay was written in Tübingen during my 1987-88 sabbatical leave supported by grants from the National Endowment for the Humanities and the Vanderbilt University Research Council. To both and also to the organizers of the Consultation on the Church and Contemporary Cosmology I wish to express my appreciation.

Today the world and all life within it are seen to be vastly more complex and much less susceptible to facile comprehension than was previously possible.

The watershed for modern sensibilities in the West was the Enlightenment and the Industrial Revolution of the seventeenth and eighteenth centuries. By elevating reason and science to a position of supreme importance as a means for understanding and developing the world in which humans live, these movements introduced fundamental changes to our self-awareness and our ability to use our environment, and probably nothing short of a nuclear winter could return civilization to the previous epoch. But do the advances in modern science and thought imply that we today are "superior" to pre-Enlightenment and pre-industrial individuals? Cultural chauvinism, as prevalent as it is among most peoples, tends to result in self-deception and arrogance, characteristics that are as unbecoming as they are interfering to human enterprises. The human mind, as anthropologist Claude Lévi-Strauss has pointedly described, must be considered equally adept in ancient (excluding pre-human and proto-human life forms) as in modern times: to solve the problem of how to fell a tree, both could invent an ax -- albeit out of different materials, from stone to highly tempered steel, depending on the accumulation of technological experience.[1]

The point is that the cosmology of a people such as the Israelites of three millennia ago is not to be dismissed out of hand even if it is directly contrary to or ignorant of much that the modern sciences have established. For it represents that culture's effort to understand the world in light of evidence available to them, and it has in fact attained the status of a classic vision with uncommon tenacity and influence throughout subsequent history. We need not share it, but we owe it the effort to understand it on its own terms as well as to interpret it in ours. Added to this humanistic agenda is the theological task for persons in the Judeo-Christian tradition to determine to what extent and in what categories the biblical version of the relationship between God and the world can yet be appropriated. A common tendency in this regard—holding to a modern world view while at the same time making extensive use of biblical language and images—can lead to no little confusion.[2]

A word about the definition of cosmology is in order. The term designates a group's comprehensive view of reality and represents the effort to grasp the nature of the whole and thereby also the place of all parts within it. What this "reality" is thought to embrace determines for each cosmologist the method to be employed: theological, philosophical, scientific, humanistic. Issues in cosmology range from the origin and order of reality to its meaning and destiny. To recover the cosmology of a given culture, such as ancient Israel's, one must be guided in large part by the perspectives that prevail there. For the Hebrews, reality included the non-physical world as much as the physical, and the relationship between these assumed fundamental importance.

They regarded the spheres of social and religious life as a central part of this, and consequently cosmology should have immediate implications for ethics: "the powerfully coercive 'ought' is felt to grow out of a comprehensive factual 'is'."[3] Since the Israelites did not set out to develop a cosmological view per se, we must extrapolate it from a variety of sources and suggestive images— ever mindful of the anthropologist's caveat: "primitive cosmologies cannot rightly be pinned out for display like exotic lepidoptera, without distortion to the nature of a primitive culture."[4] In the discussion that follows, we will begin with a rather straightforward description of the cosmos according to ancient viewpoints, after which we will enumerate some of the main images used to speak of this cosmos. At the conclusion is a paradigm that may be helpful for modern appropriation of the biblical cosmology.

I. The Cosmos

There is no specific, all-embracing term in Hebrew comparable to cosmos or universe. In order to speak inclusively of all reality the Hebrew Bible employs various phrases such as: "the heavens and the earth" (Genesis 1:1; 2:4; over seventy-five instances in the book of Psalms); "the heavens and earth and sea," often with an added comment such as "and all that is within them" (Exodus 20:11; Psalms 69:34; 146:6); or "heaven above, earth beneath, and the waters under the earth" (Deuteronomy 5:8). Another simpler yet less descriptive way is the common word "all" or "everything" or "the entirety" (kōl, often with the definite article; Jeremiah 10:16; Isaiah 44:24; Ecclesiastes 3:1; Psalm 103:19; Sirach 36:1). One other terminological feature, which is evident in the Hebrew text but rarely in translations, is that a few of the words for prominent parts of the universe occur normally without a definite article, as if they were proper names: tēbēl for the earth's surface -- "Terra Firma" (e.g., 1 Samuel 2:8; 2 Samuel 22:16); tĕhôm for the waters of the abyss -- "Deep" (e.g., Genesis 1:2; Exodus 15:6; Job 38:16); and šĕ'ôl for the underworld --"She'ol" (e.g., Genesis 37:35; 1 Samuel 2:6; Proverbs 9:18), similar to Hades in Greek. There is good reason to suspect that such usage betrays both a mythic background for Israel's conceptions and perhaps also ongoing popular beliefs as well.

The Israelites of the biblical period had a relatively uniform view of what they would consider the physical universe, and it was a conception that was shared widely throughout the ancient Near East, to be sure with some variety in descriptions and implications.[5] Evidences of it date back to Sumerian culture ca. 3000 B.C.E., but it is especially articulated in the old Babylonian creation myth, the Enuma Elish, stemming from the early part of the second millennium B.C.E.[6] In the Hebrew Bible one finds cosmological references above all in Genesis 1; Psalms 104, 74, 148, 33; Job 38-41; and in numerous other passages and allusions.

The universe, to the Hebrew mind, is a closed entity, consisting of three tiers but with multiple parts at each level. The earth is a flat disk and ends all around with either mountains or sea. Certainly this must have been the area we know as the Middle East, including the Fertile Crescent and the large desert areas, but not much beyond this. While there were sea-faring peoples such as the Phoenicians, for Israelites the sea represents the border of the earth, beyond which one would not venture. The mountains support the firmament, a transparent, massive dome stretching over the entire world, i.e., the dry land, the fresh water lakes, and the sea coasts. This firmament (Hebrew *rāqîa'*, meaning a plate beaten or hammered out, also used for a thin metal overlay) is not just the arch of heaven but also serves the function of holding back the waters above the earth, which give the sky its blue color. The earth is thus surrounded by primeval waters, above and below. There are sluices or "windows" in the firmament through which water from the upper layer can be let down to the earth in the form of rain and storm. Under the firmament are all of the heavenly bodies, the sun, moon, and stars. These are not necessarily considered to be the source of all light, for the creation account indicates that they are created after the light is, which distinguishes day from night (Genesis 1:3-5, 14-19). The earth itself is supported from below by pillars sunk into the lower waters, and fresh water lakes and rivers share the surface with dry land. There is a variant picture of this in Job 26:7—the earth hung over the void like a cloth suspended in mid-air (see also the reference to the "skirts of the earth" in Job 38:13). Down in the heart of the earth is She'ol, the underworld and the abode of the dead, to which every grave and burial cave give access. God dwells in the heavens with a vantage point over the entire world and can from there go to the earth or even to She'ol (Psalm 139:8). It did not seem to occur to the ancient Israelites to question the extent of this cosmos, to wonder how far the waters of the abyss or of the upper regions might reach, to speculate about the base on which the pillars of the earth could be anchored, to explore the regions beyond the mountains or over the seas, to consider time outside of "known" history, or to pose other such questions that their cosmological conception might naturally raise for us. Their world was encompassed by that which they observed, experienced, and could on this basis imagine. It was a world ordered and sustained by their God.

It may be of interest to look briefly at the Babylonian Enuma Elish to see how the cosmological picture just described could be given mythic form at a distance from biblical Israel of 1000 kilometers and 1000 years. For the ancient Babylonians, their experience of reality was so effectively expressed in this myth that the account was recited and reenacted each year in their New Year's festival, thereby ensuring that the divinely ordained status quo would continue. The gods and goddesses, more than mere characters in the story, are representations of various aspects of the cosmos. Water plays a chief role, as it does at the beginning of Genesis 1 and in other biblical cosmological texts. At the very origin exist only the male Apsu, the fresh water, and his consort Tiamat, the salt water. From their commingling emerges a generation of gods, not yet assigned their respective domains. When these younger gods cause so much noise that they provoke Apsu into plotting to destroy them, the gods are paralyzed with fear until the "all-wise" Ea manages to overcome and kill Apsu. Thus supplanting Apsu, Ea becomes the god of both arable land and fresh water, the liveable part of the earth separated from the salt water, and he immediately begets Marduk. Tiamat responds by preparing for a mighty battle to destroy the gods who have slain her mate. This time the battle against the ominous parental "ground of being" is led by Marduk, the subsequent founder and patron deity of Babylon itself.[7] After he has vanquished Tiamat, he divides her body into two parts, one half becoming the waters above and the other the waters below. The rest of the cosmos is delineated and regulated, with gods and goddesses stationed all around, altogether three hundred in the heavens and three hundred on the earth: sky, stars, sun, moon, storm and wind, and the like. Humans are then brought into existence at the instigation of Marduk but through the work of Ea. They are made from the blood of Kingu, Tiamat's companion in battle, and they are created primarily to relieve the gods of labor and to supply sacrifices of food and sweet aromas.

It is apparent that these two cosmological conceptions, the one culled from various Israelite texts and the other from the much earlier Babylonian myth, have striking similarities. In both there is preexistent chaotic matter, out of which an ordered cosmos finally emerges—not by chance but through the actions of deity. In both it is the divine world which establishes the mundane sphere and which maintains control over it. In both the universe is comprised of comparable components, most distinctive perhaps being the division of the waters and the vault of heaven.[8] Yet the differences are not less notable: For Israel the principle of a primeval chaos is minor, and *tĕhôm* is virtually impotent in the face of the absolute sovereignty of their God. Indeed, the Israelite world is one which derives from God and which gives evidence of the divine nature, but it is not identical with God nor embodies God in the ways in which the Babylonian deities are held equal to sky, star, storms, or whatever else they represent in the cosmos. Perhaps the most significant difference concerns the view of humanity. In Israelite thought the human race is not put on the earth merely as an afterthought, born out of a punitive act and destined to be servile to the gods, but is rather a crowning point of creation, with a status just below God's. Human autonomy, the source of repeated conflict throughout biblical history, is deliberately modified by the charge to be responsible to one another and to the world. Whatever the cosmologies throughout the ancient Near East might have in common with respect to the layout of the physical and divine spheres—and there is considerable that is shared—the theological evaluations are not thereby also identical.[9]

II. The Cosmos Imaged

To articulate a cosmological conception, one typically needs to draw on images and categories from everyday life. No less in the distant past than today, one moves from the known to the unknown, utilizing metaphors suggestive of the phenomena and realities that elude our full knowledge but not our imagination and intuition. In the historical recovery of Israelite cosmology, these images hold special signficance because of their status as native categories, the linguistic means chosen by the Israelites to express themselves, often in poetic form. While they could not avail themselves of scientific terms, their own symbols were sufficient to their task. With the images they could also indicate connections perceived between spheres of reality, from cosmic to mundane. Because of the dominant role of religion in Israelite life and thought, many of these images are expressed in terms of God's character and actions, and we should be prepared to understand these as statements also about the universe which God creates and superintends. The Hebrews did not distinguish neatly between sacred and profane, as is the modern tendency, and for them any phenomenon could have potentially cosmic significance. There is, to my knowledge, no comprehensive treatment of the range of Israel's cosmological images. In the following we must content ourselves with developing a taxonomy and supplying some examples and representative biblical references.

1.   **Nature Images.** Cosmological images selected from nature point beyond themselves to indicate the theophanic power of God, the orderliness of the universe, or the mystery of the world. The **mountain**, widely associated with deities throughout the ancient world, is imbued with cosmic significance in Israel also.[10]   Mount Sinai or Horeb is where God is revealed, the laws governing human behavior and religious cult are given, and the covenant is sealed (Exodus 19ff.). The sacred Mount Zion, Jerusalem, where God dwells (Isaiah 8:18) and "built his sanctuary like the high heavens" (Psalm 78:69), symbolizes divine presence and protection for the people (Psalms 48; 125). The **sea**, like the waters in the cosmogonic myths, is conquered by God when it is divided for the Israelites to make their exodus from Egypt (Isaiah 51:10; Exodus 14:21-19). The chaos-monsters living in the sea, Leviathan and Rahab, are mere playthings for God (Job 41; Psalm 104:25-26) or have been slain (Psalm 74:13-14; Isaiah 51:9). The **heavenly bodies** "rule over" the day or night (Genesis 1:14-18; Psalm 136:7-9), marking the course of time and the directions on the earth. The sun proceeds through its circuit like a runner (Psalm 19:5) or a horse-drawn chariot (2 Kings 23:11). The moon, together with the sun a symbol of permanence (Psalm 72:5; 89:36-37), figures prominently as the indicator of months and cultic festivals and as an eschatological sign, e.g. that it will turn to blood (Joel 2:31). The stars, used for signifying a number beyond

fathoming (Genesis 15:5), are studied (note the reference to eleven stars, probably animal constellations, in Genesis 37:9), although in orthodox religion astrology is rejected (Jeremiah 10:2). All of these heavenly bodies are felt to have some influence over humans (Job 38:33; Psalm 121:6; Judges 5:20; Malachi 4:2), yet they are subservient to divine power and purpose (Joshua 10:12-14; Isaiah 13:10; Amos 8:9; cf. also their bowing down to Joseph in his dream, Genesis 37:9).

Each of these images—and others with cosmic significance could be added (e.g., clouds, wind, rain and storms, lightning)—was deified in many of the neighboring cultures. Israelites at various junctures seemed inclined to follow suit, despite efforts by orthodox Yahwism to desacralize and de-mythologize the natural world around them. The appeal of fertility worship, especially in its Canaanite dress, consisted in its claims to guarantee the life-giving character of the earth and the womb, and polytheistic religion in general could offer its adherents additional opportunities to control their fate. The problem for Israel's faith was to acknowledge the world as good but not holy, as a source for life but not ultimately a controllable or manipulatable one, as a sphere distinct from humans and yet one in which all persons must act responsibly or reap the consequences. This was accomplished by emphasizing God's creative authorship of the world and the sustaining or devastating power that God continues to have over all that exists.

A series of other images also serves this purpose by highlighting the wonder and mystery of the world. They are especially to be found in the proverbs, which probably had a wide currency throughout the populace. The **animal world** provides the ancients, as it does often for us as well, with some of the best examples. Too remarkable to understand are the flight of an eagle and the movement of a snake (Proverbs 30:19). With "wisdom" the ants store up food for the winter, the badgers make their homes in rocks, the locusts march in rank, and the tiny lizard manages to live in kings' palaces (30:24-28). The lion, the cock, and the goat stride with arrogance and disdain (30:29-31). The stork, turtledove, and other birds instinctively know the time to migrate (Jeremiah 8:7). Wildlife give birth, roam the land, display their might, spread their wings and fly (Job 39). Samson's riddle is a paradox of lion and bee (Judges 14), and both Balaam's ass (Numbers 22:28-30) and Eve's serpent (Genesis 3:1-5) know enough to argue persuasively. Peace between natural enemies (wolf and lamb, lion and calf, bear and cow, asp and child—Isaiah 11:6-9) signals the new age yet to come.

2. Anthropological Images. The biblical literature, as is the case with most other religious traditions, makes extensive use of anthropomorphisms to speak of God, and many of these have cosmological implications as well. Yet it is not only the deity but the cosmos itself that is explicitly envisioned with human characteristics. The Hebrew word for **navel**, *ṭabbûr*, is used one time (Ezekiel 38:12) to identify Jerusalem as the center of the earth, the power omphalos image which is applied in other civilizations to Delphi, Rome, and elsewhere.[11] Commonality between humanity and the animal world is most often observed by calling both **flesh** (Hebrew *bāśār*), which at death returns to the dust of the earth from which it originally comes (Job 34:14-15). The underworld can open wide like the **mouth** (Isaiah 5:14) with ravenous appetite. The wind is frequently called by the same word (*rûaḥ*) that designates human **breath**, just as it is used to describe the vital power stemming from God. The **heart**, representing for the Israelites not so much the seat of emotions as the hidden-most recesses of thought and will, is an image for the fathomless seas (Ezekiel 27:25-27; Jonah 2:3). Hebrew anthropology does not envision a **person** as a being divided within itself, not even with a separation between body and soul. The entire being is alive, united into a whole and depending vitally on all its parts. There is no direct parallel drawn between this characteristic of a human being and the ecological whole of the universe, but the comparison may be implicit when the body parts are used as images. Nature is poetically imaged as expressing **emotions** in human fashion: the heavens, mountains, and forests sing for joy, the depths of the earth shout, nature claps its hands, groans in pain, trembles and quakes in fear (Isaiah 44:23; Jeremiah 51:48; Judges 5:4-5). **Birth** can be pictured as a coming forth from the depths of the earth (Psalm 139:15), from the womb of the Terra Mater, and this applies not only to humans but to all other forms of plant and animal life as well (Genesis 1:12, 20, 24). The image is present also in Job's statement: "Naked I came from my mother's womb, and naked shall I return"—to the earth, is clearly intended in both cases (Job 1:21). **Death** is accounted for in Genesis 3 as being the result of human rebellion, but the Hebrew Bible continues at many junctures to struggle to understand it, especially the problem of undeserved or premature death. In an attempt to lessen its threat, the normal maturing processes in nature are introduced as a comparison (Job 5:26), yet other aspects of nature—that a seemingly dead tree stump can, unlike humans, spring back to life if its nutrients are present, or that a solid rock can be irreversibly eroded by the power of water (Job 14:7-19; see also Ecclesiastes 3:18-22)—have the opposite effect of removing hope and comfort for the people.

3.   Domestic Images. The fundamentally **patriarchal nature** of the Israelite family seems to be reflected in some of the hierarchical structure perceived in the universe, particularly with respect to the relation of the divine to the human sphere. God takes Israel as his bride (Jeremiah 2:2) and keeps her even though Israel is repeatedly unfaithful (Hosea 1-3; Jeremiah 3:20; Ezekiel 16). As a father does, God provides for (Psalm 78:23-29; Jeremiah 3:19) and protects (Psalm 146:9) his children and redeems his kin (Isaiah 43:14). Like a **mother**, God clothes (Genesis 3:21) and yearns for the wayward child (Jeremiah 31:20).[12] Means for **economic livelihood** also become images of cosmic activity: pottery to symbolize the molding of humans (Genesis 2:7; Isaiah 45:9) and nations (Jeremiah 18:1-10; Isaiah 29:16; 64:8), as well as human frailty (Lamentations 4:2); agriculture to indicate the rich provisions of the earth (Genesis 2:8-9, 15), the orderliness of the world (Isaiah 28:23-29), and the utter dependence of the world on life-giving water (Jeremiah 14:2-6); shepherding to emphasize the need for proper care and protection against external threats (Psalm 23; Ezekiel 34).

4. Political Images. The organization of the community into political entities supplies further images for interpreting the cosmos. The **tribal structure** of the early period is based somewhat on a cooperative economic principle, and this may correlate to the conception of cosmic order and justice believed to be established and maintained by God. The advent of the **monarchy** fosters more of a hierarchical projection, symbolized especially by the image of God as king, "at whose wrath the earth quakes" (Jeremiah 10:10; also see Psalms 96-99). The idea of a heavenly cortege (Isaiah 6) and counsel (Isaiah 40:13), known also among Israel's neighbors, is another example of the power of the divine realm. Dominion within the cosmos figures prominently at various points, especially in Genesis 1-2 where the sun and moon are established to rule the day and night and humanity is given charge over all fish, birds, and animals (see also Psalm 8:5-8). It should be observed, however, that, since rulership according to the royal ideology of the ancient Near East is not to be conducted oppressively or despotically but with justice and compassion, the character of this dominion is defined as something quite other than the arbitrary and exploitative exercise of authority (Deuteronomy 17:14-20; 2 Samuel 12:1-14). A final political image to mention here is the **military**, a common source for cosmological as well as theological language. Just as God can be pictured as the divine warrior (Exodus 15:3; Isaiah 42:13), so can earthquakes, solar and lunar eclipses, and wastelands parallel the destruction brought by war (Joel 2:3, 10-11; Jeremiah 4:23-28). In the apocalyptic vision of the end of this age, war spreads throughout the cosmos as good and evil do violent battle for supremacy and order (see, e.g., the War Scroll from Qumran).

5. Ethnic Images. The Israelites' sense of identify plays a major role in biblical traditions, and this figures into their cosmological thinking insofar as they are concerned to understand their own place as a people in the vastness of all other life. The backdrop is set in the etiological story of the Tower of Babel, the concluding episode in the primeval history in Genesis 1-11. Here the people of the world, with one single **language** in common, seek presumptuously to build a tower, like the Mesopotamian ziggurats, that would bring them to the upper level of the universe and secure for them divine-like stature.[13]   In judgment against this desire, God "confuses" (Hebrew *balal*, a pun for *babel*) their speech, thereby creating the multiplicity of languages and nations scattered over the earth. Out of this vast array of people comes the **election** of Israel, a theme which runs like a scarlet thread through much of the Hebrew Bible. The bountifulness of the land ("flowing with milk and honey," e.g. Exodus 3:17; similarly Jeremiah 2:6-7) is a sign of God's blessing. Yet there are expectations that accompany this favored status, and when ethnocentrism or massive injustice divert Israel from its responsibilities, the prophets can point to the relativity of this election (Amos 9:7; Ezekiel 20:9) and call on the mountains ("the enduring foundations of the earth", Micah 6:2) to serve as witnesses against the people. The sustaining image is that of **Zion**, the city of Jerusalem, situated at the center of the nations (Ezekiel 5:5), the holy mountain which God will defend against all onslaught and to which in the new age all other nations will stream (Isaiah 2:1-4).

6. Architectural Images. These are especially rich in biblical descriptions of the cosmos, and they indicate well how cosmological conceptions tend to be projected from what is familiar to the people. The **tent** is a model for the firmament (Psalm 104:2; 19:4). The **windows** of heaven let down the rain (Genesis 7:11-12), and **doors** hold back the seas from flooding the earth (Job 38:8-11). **Beams** are laid out above (Psalm 104:3) to support the upper level, as is done in two-story houses. The cosmological discourse in Job 38, replete with architectural images, argues that only God could have constructed on this scale: laying the **foundation** of the earth, setting its **cornerstone**, erecting the **gates** to the underworld, determining the **dwelling place** for the light and the darkness, and providing **storehouses** for the snow and hail (also the wind, Psalm 135:7). Equally effective is the cosmogonic account in Genesis 1, in which God, like a cosmic architect, constructs the entire universe according to a deliberate plan and with constant oversight.

7. Separation Images. To speak of the cosmos involves also making clear distinctions between things that are not merely unlike but may in fact be polar opposites. At one level myths seem often to treat binary pairs that are insolubly paradoxical, such as life/death, man/woman, water/land, good/evil, divine/human.[14] The motif of separation within the **physical world** is prominent in the cosmogony of Genesis 1: light from darkness, the waters above from the waters below, the seas from the dry land, the sun from the moon, and species from species. In Genesis 2 **male** and **female** are distinguished from each other, and in the following chapter the humans learn the difference between **good** and **evil** and thus become separated radically from God. When a notion of evil or impropriety guides such separation images, a structure for avoiding or devaluing the threatening phenomena emerges. Such is probably at work in the above category of ethnic images, whereby an ingroup/outgroup dichotomy can result in the denigration of the other. But it is especially evident in Israel's **purity laws**. Certain species—such as camel, badger, hare, swine, sea-life without fins and scales, various carnivorous birds, lizards, most insects—are strictly taboo for eating (Leviticus 11; Deuteronomy 14:3-20). Sexuality, so powerful and enigmatic to the people, involves times and acts that are considered unclean: a woman's menstruation (Leviticus 15:19-24) or giving birth (Leviticus 12:1-8), a man's seminal emission (Leviticus 15:16-18), intercourse prior to a holy war (1 Samuel 21:4-5). Leprosy or other severe skin diseases are perceived to be especially threatening among human illnesses (Leviticus 13-14), but other blemishes are serious as well (Leviticus 21:17-23). Also touching a corpse, non-life, renders a person unclean until a ritual of purification has been accomplished (Numbers 19:11-22; Leviticus 11:32-35; 39-40). In all these respects parts of reality are in some way held to be anomalous or unnatural, and consequently they appear as dangerous pollutants that must be avoided or, if that is impossible, countered by a ritual or a waiting period.[15]

8.   Time Images. Finally, cosmological understandings are also articulated by means of time expressions used by the people. The definition of a **temporal structure** of days and weeks is attributed to the work of God in Genesis 1:1-2:4, according to which each stage of creative activity is concluded by marking a new day. This, for the priestly authors of the text, is one of the many indications of the orderliness of the world (see also Psalms 74:16-17 and 104:16 concerning the cycle of seasons). The word **day**, in addition to designating a 24-hour period, can represent a substantial length of time, as in formulaic expressions such as "forty days and forty nights" (Genesis 7:12), the "days" of a person's life (Job 14:1), or a "day" of prosperity or adversity (Ecclesiastes 7:14). Temporal relativity at this point is evident when it is stated that "a thousand years in God's sight are like yesterday when it is past" (Psalm 90:4). Other words for time as normally measured in human categories, such as month and year, serve comparably as images for both special periods and cosmic time. The **sabbath** can be a picture for a fallow year, a time in which the land needs to rest and restore itself (Leviticus 25:2-7). A word used seldom in the Hebrew Bible, *ḥeled* can designate both the **human life span** in certain texts (Psalms 39:5; 89:47; Job 11:17) and at other points the world itself (Psalm 49:1; 17:14). A definite and appropriate **rhythm** to life in the world is perceived in the well-known text: "For everything there is a season, and a time for every matter under heaven: a time to be born, and a time to die; a time to plant and a time to pluck up what is planted;...a time for war, and a time for peace" (Ecclesiastes 3:1-8). Interestingly, the Israelites do not seem to have a notion of eternity or infinity but rather of **immeasurable time** (Hebrew *'ôlām*), a period stretching longer than humans can comprehend but not necessarily without end. This can refer to the remotest past (as in Psalm 93:2 regarding God) or to the most distant future (as in Genesis 3:22, that humans are not to live "forever"). In a striking text, Ecclesiastes maintains that God "has put remotest time (*'ôlām*, often misleadingly translated 'eternity') into the human mind, yet so that one cannot find out what God has done from the beginning to the end" (3:11). As inclined as people are to look into the distant past and future, this effort is in the final analysis thwarted, a point reinforced in Job 38-41 when God reminds Job that he was not present at the creation of the earth and therefore cannot understand the nature of all existence.

Perhaps along similar lines, the Israelites, especially in the apocalyptic literature late in their history, seem to sense a congruence between **primal** and **final time** -- that the world as it was at the beginning corresponds to what it will become at the end of time. Not the pre-creation chaos but the world as created by God though still not violated by human misdeeds is the image of the *Urzeit*, and this will be recovered in the apocalyptic *Endzeit*. Elsewhere in the Hebrew Bible are traces of the image of a **new creation**, almost a *creatio continua*, with God acting as the agent who again and again recreates, reforms, restores: "Remember not the former things, nor consider the things of old. For I am making something new; now it springs forth, do you not perceive it?" (Isaiah 43:18-19; see also Job 39 on the continual maintenance of creation).

These eight areas of cosmological images represent the Israelites' efforts to comment on reality observed or imagined. Lacking scientific means for probing the nature of the world, they were no less curious than people today about its workings and its meaning. That they tended to see virtually everything *sub specie divinitatis* is only to be expected, given the predominant role of religion in their world view. Yet as we have seen, the typical Hebrew mode of expressing their cosmology draws directly on the everyday contexts of their life: nature, the human body, home life, political government, their self-identity as a people, their buildings, their experience of danger and pollution, and their sense of the passage of time. They moved easily among these spheres and from them to the cosmos, almost as if the whole of reality is woven of one fabric and can be described synecdochically in terms of its parts. From our perspective, these images assume supreme importance because they are the Israelites' own chosen means for expressing themselves cosmologically. They also can indicate the level of intimacy which the people could have with the world -- the immediacy of a participant observer.

III. The Cosmos Evaluated

The Israelites do not merely speak in images about the cosmos; just as important, or more so, is their evaluation of it. They can articulate this explicitly, or it can be implied in the images used. These evaluations fit into a three-fold scheme, which at the same time may constitute a paradigm with broader relevance for the question of how, if at all, modern persons can appropriate the cosmologies of the Bible.[16] As will be seen, this paradigm turns on issues of evil, order, and the meaning of life.

At the outset it should be noted that there is a fourth evaluation possible, but in my view it is not represented in the Hebrew Bible. According to this perspective, the universe is considered a benign whole, essentially untroubled and not conflictual within itself. Things steadily improve or at least thrive, and people live in harmony with each other and with nature. For the Hebrews, however, such an assessment of reality is unwarranted because of the prevalence of evil and disorder, of whatever origin. Consequently, their evaluations fall in three other categories.

1.   The Cosmos as Rational and Reliable.

Orthodox faith as represented in the Hebrew Bible espouses the view that God has created an orderly universe and seeks to maintain it as such.[17] The heavenly bodies continually perform their ordained functions, animal species reproduce and thrive in their respective spheres, time moves ahead according to set patterns, every action yields its necessary consequence, and the structures of human existence are, if properly conducted, conducive to the good life for all. This symmetry and fundamental integrity of the world are affirmed in the mythic creation account of Genesis 1, where God observes at the end of each day of creative activity that what has been made is "good." This word (Hebrew *ṭôb*) is more than merely a value assessment; it also indicates that everything functions well, is useful and suitable, is reliable. While this is the basic nature of the universe itself as God created it and wills it to continue, the evident rupture in the everyday state of things is laid directly at the feet of humanity. This could scarcely receive more vivid portrayal than in the story of the rebellion in the Garden of Eden (Genesis 3). Through their own doings, Adam and Eve—symbolic of all people throughout history—seek their own interests and thereby introduce alienation between themselves, between them and God, and between them and nature. The harmony among all beings is broken, and disorder spreads, as depicted in the hamartiological legends of Genesis 4-11: Cain and Abel, the flood, Noah's drunkenness, the Tower of Babel.

Yet according to this cosmological evaluation, the world has not thereby reverted to a pre-creation state of chaos. Principles of order still exist, even if humans repeatedly try to subvert them. A system of justice prevails, upheld by the "act/consequence scheme" according to which every action produces a necessary result: goodness yields blessing, while evil brings punishment.[18] Thus even with the disorder caused by humans, the cosmos retains its rationality and reliability. This evaluation was widely held throughout Israel's history. For priests, it signals the efficacy of ritual; for prophets, the necessity for ethical behavior; for leaders, their role in preserving social structures; for sages, the knowable regularity of the world; for commoners, the security of a manageable and humane context for life. In Douglas' words, "It is a complex world, dangerous for the rebel, good for the conformist."[19]

2. The Cosmos as Precarious and Unpredictable.

Experience can, of course, call the justness and reliability of the world into question. An infant mortality rate of over 50%, famine and plague striking indiscriminately, violence and exploitation by the strong—all such occurrences are bound to affect one's world view. Job's friends and others of similar inclination might facilely respond that, according to the act/consequence scheme, unpleasant effects must have been preceded by wrong actions, but this solution will not satisfy many persons. Thus is posed the issue of theodicy—how to reconcile belief in a good and powerful God with the experience of pain, injustice, and evil in this world.[20] Among the most compelling aspects of the Hebrew Bible is the repeated efforts found there to struggle frankly and relentlessly with this problem, and the outcome is generally not a simple acquiescence to the orthodox doctrine of a reliable cosmos. The many lament psalms (e.g., 6, 22, 74, 137), while expecting God to mend whatever wrong or pain exists, nonetheless presuppose that human existence is precarious and threatened from all sides. Royal subjects know that they are vulnerable to the whims of a despot (Uriah and Bathsheba, 2 Samuel 11; Naboth's vineyard, 1 Kings 21; cf. the law for the king, Deuteronomy 17:14-20). Even the prophet Jeremiah, who normally expects that the wicked will be punished and justice will win out, is at points pressed to the limits of endurance (e.g., 18:18-23; 20:7-18). Job's outcry against God's administration of the world is perhaps best known to us, and the response which he receives from God (chaps. 38-41) largely begs his question and instead affirms that God has things under control even though humans are incapable of comprehending the principles that govern the universe. Notably, however, Job is reprimanded for his arrogance but not for his complaint, while his friends are judged guilty of expounding incorrect doctrines about God (42:7-9). The book of Ecclesiastes takes this cosmological evaluation a step further by acknowledging that, despite our best efforts, we cannot learn the fundamental secrets of the universe or understand what befalls us and why. Ecclesiastes is no anti-intellectualist, but rather a chastened and weary sage who has long sought for the answers. His counsel is: "Go, eat your bread with enjoyment, and drink your wine with a merry heart; for God has already approved what you do" (9:7).

3. The Cosmos as Internally Conflictual and in Need of Radical Change.

The final cosmological evaluation found in the Hebrew Bible deviates decisively from the other two. No longer is the world viewed as reliable, a context in which justice can be expected to win out in the normal course of history. Nor is it enough to maintain that the inscrutable universe holds pain or pleasure for each person in an unpredictable and nonmanipulatable manner. Rather, the cosmos is essentially dualistic, torn between the forces of good and the powers of evil, and nothing short of total annihilation of evil can resolve the conflict. This evaluation developed late in Israel's history in response to the devastation of the sixth-century fall of Jerusalem and the subsequent, protracted domination by foreign powers—Babylonians, Persians, Hellenists, and finally Romans. Disempowered or deprived people, perceiving little chance for improving their own lot and becoming free from their oppressors, look beyond themselves to the very nature of all reality for the cause of their condition. This is the response of apocalypticism, a revelatory tradition which in the Hebrew Bible has its precursors in Isaiah 56-66, 24-27, and Zechariah 9-14 but is fully represented only in the book of Daniel and in various Jewish and Christian writings of the period from 200 B.C.E. to 200 C.E.[21] With heavenly visions and bizarre symbolisms, the apocalyptists portray the swelling of conflict between good and evil. As the battle breaks out, all of nature feels it and joins in the catastrophic upheaval. The outcome ushers in a new age and a transformed cosmos, reminiscent of God's primal creation. This evaluation, while eminently hopeful of the final results, lacks a similar appreciation for the present world, which is irrationally at odds within itself. In the face of this, people who are on the side of the good need to maintain their purity and prepare for the end. In the Hebrew Bible this final cosmological assessment plays a relatively minor role in comparison with the other two evaluations, although its importance rose considerably in later Jewish and Christian writings, including the New Testament.

* * * * * *

Cosmology for the ancient Israelites was thus a multifaceted phenomenon. The historian and exegete face severe obstacles in trying to recover it, above all because the Hebrew people were not intentional in developing a cosmology and presenting it clearly for others to examine. It did not exist for them as a systematic philosophy or dogma to which the individual Israelites would confess. This should not surprise us, but it means that their cosmology—if it is to be reconstructed—must be extrapolated from all available sources—not only their literary traditions but also any indications about their everyday life-world, their social structures, and their value systems. Differences evident in these areas throughout Israel's history are, it seems, reflected more in the way people spoke of the cosmos and evaluated it, not in the actual vision of the physical cosmos itself. It was uniformly agreed that we live in a three-storied universe of limited and circumscribed extent, in which the divine (and for especially the apocalyptists, also the evil) powers hold sway over the spheres of nature and humanity. As do people in all cultures, the Hebrews spoke of this world with images and categories flowing naturally from their everyday experiences. A congruence between the cosmos and the Israelites' own life was part of this projection: the universe constructed similar to their own buildings, systems of natural hierarchy parallel to their political world, ecological interdependencies not unlike their domestic and ethnic structures, cosmic features analogous to the human body, threats and pollutants corresponding to their experience of danger. Which gave rise to the other is an open question.

Of primary importance, though, is the point that cosmology results not simply from the state of people's knowledge but that it correlates directly to the terms of existence that they face on a regular basis.

This, in turn, leads to the varying evaluations of the universe. For those who count on justice and regularity, the world is rational and reliable. For others who are perplexed by the enigmas and sufferings that abound, it is precarious and unpredictable. And for yet others who perceive only insurmountable obstacles and persistent deprivation, the world is internally antagonistic and needs to be radically restructured. All of these evaluations are, to be sure, consistent with the people's basic view of the cosmos. Yet the assessments are, perhaps, transcendent of the culture in ways that the Hebrew cosmology itself is not. Persons of the modern age, regardless of the level of their scientific sensitivities, can find in their own world parallel grounds for feelings of confidence, pessimism, or powerlessness. For them the biblical traditions offer precedents worthy of careful reflection.

NOTES

1.   Claude Lévi-Strauss, *Structural Anthropology* (Garden City: Doubleday, Anchor, 1967), 227.

2.   Langdon Gilkey, "Cosmology, Ontology, and the Travail of Biblical Language," *Journal of Religion* 41 (1961) 194-205.

3.   Clifford Geertz, *The Interpretation of Cultures: Selected Essays* (New York: Basic Books, 1973), 126. These ethical implications of Israel's cosmology—in particular its cosmogony—are treated in some detail in my article, "Cosmogony and Order in the Hebrew Tradition," *Cosmogony and Ethical Order: New Studies in Comparative Ethics*, ed. Robin W. Lovin and Frank E. Reynolds (Chicago/London: The University of Chicago Press, 1985), 133-57. See other essays in the same volume for similar discussions of a wide range of cultural and religious systems.

4.   Mary Douglas, *Purity and Danger: An Analysis of Concepts of Pollution and Taboo* (London: Routledge & Kegan Paul, 1966), 91.

5.   See Walter Harrelson, "The Significance of Cosmology in the Ancient Near East," *Translating and Understanding the Old Testament: Essays in Honor of Herbert Gordon May*, ed. H. T. Frank and W. L. Reed (Nashville/New York: Abingdon Press, 1970), 237-52;   H. and H. A. Frankfort, John A. Wilson, Thorkild Jacobsen, William A. Irwin, *The Intellectual Adventure of Ancient Man: An Essay on Speculative Thought in the Ancient Near East* (Chicago: The University of Chicago Press, 1948).

6.   Translations of the myths are available in several collections, e.g., James B. Pritchard, ed., *Ancient Near Eastern Texts Relating to the Old*

Testament, 3rd ed. (Princeton: Princeton University Press, 1969); the Enuma Elish is found on pp. 60-72.

7.   Not surprisingly, the later Assyrian myth (first millennium B.C.E.) substitutes the Assyrians' own patron deity, Assur, for the hero Marduk. A parallel replacement had been effected by the Babylonians themselves, for the pre-Babylonian story of the third millennium B.C.E. apparently had Enlil of Nippur as the main character. Thus the cosmogonic myths attempt to attribute to the very nature of things the supreme importance of their respective cultures.

8.   It has long been observed that the Hebrew word *těhôm* (in Genesis 1:2 and elsewhere) -- "the deep" or "Deep" -- is strikingly reminiscent of Babylonian Tiamat, the waters of the abyss. However, etymologists now argue against a direct connection between the two words, which were instead perhaps derived independently from a common proto-Semitic root.

9.   See "Cosmogony and Order in the Hebrew Tradition," 137-43.

10.   See especially Frank Moore Cross, *Canaanite Myth and Hebrew Epic: Essays in the History of the Religion of Israel* (Cambridge: Harvard University Press, 1973), passim; and Richard J. Clifford, *The Cosmic Mountain in Canaan and the Old Testament* (Cambridge: Harvard University Press, 1972).

11.   The only other occurrence of *ṭabbûr* in the Hebrew Bible is in Judges 9:37, where it seems to refer to the center of the Israelite territory without the same religio-historical valance present in the Ezekiel text. The cosmological omphalos image, though without using the specific word for navel, is present also in Psalm 74:12 and Ezekiel 5:5.

12.   For a discussion of the female metaphor, see especially Phyllis Trible, *God and the Rhetoric of Sexuality* (Philadelphia: Fortress Press, 1978), 31-59; and Samuel Terrien, *Till the Heart Sings: A Biblical Theology of Manhood and Womanhood* (Philadelphia: Fortress Press, 1985), 51-70.

13.   Genesis 10, preserving what is certainly a different tradition about the spread of population, simply enumerates the offspring of Noah and the diverse nations and languages that stem from them.

14.   See Lévi-Strauss' classic essay, "The Structural Study of Myth," in *Structural Anthropology*, 202-27.

15.   See the important anthropological study by Douglas, *Purity and Danger*, especially pp. 41-57 on the abominations detailed in Leviticus.

16.   To compensate for the brevity of the following discussion, I refer to my article, "Cosmogony and Order in the Hebrew Tradition." This paradigm is not developed there, but the discussion of the ethical implications of Hebrew cosmogony covers in greater detail all three of these evaluative perspectives. In her *Natural Symbols: Explorations in Cosmology* (New York: Pantheon Books, new edition 1982), 103-6, Mary Douglas develops a typology for cosmologies based primarily on social structures and ideas of ritual, sin, and self. These types are somewhat related to the evaluative categories in this

paper, but the fact that I am not employing a strict sociological method has resulted in notable differences, particularly with respect to the evaluation of the universe as precarious and unpredictable but also regarding the social groups that are assigned to each.

17.   The importance of the Hebrew principle of order and its relation especially to Egyptian *ma'at* are developed by Hans Heinrich Schmid, *Gerechtigkeit als Weltordnung: Hintergrund und Geschichte des alttestamentlichen Gerechtigkeitsbegriffes* (Tübingen: J. C. B. Mohr [Paul Siebeck], 1968); also see his "Creation, Righteousness, and Salvation: 'Creation Theology' as the Broad Horizon of Biblical Theology," in *Creation in the Old Testament*, ed. Bernhard W. Anderson, Issues in Religion and Theology, 6 (Philadelphia: Fortress Press; London: SPCK, 1984), 102-17.

18.   See especially Klaus Koch, "Gibt es ein Vergeltungsdogma im Alten Testament?", reprinted in *Um das Prinzip der Vergeltung in Religion and Recht des Alten Testaments* (Darmstadt: Wissenschaftliche Buchgesellschaft, 1972), 130-80; translated and reprinted in part: "Is There a Doctrine of Retribution in the Old Testament?", in *Theodicy in the Old Testament*, ed. James L. Crenshaw, Issues in Religion and Theology, 4 (Philadelphia: Fortress Press; London: SPCK, 1983), 57-87.

19.   Douglas, *Natural Symbols*, 105.

20.   See discussions in Crenshaw, ed., *Theodicy in the Old Testament*.

21.   See, e.g., Paul D. Hanson,   *The Dawn of Apocalyptic: The Historical and Sociological Roots of Jewish Apocalyptic Eschatology*, 2nd ed. (Philadelphia: Fortress Press, 1979); and Christopher Rowland, *The Open Heaven: A Study of Apocalyptic in Judaism and Early Christianity*   (New York: Crossroad, 1982).

"Heaven" in the World View of the New Testament

Ulrich Mauser

Pittsburgh Theological Seminary
Pittsburgh, Pennsylvania

I

The renowned physicist Carl Friedrich von Weizsäcker has published a collection of 12 lectures entitled "The History of Nature".[1] The slender book provides a splendid and fascinating introduction to modern theories about the origin and growth of the universe, ending in two chapters describing the external and internal history of the human race. It seems significant that in this small volume the word "heaven" is hardly ever used. Von Weizsäcker has no aversion to the word "heaven". A chapter on the stars is announced to deal with "the history of the heavens"[2] but almost immediately, the author slips into the choice of a different word whose use dominates the book throughout: It is the word "space". The preference for the word "space" is significant because it is more appropriate to the objective reality of the universe which contemporary physicists explore. They are concerned with the measurable and calculable dimensions of time and space which provide the framework for our knowledge of the world. This knowledge is characterized by the enormity of dimensions, both in space and time, which express the modern scientific view of the world. The universe began some four or five billion years ago.[3] We find ourselves now on a small planet within one solar system, surrounded by an immense expanse of empty space in which a vast number of other solar systems, containing some one hundred billion luminous stars, combine to make up our galaxy which is in turn accompanied by some one hundred million extragalactic nebulae the most distant of which is approximately five hundred million light-years away from us. All nebulae are speeding away from us, the most distant ones with the greatest speed, causing the universe to expand constantly.[4] In spite of that, von Weizsacker considers the cosmos to be finite, allowing the hypothesis of the curvature of space to produce the image of the surface of an unimaginably gigantic ball whose radius might measure some three billion light-years. By far the greatest space in this immeasurable vastness is occupied by a black vacuum. Outside our solar system, p.e., there is empty space for a distance of more than

*This article was published earlier in *HORIZONS IN BIBLICAL\LITERATURE: An International Dialogue*, Vol. 9, No. 2, December 1987, pp. 31-51.

a thousand times the radius of the system itself, dotted only by some meteorites and gaseous atoms.[5]

One can understand, then, that for the modern physicist the concept of space naturally displaces the concept of heaven. The traditional image of heaven is derived from the visual impression of a high dome above our world, determined by the eye of the human observer whose standpoint provides the center around which the image is perceived. But for the scientist there is no above and no below in the universe, the geocentric and anthropocentric view is abandoned, and the appearance of the heaven's vault is given up in favor of empty spaces all around us of such staggering magnitude that they defy all imagination.

Leading modern physicists provide conflicting theories for the explanation of some of the most crucial questions about the history of the universe, and they make allowance for definite boundaries which are set to our knowledge.[6] In spite of that, it appears justified to speak of a world view of modern physics which determine the consciousness and thought of contemporary society. It is frequently compared with the "ancient world view" which people of antiquity had in common, down to the Copernican revolution, and which is said to be shared by all biblical writers in Old and New Testament times. This "ancient world view" is conceived as the three-story universe in which a flat, round earth is vaulted by a domed solid substance, the heaven or heavens, on which sun, moon and stars are fixed and which has openings through which the celestial waters can provide rain, while a region of the nether-world is placed below the earth. Contrasted to the image of cosmic history which the physicists of our time have developed, there is indeed an ancient world view whose presuppositions we can no longer share. Yet, some caution is in order in making this statement. I would like to make two observations which might give us pause to refrain from premature generalizations.

1.   The three-storied universe is for the ancients not simply a spatial reality. It is concomitantly the carrier of divine powers, and the heaven especially is at one and the same time the firmament in space and the home of many gods. The heaven is, therefore, not only spatially visualized as a firm substance above the world, but also full of divine life which holds sway over the world below. In many of the religions surrounding Israel and the emerging Christian community, the celestial bodies are identified directly with gods, in others they belong to the gods' primary tools of governance. Even in Greek philosophy down to the Stoic movement, heaven is at once the visible sky and the sign for a divine order.[7] Heaven is, to be sure, a place; but it is simultaneously a region of the gods whose lives make heaven what it is. It is not purely

an objective matter whose location can be fixed on a cosmic map, but, more importantly, the abode of gods who claim veneration of human subjects. These gods are associated with stories, they are worshipped in cults, and they are obeyed in societal laws which correspond to the heavenly origin of a cosmic order. It is arbitrary to separate the spatial aspect of heaven in the ancient world view from its existential aspect in which heaven communicates its authority and power over the world with human societies and individuals who live on earth.

2.   The concept of the three-storied universe underwent considerable modifications in the ancient world. The impact of philosophical, especially Platonic, ideas and of developments in ancient astronomy changed the older concepts in such a way that the earth was no longer conceived to be a disc swimming on the ocean overarched by a heaven not too distant from the earth. The earth was now seen to float freely in space, ringed by the spheres of the seven planets and an eighth sphere of the fixed stars. As a consequence, the cosmic space was extended greatly, the older concept of the nether-world was abandoned and its powers were now transplanted into some heavenly regions.[8] It is to be expected that older ideas about the nature and activity of divinities in heaven needed to be modified accordingly.[9] While it is not certain how early these modifications gained wide acceptance, it is sure that they had taken firm hold in the Hellenistic age and became spread abroad by Hellenistic culture. It is, therefore, unwise to postulate the universal validity of the "classic" three-story universe for an interpretation of the New Testament in all its parts. Rather we have to be prepared to encounter a variety of world views, and consequently different concepts of heaven, which have left their mark in the New Testament.

II

In the New Testament, the concept of heaven is by no means inflexibly fixed to a monolithic world view. The observations above concerning heaven as the abode of the gods, and the transformation of the image of the cosmos in the Hellenistic period, are partly shared and partly rejected or modified by New Testament authors whose conceptual starting points differ leading them to quite distinct conclusions about the place and the nature of heaven. Most importantly, they all have in common the uncompromising rejection of polytheism, and the exclusive association of heaven with a single and victorious God to whom all heavenly powers are strictly subservient. But this common orientation has not produced, among New Testament writers, a single view of heaven which could be asserted to be an element of a single view of the world.[10] At least two observations can clarify this claim.

1. New Testament books exhibit, in contrast to some Jewish and non-Jewish Hellenistic works, a striking disinterest in details of a concept of heaven which are essential to providing a world view. What we are given are fragments of a concept of the world, and it is possible that some New Testament authors might have affirmed more specific statements which they inherited from their tradition, especially from Jewish sources. But the fact remains that they felt no need to go beyond highly fragmentary sections of a world view to express what was to them essential about heaven. Jewish apocalyptic and rabbinical literature developed ideas about two, three, or seven heavens.[11] The notion is most fully described in 2 Enoch which tells of Enoch's journey through the seven heavens. In the account of the journey each heaven is described and its purpose explained. Paradise, in this text, is located in the third heaven (2 Enoch 8), while God dwells in or above the seventh heaven (2 Enoch 22). Some apocalypses place sun, moon, and stars in a specific heaven, and the distances between the heavens are stated in terms of the length of the journey traversed by the seer in going from one heaven to the next. It is quite evident in these apocalyptic writings how astronomical interests and theological motivations merge. The language is a curious mixture of symbolism and objectifying statements (numbers, distances, locations, purposes) which combine guardianship for the mystery of God with the quasi-scientific desire for objective knowledge.

A third heaven is mentioned in the New Testament also, and so is its association with paradise (2 Cor 12:2-3). Paul, in his defense against super-apostles, appears to relate in cryptic terms a vision of his own[12] which led him to the third heaven and to paradise in which he heard words which cannot be communicated in ordinary speech. It is safe to conclude, then, that Paul shared a world view which contained a certain number of heavens. But beyond this conclusion we are reduced to guesswork. Some scholars assume that Paul held an idea of the universe with three heavens,[13] while such experts as R. H. Charles and H. Bietenhard concluded on the basis of the similarity of 2 Cor 12:2-3 with 2 Enoch 8 that the apostle shared the view of seven heavens.[14] What is more: Paul insists that the words he heard in the vision are incommunicable in normal discourse. This emphasis negates the apocalypticists' tendency to be as explicit as possible in furnishing objective sentences about the heavens. It is undeniable that Paul had a world view with several heavens. But this view is put to the service of a statement which uses "heaven" as metaphor for a mystery so inaccessible and incomprehensible that it resists the reduction to objectifying speech.

2. For the New Testament, as for most of the Jewish and Hellenistic world, the heavens are filled with life: heavenly powers dictate the

course of the world, and it is not decided a priori whether they stand on the side of God or whether they represent forces hostile to God's will. In fact, the position of the powers of heaven in relation to God is seen differently by different New Testament writers, and this suggests substantial variations in their concept of heaven.

The seer of the book of Revelation tells of war in heaven (12:7) which sets the pattern for a war on earth (13:7) in which the conflict in heaven is mirrored. Even the risen Christ, in the image of the rider on the white horse, is said to engage in warfare (19:11) leading the "armies of heaven" (19:14) into a heavenly battle. In adoption of Apocalyptic patterns of thought,[15] Revelation understands the hardships and sufferings of a Christian community, harassed by false teaching and persecuted by governmental powers, as the reflex of a struggle in heaven in which the power of God and his Christ are assisted by a multitude of angels and archangels, resisted by Satan, his beasts, and his troops. The details of this picture of a celestial war cannot now detain us. It is enough to say that for this apocalyptic view in the New Testament, heaven is the battle field on which hostile powers are taking their position to decide the destiny of the world.[16]

At the opposite end of Revelation's concept of heaven is the Gospel of John. In this Gospel heaven is associated exclusively with God and with the mission of God's Logos in the world. The bread of life is the "bread from heaven" (6:32) which is none other than Christ, the bread of God which has come down from heaven (6:33). The Johannine Christ says of himself "I am the bread come down from heaven" (6:41, 50, 58). In the seemingly dualistic language of John, heaven belongs to the realm of light, truth, and life which is the sphere of God above a cosmos imprisoned in darkness, life and death. John's heaven is unaffected by the struggle with opposing powers: it is home and origin of God's saving will and act, permanently opened to the cosmos in the presence of Christ, the Logos of God (1:51).

Similar to the notion of conflict in heaven, but couched in terms reflecting a different world view, is the linkage in Ephesians of the heavens with powers in rebellion to God.[17] The heavens (*ta epourania*) are occupied by principalities and powers (3:10), together with the world rulers of this present darkness and the spirits of evil (6:12), as well as the prince of the power of the air (2:2). The spatial connotation of these heavens cannot be disputed. Christ descended (*katabaino*) from above into the lowest parts of the universe, the earth, and his ascension (*anabaino*) is a rising up in victory over heaven's hosts above all the heavens (4:8-10). There he is installed as co-regent with God whose throne, at the top of the heavens, he shares (1:20f.). The concept reflects a hellenistic origin in which many layers of heavens are concentrically placed above the world and whose lowest sphere is the zone of the air, probably reaching from the earth to the moon.[18] These heavens are the home of demonic powers who enslave humans by rivetting their fascination and attention to claims arising from the powers' capacity to let the universe appear as final divine authority, thus consigning the human captives to idolatry and death.[19]

In conclusion: the employment of the word "heaven" in the New Testament reveals considerable differences. The world views reflected in these differences cannot be harmonized one with the other. They are used as vehicles for assertions about the work of God which relativize and modify the importance of the world views by themselves.

III

Throughout the New Testament statements are made about heaven in concepts reflecting a variety of world views. But it is true, at the same time, that the New Testament, in speaking of heaven, is so captivated by attention to a set of events which have the power to give new content to the word that the linkage to a given world view becomes secondary. In turning to this aspect of the matter, the attempt will be made to synthesize in four steps the theological assertions made by the word "heaven" in the New Testament.

I.   **Heaven: The Parable of God.** With the entire ancient world around the Mediterranean, the New Testament uses the word "heaven (uranos) for the visible, solid vault over the earth, the firmament, but also for the space of air above the earth. Especially in sayings and traditions of Jesus, uranos is not infrequently employed in this sense. The birds flying in the air are the "birds of the air" (Matt 6:26), the uranos can be observed for signs of weather when its atmosphere turns red (Matt 16:2f.; similar Luke 12:56), the phrase "looking up to heaven" implies the gesture of prayer in which the head is turned upward toward the sky (Matt 14:19; Mark 6:41; Luke 9:16), and the heavens can be shaken because they are of firm material (Matt 24:29; Mark 13:25; Luke 21:26). There is an area of "mid-heaven" (Rev 8:13; 14:6, 19:17) clearly indicating the spatial nature of uranos.

As firmament, heaven is above the world and the human observer in the world. But the spatial connotation of "above" can turn, in any instant, to a metaphor meaning that which is hidden from ordinary human insight and, at the same time, in control of the world. The authority given to Pilate "from above"

(John 19:11) indicates the same origin as the authority "from heaven" with which John the baptist did his work (Matt 21:24f.; Mark 11:29f.; Luke 20:4); the heaven above is, in the context of the question of authority, the source which bestows upon a human being a singular power to lead and to govern.

Being high above the earth, heaven is removed from human inspection and knowledge. The physical limitation of the human eye to reach into the distant spheres of heaven is turned into the assertion that human perception cannot by its own power penetrate into the recesses of God's mystery. To become intelligible to the human being on earth, heaven's secrets must be disclosed; using a spatial metaphor again, New Testament narratives speak of an opening of heaven to mark an event of revelation. At Jesus' baptism the heaven opens to clarify who he is whose story is about to unfold (Matt 3:16; Mark 1:10; Luke 3:21), Peter's mission receives radical redirection through the opening of heaven (Acts 10:11), above and beyond his impending execution, Stephen sees through the open heaven the Son of Man as the true ruler of the world (Acts 7:56), and the visionary of the book of Revelation sees in the open heaven Christ as King of kings and Lord of lords (Rev 19:11, 16). A spatial, even material element in the image of the opening of heaven is involved in all of these passages. But in most of them the rending or opening of heaven is accompanied by the sound of a voice which clarifies what it is that enters the earth through the open heaven. The opening of heaven is not a speechless rupture of celestial matter, but an act of disclosure which declares the portent of the moment as an event revealing God.

In line with the Old Testament tradition, the New Testament retains the faith that God has created heaven and earth (Acts 4:24; 14:15; 17:24; Rev 14:7), and the new creation cannot be expected except in the creation of a new heaven and a new earth (2 Pet 3:13; Rev. 21:1). The totality of God's creation is captured in the phrase "heaven and earth",[20] but the coordination of heaven and earth does not imply equal value given to both terms. God is more closely associated with heaven than with the earth and because of that there is an affinity of God to heaven which makes heaven the higher, superior, and ruling part of the pair "heaven and earth". God can appropriately be called the God of heaven (Rev 11:13; 16:11) since in governing heaven God rules from out of heaven over the entire world.[21]

The special closeness of God to heaven is reflected in language characteristic of the gospel of Matthew. With great frequency, in the first gospel, God is called the "heavenly father", and the "father who is in heaven".[22] God's care of his children, as the father in heaven, is connected to the way in which this care is carried out: it is the care of one who, being in heaven, sees that which is hidden to all other eyes. It is striking that the phrase "he who sees in secret" has become in Matt 6:1-18 almost a definition of God: as father in heaven God knows the truth behind all appearances, and the Christian community's trust in this heavenly father is, correspondingly, the liberation to a trust which needs no demonstration but relies on being known by God who sees in secret. The word heaven has, in these contexts in Matthew's gospel, assumed the role of describing the manner in which God cares for his people, and for the way in which this God's children trust in his care. God is father in heaven, because from heaven he sees the truth in that which is hidden, and cares for those who dare to live in the power of the hiddenness of truth. The connection between the truth in secret and God's rule from heaven plays a role also in Jesus' parables. In Matthew's gospel the parables speak of the kingship of heaven, of the way in which God from heaven governs the world.[23]

In the parables of the kingship of heaven ordinary circumstances of human life are used to describe what happens if heaven rules the earth. Very frequently in the parables, the stories told do not at all conform to ordinary human behavior; in fact they sometimes run so flagrantly against the grain of what is customary that the listener is purposely provoked. The king who forgives his servant a sum of money equal to ten times the annual tax levy of Herod the Great [24] will be extremely hard to verify in the annals of actual history (Matt 18:24, 27), and the owner of vineyards who pays the same wages to all his hired hands regardless of the length of their service will hardly be chosen as a model of justice either by a capitalist or by a socialist economic order (Matt 20:1-16). The offense of the parables is intentional; when heaven rules the earth a goodness is spread upon it which puts all human measures of justice and good order to shame. Human order and justice become mere appearances of goodness, and heaven inaugurates an unrealized dimension of grace which is covered by human convention. Heaven ruling over the earth brings about a basking in the inexhaustible grace of God which turns this earth into a field of blessing in which the most marvellous freedom is attained. The coming of the reign of heaven down to earth is the shower of heaven's riches upon an impoverished earth, and in this coming heaven represents the goodness, the grace, the wealth of God. Heaven is high above the earth. But while this sentence includes in the first gospel, a spatial element and thus part of an ancient world view, it has been transformed into an assertion about the nature of God as the father in heaven, about the way in which he governs the world, and about the trust with which this God's children rely on his rule. Seen from heaven, the deepest secrets of the earth are disclosed, and the world's justice is uncovered as a ragged loin cloth of goodness on the surface ill suited to cover the nakedness of sin. It is God's rule which brings about this disclosure, and this rule of god is the rule of heaven because heaven expresses the superiority of the hidden truth, and the victory of a quality of human life far beyond conventional good order. Thus heaven becomes the parable of God: it stands for the gracious superiority of God over the earth. "For as the heavens are higher than the earth, so are my ways higher than your ways and my thoughts than your thoughts" (Isa 55:9).

2.   The Vitality of Heaven. The New Testament, in consonance with the world view of its time, conceives of heaven and earth as firm, material substances. But this does not mean that the relation of heaven to earth, and of earth to heaven, is construed in terms of static objects which act on each other like dead bodies of matter. Quite to the contrary: heaven is full of life and it is capable of influencing life on earth by imparting its own vitality to the world. There is a movement emanating from heaven down to earth, and a corresponding movement from earth to heaven, although it is clear that the initiative of the movement is always to be found in heaven which acts in a leading and controlling position compared to which all movement from earth to heaven can be considered but a reflexive motion.

The New Testament makes statements, on occasion, about heaven by expressing action with a verb of motion. Although this cannot be found very often, it is present in very significant passages. Above all, it is said by all Synoptics that Jesus' activity began with the announcement of the coming of God's kingship (Mark 1:15; Luke 4:43) which in Matthew takes the form of announcing the kingship of heaven (Matt 4:17). For reasons stated in the previous section, this entails the idea of a coming of heaven to earth. The word phthano, used in a similar context, is equally a verb of motion (Matt 12:28; Luke 11:20). Angels, who are the messengers of heaven, descend from heaven to earth (John 1:51), completing their movement by a corresponding ascent again from earth to heaven. The angel who appears at the tomb of Jesus announcing his resurrection has first come down from heaven (Matt 28:2).

Highly dynamic is the activity in heaven in apocalyptic passages, especially in the book of Revelation. Everything that happens on earth is first decided, recorded, and often acted out, in heaven. Human history is here portrayed entirely in dependency on good or evil powers which dwell in heaven, and cultic objects on earth have their model, or rather their true reality, in heaven (throne, temple, lampstands)[25]. The initiative for all history on earth, including human history, goes out from the vitality of heaven.

In the Pauline and Deutero-Pauline epistles, the powers and principalities, with their association of other named potencies, are predominantly, perhaps exclusively, powers in heaven.[26] At least in Ephesians and Colossians they appear to be entirely hostile to the will of God representing a force in heaven which destroys peace and well-being both in the cosmos and on earth,[27] although precisely in those epistles they are also seen as liberated, or capable of liberation, from their destructive will. Even a summarizing discussion of this highly complex, and controversial, topic is here quite impossible. Suffice it to say that the powers and principalities in the Pauline corpus of the New Testament are further evidence of the vitality of heaven whose life determined the character of life on earth.

The idea of a vitality of heaven in which angels and demonic powers are alive poses enormous problems to the modern view of the world in which cosmic life is understood as the outcome and manifestation of impersonal forces whose properties can be quantified by means of the measurements, calculations, and the intuitions, available to the physicist. But the intention of the New Testament's view of the vitality of heaven can be probed without the attempt to cling to the ancient world view.

There is hardly any question that the Jewish concept of angels owes much—not everything—to the desire, arising at times of close contact with pagan civilizations and religions, to transpose pagan divinities into servants and messengers of the God of Israel.[28]   By the same token, foreign divinities are already in LXX in a few instances translated by daimonia and the tendency increased in time to identify pagan gods and their images with demons and demonic powers.[29] The primary motivation which guides this development of early Jewish theology is the preservation of the first commandment of the Decalogue, the prohibition to worship any god except the God of Israel. As in the early parts of the Old Testament the recognition of Yahweh alone leads rarely, if ever, to to the flat denial of the existence of foreign gods but to a relegation of these divinities to a subordinate status under the sole rule of Yahweh, so now in the centuries after the Babylonian captivity the tendency became widespread to acknowledge the presence of gods in heaven but strictly in the role of Yahweh's servants. Especially in apocalyptic literature the numbers of these sub-divine powers are, in comparison to former times, tremendously increased, they are assigned far more specific functions, and their names allow frequently the conclusion that they are nothing but forces of nature subjected to Yahweh's monarchic power.[30]

Notwithstanding the need for much greater specificity and precision in detail, it can be stated in the most general terms that the vitality of heaven in the New Testament, the heavens filled with angels, demonic powers, and princi-palities by several other names, is the result of a dual theological intention. It continues, on the one hand, the confession to one God alone who is understood to be identical with the god of Israel but nevertheless disclosed in novel and ultimate form as the Father of Jesus the Christ. And it preserves, on the other hand, a limited but sober acknowledgment of the reality of many powers far above human control, and thus powers in heaven, which must not be granted divine standing but which can also not simply be argued into non-existence. The vitality of heaven in the New Testament displays this dual intention. It expresses a highly dynamic concept of cosmic life and cosmic order which demands to be subjected to the obedience of faith in the one God. It is clear that the relationship of the one God to the powers of heaven is highly problematic and filled with tension. Heaven, then, is the arena in which this tension is real; it is the field of contest on which it is decided how, and why, and wherefore the supremacy of the one God de-idolizes creation and relinquishes the gods to the impotence of fraudulent imposters.

3.   **The Kingship of Heaven.** The kingship of heaven was mentioned before under the aspect of the language of parable. There is, however, yet another side of this phrase which requires consideration.

The concept of the "kingship of god" or the "kingship of heaven" grew out of the Old Testament acclamation "Yahweh rules as King". The acclamation looks at a divine action: Yahweh is worshipped as king because he acts like a king. Centuries of experience under foreign domination had enforced in Judaism a distinction in regard to the manner in which Yahweh is king. Jewish teachers differentiated between God's kingship *de jure*, by right, in which God rules over heaven and earth, and God's kingship *de facto*, in actual fact, in which he rules over heaven while the large majority of people on earth are obedient to an entirely different command.[31] This entails the faith that in heaven God's will is now and always fulfilled; there, the gap between God's right and God's might does not exist. But on earth reality marches to the beat of a different drummer so that the phrase "God of heaven" can signify not the universality but the limit of God's reign.[32] In the sayings of Jesus in the Synoptic gospels, the word heaven is sometimes used in a way which suggests a fundamental change in this situation. The petition of the Lord's prayer that God's will be done not only in heaven but also on earth (Matt 6:10) is a request for a takeover by God in the power struggle for the domination of the world. In Jesus' word and act, the coming kingship of God is beginning to take over the earth to make it conform to heaven. Heaven is to regain its lost leadership over the earth, and in this process human rules and customs are radically challenged.

Therefore, in some sayings of Jesus the word "heaven" assumes a strongly antithetical, if not polemical, note since it is directed against deep-seated human convictions and habits which defy the rule of heaven over the earth. Even that is not saying enough. "Heaven" can become, in Jesus' words, a direct opposite to the word "human". When Jesus is challenged by Jewish authorities to give account for the origin of his authority he answers with the counter-question whether the authority of John the baptist was from heaven or from human sources (Matt 21:23-25, Luke 20:1-4). The counterquestion assumes that a claim derived from human insights is, for that reason alone, not a claim based on the rule of heaven: heaven and human will have become centers of opposing camps. Some of Jesus' harshest sentences employ the word "heaven" in similar ways. "It will be hard for a rich man to enter the rule of heaven" because readiness to let heaven govern the earth would, in the case of the rich young man, demand the selling and distribution of his wealth to gain "treasure in heaven" (Matt 19:21, 23; Mark 10:21; Luke 18:22). The eight beatitudes in Matt 5:3-10 describe the results of the coming of the kingdom of heaven, as indicated by the bracket in the first and eighth beatitude with their identical phrase "theirs in the kingdom of heaven". The first four beatitudes, and their counterparts in Luke, announce the change which will come upon those whose condition in life contradicts the reality of the kingdom of heaven. Then the poor will be enriched by the power of heaven, the mourners will be comforted, the powerless will inherit the earth, the starving will have enough to eat (Luke 6:21), and those subjected to injustice will be fed with satisfaction. In the power of heaven, human conditions groaning with distortion of what God's kingship establishes on earth, are so reversed that the coming of the rule of heaven turns the accustomed order of things upside down. The disciple of the agent of the kingship of heaven is, therefore, also expected to act in ways which cancel out the safety and convention of orders designed to protect in human society the dignity of life: the disciple will, like his master, have no shelter but live more seriously exposed than the animals in the fields, and he will have to disregard even the sacred obligation of providing burial to the father when the call to discipleship is heard, leaving the burial in earth to those who are children of the earth and consequently already dead since the power of heaven has not yet brought them to life (Matt 8:19-22; Luke 9:57-60)

Sayings like these are extremely harsh because they reckon with a reality of heaven so seriously that the accustomed world of proven practices and healthy laws is called into question. When heaven rules the earth, the so-called "real world" stops to remain a solid mass which can never be shaken. The coming of heaven to earth involves a confrontation in which heaven asserts its superior rights against orders on earth which have been taken for granted and which frequently are imbued with the claim of divine sanction. There is harshness in the coming of heaven to earth. But that must not disguise the other aspect of the matter: the "real world" of the earth visited by the power of heaven is the world of signs and wonders, of healings and rejuvenation. "The kingdom of heaven is at hand", and in consequence of that "heal the sick, raise the dead, cleanse lepers, cast out demons" (Matt 10, 7f.). It is neither possible nor necessary to engage us, at this point, even in a cursory discussion of the miracle stories in the gospels. But it is possible and necessary to state in very general terms the overall impression which the reader of the gospels can hardly fail to verify: in the act and world of Jesus, the dynamics of heaven are so released that the well-known world of orders, laws, and customs creaks and crumbles, and the unknown world of marvelous restoration emerges before our eyes.

It should be manifest that the word "heaven", in the context of Jesus' sayings and deeds, has almost entirely lost the connection to an ancient world view. It describes, rather, the arrival of a new and superior quality of goodness on an old and weary world, tied completely to the story of the man Jesus in whom this arrival occurred. Heaven is defined through the gospel, not through cosmological concepts.

4.   TheVictory of Heaven. We have not yet reached the point, however, at which heaven is decisively determined in the New Testament. The point is the resurrection of Jesus Christ from the dead.

Already in the oldest parts of the Pauline corpus of letters, the association of resurrection and heaven is clear. The Christian community in Thessalonica is encouraged to "wait for (God's) Son from heaven, whom he raised from the dead" (1 Thess 1:10); in his parousia "the Lord will descend from heaven with a cry of command" (1 Thess 4:16), and the community beset by afflictions and persecutions will then find her rest, "when the Lord Jesus is revealed from heaven with his mighty angels in flaming fire" (2 Thess 1:7). The language which identifies Christ's resurrection from the dead with his being in heaven (Eph 6:9; Col 4:1) defines heaven at least in three ways.

First, Christian confessions had very early begun to read Psalm 110 christologically.[33] The psalm's opening sentence, "the Lord says to my lord: 'sit at my right hand, till I make your enemies your footstool'" was specifically applied to the resurrection (Mark 16:19; Acts 2:34, Rom 8:34; Eph 1:20; Col 3:1). It understands Jesus' resurrection from the dead as the exercise of God's power as king, the enthronement of Christ as God's co-regent. The part of God's creation which is capable of witnessing this enthronement is heaven (Acts 2:34)[34] Paul can identify the act of God's raising Christ "from the dead" with the statement that the risen Christ is "in heaven" or "from heaven". The waiting for God's son "from the heavens" corresponds to God's having raised him "from the dead" (1 Thess 1:10), and the Christ who was raised "from the dead" is identical with the "man in heaven" (1 Cor 15:20, 47). The correspondence between the phrases "from the dead" and "from or in heaven" does of course not mean that heaven is the world of the dead. To the contrary, heaven is the place where the victor over death is at home. Heaven is the royal aspect of God's created works worthy to be the palace in which this coronation takes place. It is superior to the earth because earth was the field on which the Son of God was slaughtered and the justification of his life by God was performed in the presence of heaven. Heaven therefore, is the creation of God in its mystery to be home and witness of the life-giving power of God which annuls the claim of death.

Second, the risen Christ is expected in his coming as Lord of all to be "revealed from heaven". That implies that he is, till his parousia, hidden in heaven. In adoption of a frequently stated apocalyptic idea,[35] heaven is here considered as the place where the true character of the dead is preserved until it is revealed in the end whether they were just or unjust. The eternal life of the risen Christ is in heaven, because until his coming in power his true character, the fulness of his achievement, is not manifest to those who live on earth. Heaven is that aspect of God's creation which veils and preserves the victory of resurrection up to the time when this veil will be removed and the victory will appear in the fully disclosed truth of his triumph.

The hidden and preserved triumph over death in the resurrection of Christ includes the idea that with him the true life of the believer, together with its benefits, is kept in heaven. Christian citizenship is in heaven (Phil 3:20), believers have a house and home which is in heaven (2 Cor 5:1), they have an inheritance kept for them in heaven (1 Peter 1:4), their hope is laid up for them in heaven (Col 1:5).

Third, when the ultimate disclosure of the truth of Christ's triumph will also reveal the truth of the life of those who shared his power in faith, then they will be disclosed as the participants of his suffering and of his resurrection. The coming in power of the Son of Man will be a coming with the clouds of heaven (Matt 26:64; Mark 14:62) at which time his sign will appear in heaven (Matt 24:30). And that time will mean the coming down from heaven of a new creation, a new city of God, in which the earth is not destroyed but recreated under the leadership of heaven (Rev 21:1-2). It will be the rejuvenation of the earth under the rule and blessing of heaven in the final revelation of the power of God who in his Christ has triumphed over death who will then be all in all.

* * * *

In conclusion, we can state that the word "heaven" in the New Testament has been drawn into the sphere of power determined by the act of God in Christ. This determination shapes the meaning of the word to such an extent that it is not an exaggeration to say that heaven is defined by the Christ event. Of course, all statements in the New Testament about heaven partake of elements of an ancient world view which we can no longer consider authoritative. But within this vehicle of an ancient view of the world, heaven is theologically explicated in a manner which allows the isolation of the theological intentions of the texts from the garb of a set of cosmological concepts which have lost their persuasiveness.

NOTES

1. C.F. von Weizsäcker, *The History of Nature*, the University of Chicago Press, 1949.

2. "This chapter and the next are devoted to the history of the heavens", von Weizsäcker, *Nature*, 75.

3. Somewhat different figures are reached depending on the method used in the computation. Three basic methods of calculation produce numbers varying from two billion to six billion years. The medium four to five billion is arrived at by the elimination of the extremes, von Weizsäcker, *Nature*, 42-45.

4. von Weizsäcker, *Nature*, 36-39.

5. von Weizsäcker, *Nature*, 34 and 40.

6. With the cautiousness and modesty characteristic of many contemporary physicists, von Weizsäcker advocates in respect of boundary problems, like the question of infinity, an "honest nihilism" which he considers to be "the negative counterpole of Christianity. We shall not understand one pole without the other", *Nature*, 74. See the entire chapter "Infinity", *Nature*, 6-74.

7. H. Traub, "Uranos", *TWNT* 5 (1967), 497-502.

8. Martin P. Nilsson, *Greek Piety*, Oxford: Clarendon Press, 1948. 96-103. The discovery of a strictly heliocentric system of the universe by Aristarchos of Samos at the beginning of the 3rd century B.C., and its defense by Seleukos, did not win the approval of the experts of the time, and could, therefore, not shape communal awareness.

9. Following Aristotle the planetary regions were distinguished in sublunary and superlunary spheres. Since the planetary spheres were the abode of the gods, and the sublunary region an area of defective quality, the air between earth and moon became the home of spirits and demons, half-way between gods and humans, who dominated that space. Nilsson, *Piety*, 100.

10. One of the most knowledgeable experts in the field of Jewish cosmology, H. Bietenhard has come to the conclusion that it is "completely impossible to speak of a world view of the New Testament", H. Bietenhard, "Die himmlische Welt im Urchristentum und Spatjudentum", *WUNT* 2, Tübingen: Mohr, 1951, 257 (my translation).

11. Bietenhard, *Himmlische Welt*, 8f., 11.

12. See, however, the differing opinion of H. D. Betz, *Der Apostel Paulus und die sokratische Tradition*, Tübingen: Mohr, 1972, 84-92.

13. Most commentators of 2 Cor. 12:1-3 present Jewish texts which mention different numbers of heavens, without deciding if Paul held to a view which knew of only three heavens: see the commentaries by C. K. Barrett (309f.), R. Bultmann (German ed., 223), A. Plummer (343), A. Schlatter (*Paulus, der Bote Jesu*, 662), H. Windisch (371-73).

14. W. R. Morfill and R. H. Charles, *The Book of the Secrets of Enoch*, Oxford: Clarendon, 1896, XL. H. Bietenhard, *Himmlische Welt*, 166 (with

62 Ulrich Mauser

15. John J. Collins, "The Mythology of Holy War in Daniel and the Qumran Scrolls: A Point of Transition in Jewish Apocalyptic, *VT* 25 (1975) 596-612.

16. Scattered elements of an apocalyptic concept of holy war are found also in the Synoptic traditions, and—with much less frequency—in some letters in the New Testament. O Betz, "Jesu heiliger Krieg", *NovT* 2 (1957), 116-137. O Böcher, "Polemos", *EWNT* III, 307-308.

17. H. Odeberg, "The view of the universe in the epistle to the Ephesians", Act. Univ. Lund, 1934. F. Mussner, *Christus, das All und die Kirche*, 2nd ed., Trier: Paulinus Verlag, 1968, 9-28.

18. W. Foerster, "aer", *TWNT* 1 (1933), 165.

19. H. Schlier, *Der Brief an die Epheser*, Düsseldorf: Patmos, 1957, 102-105.

20. In analogy to Old Testament tradition, the phrase "heaven and earth" permits expansions in the New Testament also: the sea is added in Acts 4:24; 14:15; the sea and the fountains of the water in Rev 14:7.

21. H. Traub, "Uranos", *TWNT* 5 (1967), 520.

22. The passages are collected by Traub, "Uranos" 520. Traub disputes, with good reason, the simple identification of the word "father" with "God".

23. It is true that "heaven" can, in Jewish usage, function as substitute for the word "God". This can lead to the conclusion that Matthew's phrase "kingship of heaven" is nothing more than a translation of Mark's "kingship of God" into a Jewish pattern of speech. If this was the case, the word "heaven" in Matthew's usage of "kingship of heaven" would carry no specific meaning but function only as a substitute. But the meaning of "kingship of heaven" is so akin to the meaning observable when the word "heaven" is used outside this phrase in Matthew, that the conclusion is safer that the concept of heaven retains its genuine meaning in Matthew's use of "kingship of heaven". cf. Traub, "Uranos", 521.

24. E. Schweizer, *Das Evangelium nach Matthaus*, Göttingen: Vandenhoeck & Ruprecht, 1973, 246.

25. Similar to apocalyptic ideas about heaven as the place where the originals, or models, of earthly realities are stored, is the concept of heaven in Hebrews which knows of heaven as the cultic tent and holy place (9:11f., 24, O. Michel, *Der Brief an die Hebräer*, Göttingen: Vandenhoeck & Ruprecht, 1949, 202f.)

26. The latest monograph in English on this much discussed topic is W. Wink, *Naming the Powers, The Language of Power in the New Testament*, Philadelphia: Fortress, 1984.

27. E. Schweizer, *Der Brief an die Kolosser*, EKK, Zürich-Neukirchen: Benziger und Neukirchener Verlag, 1976, 68f.

28. Typical is the concentrated remark in Philo, De gig. 6 where, in reference to Gen 6:2, the *aggeloi theou* of Gen 6:2 (LXX: *hoi huioi tou theou*)

are explained to be those beings "which are called daemons by other philoso-phers, but which Moses used to call angels".

29. H. Strack, P. Billerbeck, *Kommentar zum Neuen Testament aus Talmud und Midrasch IV*, München: Beck, 6, Aufl., 1975, 501ff.

30. The eighteen angelic names in 3 Enoch 14:4 are made up of stems indicating the natural phenomenon over which the angels rule and the theo-phoric ending *'el*. Similar are the lists in 1 Enoch 6:7 and 8:3.

31. This is pointed out very frequently. Particularly detailed is the discussion in T. W. Manson, *The Teaching of Jesus*, 2nd ed., Cambridge: University Press, 130ff.

32. Strack-Billerbeck, *Kommentar I*, 173.

33. B. Lindars, *New Testament Apologetic*, Philadelphia: Westminster, 1961, 45-51.

34. The complicated problems associated with the ascension to heaven are omitted in this article. See G. Lohfink, *Die Himmelfahrt Jesu*, StANT XXVI, München: Kösel, 1971..

35. H. W. Kuhn, *Enderwartung und gegenwärtiges Heil*, StUNT 4, Goötingen: Vandenhoeck & Ruprecht, 1966, 181-188.

From Organism to Mechanism to History:

The Bifurcation and Reintegration of Western Culture

James B. Miller

United Campus Ministry of Pittsburgh
Pittsburgh, Pennsylvania

[**A note of apology to the reader:** Please excuse the length of the following. The only rationale I can offer is that even in an effort to do a sweeping summary of cultural history 3,000 or so years of cultural development do not package easily in a brief space, especially when the most recent centuries are rich with innovation and the current cultural situation is one of high flux. I have tried to put as much as possible in the end notes to provide references and explanatory comments for those who might be interested in further inquiry. I believe, however, that the text can be read without such references.]

As I begin this paper, three caveats must be offered. First, by cosmology I will mean the broad worldview which orients a culture. It is those understandings of the world as a whole which inform the language, practices and institutions of a culture. It is the cosmic sense of place, of orientation, which individuals absorb tacitly by simply growing up in their particular culture.

Second, when dealing with the worldview of a culture, I will assume that it is not adequate to treat simply the notions about the structure of the world as such. It is also necessary to attend to how that structure is known. In other words, cosmology also implies epistemology. And with these two in attendance can metaphysics be far behind? Therefore, the following survey will give explicit attention to epistemological developments and more implicitly to metaphsyical ones.

Finally, I must admit that it requires a significant degree of immodesty to attempt to summarize three-thousand years of cultural history in even eighty-plus pages. Yet, in order to understand the contemporary relationship between Christian theology and the natural sciences as it is developing, it is necessary to have a sense of how theological expression and understandings of the character of the cosmos have interacted throughout Western history. Given the apparent necessity of this task for our present discussions, I will try in the following pages to paint in broad stroke and bold colors an historical tableau which does not too severely distort the actual history which deserves representation in the subtlest and most nuanced hues and textures.

In painting this picture I will employ the artifice of a typology, dividing the history of our culture into three periods: the pre-modern (from our ancient roots to Copernicus), the modern (from the Copernican revolution to the early years of this current century), and the post-modern (the contemporary period which is still undergoing definition). Of course, none of the divisions between these periods is clear cut. The roots of the modern cosmology reach back into the pre-modern period and to a degree the formation of the post-modern worldview involves a recovery in a new context of suppressed elements of the pre-modern cosmology. Similarly, just as the modern view only slowly displaced the pre-modern one, so also the post-modern view is coalescing against what remains in many aspects a predominately modern cultural background.

As a strategy for painting this cultural picture I will center on the formation of the modern cosmology: on its emergence from the pre-modern world, the view of nature and the understanding of knowledge it entails, its legacy toward the contemporary period, and general features of the world view which is coming to displace it.

First then, it is necessary to set the pre-modern stage. Yet, as noted, to identify all of the natural philosophy, metaphysics, epistemology, and Judeo-Christian theology preceding Copernicus under one heading is an act of gross oversimplification. But since any systematic treatment of a subject must rest on unargued but crucial premises, so any historical consideration has a beginning point which presumes the character of all preceeding history. Thus, I presume as follows.

The immediate cosmological setting for the emergence of the modern worldview was the convergence in medieval thought of Biblical theologies of creation and salvation with Aristotelian metaphysics and the cosmology of Ptolemy. There is debate as to the success of the resulting synthesis and of the degree of tension which existed between Biblical and classical Greek worldviews. Some see these worldviews as very disparate and so view the resulting synthesis as tenuous and strained. For others these worldviews were open to reconciliation and they see such a feat as one of the central accomplishments of the medieval theologians.[1]

In one sense there could be no conflict between the Biblical and the Greek traditions. They were responses to different concerns. Greek cosmologies were explicitly speculative. They were deliberate attempts to provide a rational account of the world as it was found in experience. They were intentionally explicit cosmologies. In contrast, the cosmological elements observed in the Hebrew scriptures and New Testament serve as the tacit background for intentionally theological expression. Thus, while the Greeks provided a variety of articulate cosmological systems, the Bible has within its writings no explicit cosmology.[2]

Yet, in another sense the cosmological perspectives of the Greek natural philosophers and the Biblical writers seem far from compatible. On the one hand, the movement in Greek cosmology from the Ionians in the sixth century B.C. to Ptolemy in the second century A.D. was one involving a significant degree of demythologizing and rationalization. The process of speculative cosmology deliberately sought to reduce the mythological content often found in accounts of the origin and structure of the cosmos. On the other hand, the Hebrew and Christian view of nature was thoroughly theological in intention and so the Biblical writings include significant mythological elements.[3]

Further, while Greek cosmology removed the gods as explanatory principles for understanding nature, Nature itself tended to be given the divine-like characteristics of eternity and self-sufficiency. Humanity was viewed as subordinate to Nature. In sharp contrast, the Biblical writers consistently viewed nature, as well as humanity, as creature, but, in addition, viewed humanity as standing above nature in the scheme of creation.[4]

Still, to relate Greek and Hebrew cosmological perspectives in terms of simple opposition is to misconstrue the intellectual and cultural dynamics of the early stages in the development of Western culture. For the Biblical writers, by their unavoidable tacit dependence upon cosmological views, drew upon the prevailing cosmological perspective of their day though not without theological modification. Thus, for example, the Priestly writers, to whom the cosmogony of the first chapter of Genesis is attributed, borrowed their cosmological scheme from the prevailing Babylonian cosmology found in explicit form in the *Enuma Elish*, "the Babylonian Genesis."[5] It is worth noting that the developmental or progressive cosmogony of the Priestly authors is also similar in form and order to that of the pre-Socratic Ionians though more mythological in tone. The monotheism of the Priestly account actually places it closer to the Ionian cosmology than to either the Babylonian cosmology or earlier Greek cosmologies like that of the Hesiod.[6]

In addition to the more normal processes of commerce and inter-cultural migration, the Greek conquest of the Middle East resulted in the transmission of Greek culture into that region. Alexander the Great was the student of Aristotle. So, prior to the formation of the New Testatment, there had been an association of Helenic philosophy with Hebraic traditions, in particular an influence by logos philosophy on the Hebrew wisdom tradition. This association was perpetuated in the New Testament.

Further, late Hebrew apocalypses (*Daniel*), those of the Inter-testamental period (*Enoch*) and those of the New Testament (*Revelation*) were expressed against cosmological backgrounds not only Babylonian and Persian but Greek as well. In these apocalypses there is an emphasis on discontinuity, on a division between the present age and the age to come. This discontinuity represents a form of historical dualism. However, this discontinuity is not an ontological one. It is instead a way of expressing the moral distance between Yahweh's kingdom and the actual present history of the people.

In addition, the Biblical distinction between Creator and creature is again not an ontological one but rather one marking authority. In the Biblical cosmogony Adam, who is created by the divine sculptor in the divine image and in whom the divine breath (or spirit) is breathed, is also a creator in his own right as he completes the creation of the beasts of the field and the birds of the air by giving them their names (Gen. 2.18-20). Thus, while there are dualistic themes in the Biblical writings, these are not of an ontological but rather of a moral or authoritative nature.

Still, just as it would be erroneous to view the Biblical writings as expressive of a monolithic theological tradition, so also it would be erroneous to view speculative Greek philosophy as being a single unified tradition. As in most of the ancient cultures, early Greek cosmologies or cosmogonies were significantly mythological. However, among the pre-Socratic Ionians, especially Anaximander, there began a process of speculative rationalization which deliberately set about to eliminate the mythological elements from cosmology. Similarly, the Pythagoreans sought to fashion a cosmology from geometry and number.[7] Perhaps the most radical form of demythologizing in classical Greek thought is found in Democritus, his contemporary, Leucippus, and their later disciple, Epicurus. For these the whole of the cosmic order was to be accounted for in terms of two factors, atoms of being and motion. All else was nothing.

In the midst of this movement to eliminate the mythological from cosmological speculation, there also appeared a counter trend; namely, the theological cosmologies of Plato and Aristotle. In fact Plato's most explicit and extended discussion of cosmology, *The Timaeus*, is written in part in the form of a myth. While Aristotle's physics and metaphysics were more thoroughly rationalized than Plato's cosmology, they also included a significant theological element. In addition to this persistent theological component, both Platonic and Aristotelian cosmologies manifested a dualistic element.

The Ionians, the Pythagoreans and the atomists all tended toward cosmologies which were not only naturalistic but also holistic. Plato and Aristotle likewise viewed the cosmos as an ordered whole. Nevertheless, for Plato, the world of immediate empirical experience was fundamentally distinct from a realm of pure ideas beyond this world. This cosmological distinction bore with it a value distinction. The ideal was of greater value than the empirically real. The ideal was the domain of eternal perfection while the world of sense experience was the domain of the transient and the imperfect. Although Aristotle eschewed such idealism, favoring instead an empirical realism, he did nevertheless describe a cosmos ordered in a hierarchical fashion where God was ontologically unique and separated at the top of the hierarchy from the rest of the cosmos.

With the exception of the contrast between Aristotle's realism and Plato's idealism, Aristotle's cosmology retained much of the Platonic world picture. According to both Plato and Aristotle, the earth occupied the center of the universe. It was surrounded by moving celestial spheres carrying the planets and a final sphere bearing the fixed stars.[8] While everything on earth was transitory, the celestial bodies were imperishable and perfect.

The theological element in the two cosmologies appeared in both similar and different respects. For Plato the cosmos had a beginning. It was the creation of God. For Aristotle, on the contrary, the world was best conceived as eternal. At the same time Aristotle held that the motion of the cosmos originated with a divine "unmoved-mover," ontologically unique and separated from the cosmos. Thus, though articulated in different manners, both Plato and Aristotle associated the structure of the cosmos with a divine providence and they both viewed the cosmic structure as a hierarchical one with the earth at the lowest level and the divine at the highest.

Lastly, both Plato and Aristotle conceived of the cosmos in organic terms. For Plato the cosmos as a whole was like a single organism moved by a world soul.[9] While Aristotle's cosmology, again, was less mythological than that of Plato, it nevertheless also contained an essential organismic element, especially in its explanation of motion in terms of the final causality of the heavenly bodies conceived as divine beings.[10]

While the heirs of Plato tended to develop the theological dimensions of his cosmic scheme, the heirs of Aristotle further refined the astronomical geometry by which the observed movement of the heavenly bodies could be understood within the rational system of his cosmology.[11] The most significant achievement in this regard was that of the Egyptian astronomer, Ptolemy. In his *Mathematike Syntaxis* he developed and articulated the Aristotelian cosmological heritage in such a formidable fashion that this work became the standard cosmological text in Western culture (Islamic as well as Christian) for the next 1,400 years.[12]

The process by which this Greek tradition of cosmological speculation became integrated with the Biblical heritage of Christianity is a complex one. However, very early in the life of the Christian community there were those who sought to show, largely with apologetic motives, that Christian Biblical theology was not only compatible with but completed the speculative theologies of the classical Greeks. Both the "creation" theology of Plato and the Platonic-Aristotelian visions of a hierarchically ordered cosmos were seen to be especially congenial to the Biblical tradition.

In *The Theologian and His Universe* N. Max Wildiers has summarized this complex process in a helpful manner.[13] From Origen and Pseudo-Dionysius in the third century through Augustine to the "School of Chartres" and Thomas Aquinas in the twelfth and thirteenth centuries respectively, there were two interwoven processes of theological development. One was a movement which more and more found, within the metaphysical and cosmological systems of Plato and especially Aristotle, rational structures by means of which to articulate a revealed Biblical faith. The second movement was one from a cosmological perspective which was predominately Platonic or Neo-Platonic to one which was predominately Aristotelian.[14] In the fifth century Augustine initiated an important theological distinction when he affirmed that God could be known by "reading" two books: the book of revelation (the Bible) and the "book of nature." Augustine was careful to note, however, that the value of the second "book" was in its ability to point to the truth present in the first.[15] A number of cosmological themes recur in the writings of the Church Fathers and pre-scholastic theologians which were particularly significant in the formation of the medieval worldview. These were (1) that the cosmos was an ordered whole, (2) that that order was both organic and hierarchic, (3) that the human being was a microcosm and (4) that the human being was a center mediating between the ontologically distinct domains of the terrestrial and the celestial.

Wildiers argues that, given access in the thirteenth century to authoritative new translations of Aristotle's works, the Platonic/Neo-Platonic dominance in Christian theology was replaced by an Aristotelian one. In their different ways the works of Bonaventure and Thomas Aquinas were especially significant contributions to this shift and are paradigmatic of the medieval effort to provide a synthesis of Biblical theology and Greek natural philosophy. In the works of Thomas Aquinas this synthesis can be seen most evidently. Aquinas also exhibited a theological method which embodied in generalized form Augustine's distinction between the "two books."[16]

The outcome of these two movements was a worldview which became the tacit cosmology orienting the reflective thought (theological and natural) of medieval culture for the next three centuries. Thus, on the eve of the Copernican revolution there was in place a worldview theologically Christian and cosmologically Aristotelian and Ptolemaic. The chief features of this worldview were: that the cosmos was an ordered whole; that the order was a hierarchic one with greater value/perfection ascribed to the "higher" reaches; that the dynamics of the cosmos were understood in organismic and teleological terms; that the earth was at rest at the center of the cosmos; that there was an ontological distance between the heavens and the earth, between the celestial and the terrestrial spheres; and that man was a microcosm in whom the celestial and the terrestrial met.[17]

The cosmological vision of the modern world was formed slowly in response to shifts in philosophical cosmology which were themselves immersed in a shift in astro-physical cosmology. While a large company of individual actors performed vital roles in this drama of intellectual and social transformation, the movement was bracketed by two figures whose particular contributions can be taken to characterize the nature of the change. These two were: Rene Descartes and Immanuel Kant. Before considering more closely their distinctive influences, summary attention needs to be given to the beginning of the shift in astro-physical cosmology within which they were participants and from which their philosophical contributions emerged.

Contrary to the manner in which it is often portrayed, modern science did not arise initially as an empirical challenge to a physics derived from metaphysical speculation. Science in the modern sense is ordinarily dated from the publication in 1543 of Nicolaus Copernicus' *On the Revolution of the Spheres of the Universe*. However, this was not an empirical work by any means. It was instead a challenge to the prevailing Aristotelian/Ptolemaic cosmology originating in Copernicus' commitment to a Platonic and, more especially, a Pythagorean cosmological perspective. The challenge was thoroughly philosophical.

The system of Ptolemy was an extremely complex one. Beginning with a set of cosmological and metaphysical presuppositions (e.g., the perfection of the heavens, perfection as manifest in immutability, circular motion as the perfect form of motion, etc.) Ptolemy had developed a system of cosmic geometry by which to account for the observed motion of the heavenly bodies. In order for this geometric system to work, however, it was necessary to include three elements which significantly added to the complexity of the system. These were: the eccentric, the epicycle and the equant.[18]

It was the last of these which Copernicus found especially troublesome for the equant undercut the principle of uniform, and therefore simple, circular motion; a principle which lay at the foundation of his vision of the perfection of the heavenly movements. Copernicus argued that this significant flaw could be overcome by assuming that the sun and not the earth was at the center of these motions. Neither this assumption nor its consequence for the motion of the earth (i.e., an annual revolution about the sun and a daily rotation on its axis) were original with Copernicus. Some of the ancient natural philosophers had already allowed for a two-fold motion of the earth about a cosmic center.[19] From Copernicus' perspective he was not proposing a radically new position but rather recovering an ancient view which had been lost amid the ascendancy of Aristotelian thought. As a consequence his system was often referred to, by his supporters and opponents alike, as Pythagorean, Copernic-Pythagorean or even Aristarchian.

A second way in which Copernicus was moving against the presuppositions of his day was with regard to the truth of astronomical systems. For most of his contemporaries such mathematical schemes primarily served practical purposes. They were valuable as an aid to astrological calculations or for establishing the dates of civil and religious events. However, such systems were seen neither as avenues of knowledge nor as reflections of the "true" order of the cosmos.

Andreas Osiander, Copernicus' editor, added a preface to his author's work which reflected this attitude. It was held there that the arguments within the work were not to be taken as expressions of truth but instead were offered "only to provide a correct basis for calculation."[20] In one of those ironies to which human history seems especially prone, Osiander, the Protestant, was providing Copernicus, the Roman Catholic priest, with precisely the equivocation which Roman Catholic authorities would later urge upon Galileo. However, unlike his more cautious younger colleague, Copernicus was prepared to challenge the adequacy of the dominant received astronomical tradition.

Copernicus referred to his position as "almost against common sense." This an indication of the contrast between Copernicus' Pythagorean and Platonic epistemological orientation and the prevailing medieval Aristotelianism. For Aristotle, knowledge was founded on ordinary sense experience. Both knowledge of the physical world and metaphysical knowledge were rooted in the experience of the senses. For the Platonist, on the contrary, the world of the senses was at best an imperfect copy of the ideal domain. Genuine knowledge was to be gained from an intuition of the ideal forms. It is this epistemological attitude which Copernicus brought to his effort to reform the Aristotelian-Ptolemaic astronomical scheme.

It should be noted that Copernicus' drive toward simplicity was not altogether successful. Though he succeeded in eliminating the equant and eccentrics, his system still retained epicycles. This remaining "complexity" was due in large part to his continuing metaphysical commitment to circular motion as that motion appropriate to the perfect heavenly domain. Thus, Tycho

Brahe (1546-1601) was able to offer an alternative to the Copernican system which possessed equivalent "simplicity" yet which retained the earth at the cosmic center while allowing the other planets to revolve about the sun which itself revolved about the earth.[21] It was Johannus Kepler, another Polish mathematical astronomer, who demonstrated that a "simple" Copernican model of the motion of the planets could be derived by assuming that their orbits took the form of elipses rather than circles. For Kepler it was the aesthetic "simplicity" of the system rather than metaphysical assumptions about the perfection of circular motion which was the guiding influence.[22]

Since both Copernicus and Osiander were aware of the challenges *The Revolutions* presented to the dominant cosmology, they shared an anticipation of the conflict which this work would initiate. Yet, Copernicus himself was spared the burden of the controversy which was about to erupt. He received his own copy of the published work as he lay on his death bed. It was for others, convinced of the truth of his system, to bear the weight of the ensuing conflict. Of these Galileo Galilei is most commonly cited as the champion of Copernicanism and also as the chief victim of its repression by religious authorities. But such a judgment is simplistic and does not do justice to the nexus of issues surrounding Galileo's trial, condemnation and subsequent house-arrest.

It has been said that if Galileo were alive today he would be Carl Sagan.[23] Such a comparison gives witness to the entrepreneurial and assertive elements which were significant aspects of Galileo's personality. While many think of him, for instance, as the inventor of the telescope, he was instead one of its earliest technical refiners, promoters and salesmen.

The trial of Galileo itself was the outcome of a variety of factors. These included not only his own aggressive personality but also the atmosphere of the religious beligerence stemming from the conflicts over authority which were central to the Protestant Reformation. Perhaps the most important of these factors was Galileo's challenge to the intellectual hegemony of Aristotelian thought, a dominance which was explicit in the arena of astronomical cosmology and terrestrial physics and implicit within the domain of medieval Christian theology.

Galileo's use of the telescope for astronomical observations led to several significant discoveries, discoveries which undermined the metaphysical presuppositions of the Aristotelian-Ptolemaic cosmological system. Yet, these discoveries in no way provided demonstrative proof of the validity of the Copernican position.[24] Still, they did challenge the authoritative Aristotelian view of the structure of the cosmos.

At the same time this distinction offers an example of the broader dualism which permeated Descartes' system as a whole from its initial inception. This distinction can be seen as early as 1628 when, in his *Rules for the Direction of the Mind*, Descartes identified the task to which his sense of calling had led him. His object was no less than to establish a body of comprehensive knowledge which was "scientific"; that is, "true and evident." It was his intention to reject all "merely probable knowledge and make it a rule to trust only what is completely known and incapable of being doubted."[30] Here it can be seen that doubt had a systemic function in the development of Descartes' "unified science." But if doubt was the means by which to cut away all that was "merely probable," what was the route to knowledge which could be "completely known and incapable of being doubted"? This route was a dual one.

On the one hand, there was the path of "intuition" or "the conception which an unclouded and attentive mind gives us so readily and distinctly that we are wholly freed from doubt about that which we understand."[31] On the other hand, indubitable knowledge could also be attained by means of deduction from first principles. As Descartes put it: "by [deduction] we understand all necessary inference from other facts that are known with certainty...."[32]

While these two were the only paths by which reason could attain certain knowledge, they were not finally the only paths to knowledge which was sure. For Descartes also declared that

> These two methods are the most certain routes to knowledge, and the mind should admit no others. All the rest should be rejected as suspect of error and dangerous. But this does not prevent us from believing matters that have been divinely revealed as being more certain than our surest knowledge, since belief in these things, as all faith in obscure matters, is an action not of our intelligence, but of our will.[33]

It is worth noting in anticipation that here, in Descartes' early reflections on reason as a source of knowledge and on the relation of reason to revelation, there was an expression of the limits (or boundaries) of rational knowledge which later found far more focal development in the works of Immanuel Kant who anchors the "critical" pole of the modern critical consciousness. Still, here in his earliest consideration of how knowledge is acquired, Descartes manifested a functioning dualistic perspective.

It should also be clear that the model of knowledge which substantively informed Descartes' system was that of mathematics and especially axiomatic geometry. Again, in anticipation, the orderly structure of mathematics and geometry can be seen to have played a formative role in the development of Kant's epistemological system. In both cases the attraction to mathematics as a key to understanding the structure of human knowing was a perpetuation of the Platonic and Pythagorean perspectives on the fundamental character of the cosmos.

Before going on to Descartes' more specifically cosmological proposi- tions which asserted a dualistic division in reality, one additional characteristic of his larger project needs to be identified. This was his "reductionistic" approach. First, he held that his development of a "unified science" had to occur in a particular order. He proposed to move from the simplest to the more complex [34] This was the methodological mirror of Descartes' notion that the most complex phenomena and objects are themselves built up out of that which is simple. Thus, he stated his fifth rule "for the direction of the mind" as follows:

> Method consists entirely in the order and disposition of the objects towards which our mental vision must be directed if we would find out any truth. We shall comply with it exactly if we reduce involved and obscure propositions step by step to those that are simpler, and then starting with the intuitive apprehension of those that are absolutely simple, attempt to ascend to the knowledge of all the others by precisely similar steps.[35]

In axiomatic geometry one begins with simple definitions and axioms intuitively validated and from there builds up deductively a series of rational conclusions which account for the character of complex geometric figures and relationships. Similarly, given Descartes' method, when confronted with a complex object or phenomena, the simplest constituents are sought in order to provide the foundation from which to build up the understanding.

As noted above, Descartes suppressed *Le Monde*, the first composition in his effort to fulfill the program which he had originally outlined in *Rules for the Direction of the Mind*. However, in the safety of Protestant Holland he did have published *Discourses on the Method of Rightly Conducting the Reason and Seeking for Truth in the Sciences*. This was his first general public presentation of his views (*The Rules* like *Le Monde* was not published until after Descartes' death). It was here that his cosmic dualism first became publicly explicit.

Descartes' "Method" was one of doubt. His program was to skeptically chip away at all apparent knowledge until there was a "clear and distinct" residue which was certain. He was prepared to doubt, in principle, even the most "clear and distinct" presuppositions of mathematics on the grounds that he could possibly, though not probably, be deceived about these. This theoretical doubt he called "hyperbolic."

Applying this program he arrived at the one affirmation about which there could be no doubt: "I think therefore I am." He could not even "hyperbolically" doubt his own existence for the very act of doubting required his existence. Thus, his existence as a thinking entity was beyond doubt. However, for Descartes such an affirmation of personal existence did not necessitate the affirmation of the existence of his body.[36] This distinction between body and mind (or body and soul) in the human was a manifestation of a fundamental metaphysical dualism. Within the cosmos there were two distinct substances: material substance and mental (or spiritual)'substance. The former was extension; the latter was thinking. The behavior of the former could be fully described in the terms of mathematical physics (mechanics), while the latter could be understood only in metaphysical or ultimately in theological terms. Thus, while the human being as a soul was free and indeterminate, the human body had the characteristics of a living machine. With respect to the body alone, Descartes saw human beings as indistinct from other animals.[37]

Descartes, however, was not simply satisfied with this fundamental dualism between body and soul. For it was clear to him through a consideration of his personal experience that mind and body were intimately related.[38] But, how was this intimate union possible when the body and soul were comprised of distinct substances? A review of Descartes' struggle with this question reveals that he never was able to arrive at an entirely satisfactory answer. However, his effort did lead him to propose a physiological point at which the union of body and soul occurred: namely, the pineal gland.

It is worth noting that this dualism of substances, which produced a radical distinction between human beings and all other created things, was quite compatible with strands of Christian theological development. This is especially true for those strands which gave an ontological interpretation to Paul's distinction between the "flesh" and the "spirit" and those which tended to view salvation in terms of the transcendence of the soul beyond material existence.[39] At the same time, Descartes was challenging the Aristotelian (and one might suggest more Biblical) view, maintained in medieval scholasticism, that the concept of "soul" was broader than that of rationality and was more generally to be identified with the concept of "life."[40]

This metaphysical dualism, then, permeated Descartes' natural philosophy and significantly affected his procedure as a "scientist." To the extent that this philosophical commitment was the deductive ground of his conclusions about the particular structure of the cosmos, Descartes carried forward a philosophical tradition which was more medieval than modern even as he challenged the specific content of medieval natural philosophy. His physics, as a deductive enterprise, was to a large extent an outgrowth of his metaphysics. This metaphysical dependence can be seen in the way he dealt with specific theoretical questions such as: the existence of atoms, the extent of the universe and the existence of a pure vacuum.

For Descartes the answers to these questions lay in his understanding of the nature of material substance as extension and in his theological commitment to a traditional understanding of divine omnipotence. Thus, in principle, there could be no smallest indivisible material part (atom) because the very nature of matter was extension. But even if one could conceive of a smallest material part which was not divisible by any means within the created cosmos, nevertheless, any such part would not be immune from the power of God to divide creation as God chose.[41]

Similarly, one could not place a bound on extension; thus, the material cosmos as extended substance could not be bounded. Here, however, Descartes chose not to claim that the universe was infinite in extension and chose instead to say that it was "indefinite." The choice of words, which might seem a quibble, was a further concession to a theological view which reserved the term infinite for the divine.[42]

Finally, the question of the existence of a vacuum was answered as a direct consequence of Descartes' identification of material substance with extension. It was inconceivable that one could have extension (space) without material substance (content) for the two were metaphysically united. Therefore, while a vessel might not contain any sensible content (e.g., an "empty" pitcher), nevertheless, in order for it to have interior extension at all meant that it possessed a content, for in principle extension meant material substance.[43]

Given Descartes' deductive method and his formative metaphysical and theological commitments, it would be easy to conclude that his natural philosophy was no more a contribution to the emergence of "modern science" than the metaphysics of the ancient and medieval philosophers because it lacked any significant empirical or experimental component. However, such an assessment would not be accurate. For although he failed in his search for a certain and unified science based on the clear and distinct deliverances of reason alone, a science unencumbered by past authorities, his methodological skepticism did enable him in fact to consider theoretical presuppositions significantly different from those received from the natural philosophers of the past. As a consequence, for example, he lay the groundwork for a reconception of the nature of motion.

This reconception was to become a foundation for the further development of "classical mechanics", a development which came to flower in the works of Isaac Newton. In particular it was Descartes' conception of motion as a state rather than a process, his affirmation of the universal conservation of motion and his conceptual formulation of the principle of rectilinear inertia which formed a legacy for the "enlightened" scientists who succeeded him. At the same time, Descartes' commitment to a strictly mechanical interpretation of the motion of objects (i.e., that their motion was due exclusively to the direct impact of other objects) resulted in an interpretation of the motion of the heavenly bodies in terms of multiple interacting vortices. This interpretation of celestial motion was exceedingly complex if not, in fact, mathematically indeterminate. Without an experimental component in his natural pholosophy, Descartes provided logical explanations which were not amenable to empirical testing. In this regard Descartes was the "father of modern philosophy" while having one foot planted firmly in the speculative methodology of previous ancient and medieval natural philosophers.

It remained for Isaac Newton to fulfill in a comprehensive way the philosophical effort begun in Copernicus' cosmological speculations, refined and extended in Galileo's empirical observations and experiments, and reconceived in Descartes' deductive physics. This accomplishment is sometimes referred to as the "Newtonian Synthesis" but this expression is somewhat ambiguous.[44] On the one hand, the term "synthesis" can be taken to refer to Newton's success in drawing together the theoretical insights of a number of his predecessors including Galileo, Kepler, Descartes, Borelli and Hooke to name but a few. In this regard Newton was able to provide in a single set of concepts an explanation for a wide range of natural phenomena.[45] In addition, he was able to describe the causal mechanisms which he identified for these phenomena in coherent mathematical terms. And finally, Newton's system represented a unified mechanics (celestial and terrestrial) articulated in one set of concepts and mathematical expressions.

This triumph of mathematical reason was the final major step away from a cosmos conceived as an organic union of spirit and matter and toward a vision of the cosmos as a determinate mechanism. While the speculations of Copernicus and the terrestrial mechanics of Galileo had been spurred on by their allegiance to the Pythagorean and Platonic view of reality as mathematical form, these progenitors of "modern science" had yet retained an understanding of the cosmos as an organic whole. However, in Newton's conceptual system the motions of the bodies of the heavens and those of the earth could be fully taken into account by means of a set of pure mathematical expressions. Thus, geometric models rather than organic ones became the appropriate forms for explanation. The cosmos was to be most appropriately conceived as a great determinate machine rather than as a living organism.

In concert with the cosmic physics of Newton a broader philosophical cosmology was taking shape which included not only an understanding of the general structure of the universe but also an understanding of how that universe was known. This more general cosmological orientation has been called the "mechanistic philosophy" and it lies at the core of the formation of the fundamental dualism which came to characterize the modern and critical perspective. While specification of such a broad orientation is always historically problematic some of its general features can be listed as follows:

> God is the ultimate source of all motion; human reason can explain all the workings of nature; the natural world is nothing but a machine, the operation of which occurs by physical necessity;... all natural phenomena are produced by the effects of matter in motion;... there is an absolute dychotomy between matter and spirit; bodies can interact only by impact;... there is a fundamental distinction between primary and secondary qualities — a distinction which follows from the proposition that the real world is not necessarily as we perceive it. Primary qualities such as shape and size belong to objects as they really are; but secondary qualities such as heat and colour, have no independent existence.[46]

As this list indicates the Newtonian cosmology itself raised some issues for the mechanistic position. For example, the "law of universal gravitation" assumed the possibility of a force acting at a distance rather than through the immediate impact of adjacent bodies. In this regard, Descartes' cosmic vortices were more consistent with the "mechanistic philosophy" than was Newton's gravitational law. However, Newton's law had the great advantage of being capable of expression in a clear mathematical form so as to generate predictions of the actual motions of the planets; predictions which could be tested.

It was Laplace who not only carried forward Newton's project with precise mathematical rigor but also expressed the "mechanistic" view of the determinateness of the great world machine. He stated with confidence that given the precise positions and velocities of all the bodies of the universe and a knowledge of all forces operating on those bodies the entire history of the cosmos, the future as well as the past could be seen.[47] Further, Laplace exhibited the fundamental distinction between the material universe and the domain of the spirit when he responded to Napoleon's query about the place of God in his system with the reply, "I have no need of that hypothesis."[48]

Within the broader philosophical reflection on the nature of the cosmos there were epistemological issues concerning how knowledge of such a cosmos was possible. Descartes had turned attention to the rational subject whose certain existence was known in the act of knowing. John Locke developed an analysis of the structure of empirical knowledge as grounded in sensory experience. For both Descartes and Locke the question of the reality of the material world was not at issue. Bishop Berkeley, however, argued that the sensations of the knower were not identical with the thing known and that what was known was not things but ideas.[49]

David Hume took Berkeley's "ideal philosophy" one step further and argued that the only legitimate rational position for the knower was a moderate skepticism. For Hume all that the knower knew in his effort to know the material world were his own sensations or ideas. Hume's skepticism embraced, in principle, not only knowledge of the existence of the material world, other minds and even the mind of the knower himself, but also the reality of such "scientific" concepts as causality. From Hume's perspective reason gave no sanction for concluding that there was a causal relationship between two events merely because they were habitually experienced in a sequential order. In this sense, "causality" was not a characteristic of the world but rather a way in which the knower ordered experience.

One response to Hume came from a fellow Scot, Thomas Reid. In contrast to the esoteric idealism of Berkeley which seemed to lead necessarily to the skepticism of Hume, Reid argued in favor of a "common sense realism." First, he observed that pragmatically even the skeptics were not skeptical in the practical affairs of life. But he went on to offer an alternative epistemological scheme as a substitute for theoretical skepticism.

For Reid the knower knew not simply sensations or ideas but, more particularly, the things represented in those sensations. Empirical experience was made possible, according to Reid, by principles in the constitutiion of the mind which were anterior to and independent of that experience. The guarantor for the correspondence between experience and things experienced was God. Thus, Reid answered Hume's skepticism by offering in its place what amounted to a theological positivism. God created the human mind to be able to experience the world as it is and guaranteed the correspondence between experience of the world and the world as it is in itself.[50]

It was, however, yet another respondent to Hume who developed a critical justification for empirical knowledge. This justification was one based on the a priori structure of human reason itself without any necessary recourse to the divine. The respondent was Immanuel Kant.

Kant was a younger contemporary of both Hume and Reid. His subsequent reputation as one of the preeminent shapers of Western philosophy is based upon works which appeared after his fifty-seventh birthday. If he had come to be known only in relation to his earlier works, he would probably have been recognized by scholars in the history and philosophy of science but by few others. Nevertheless, these earlier works indicate that Kant's later philosophical development was firmly rooted in the sciences of his day, especially Newtonian physics. Of particular note is a work on theoretical cosmogony. This was Kant's *Universal* [or *General*] *Natural History and Theory of the Heavens* written sometime prior to 1755.[51]

This essay was an almost lyrical speculation on the origin of the universe. It combined the celestial mechanics of Newton with Thomas Wright's speculations on the structure of the Milky Way and other stellar systems. Of special note is the evolutionary character of Kant's picture of the formation of the cosmos. This was not empirical science but neither was it sheer metaphysical reflection. It was instead an extrapolation from observations and the "laws of mechanics" to form a theory of the emergence of the observable universe. At the same time this "theory" was expressed in language which was as religious as it was scientific.[52] In this work there was a combination of the "law of universal gravitation," a theoretical commitment to the consistency of natural law in the cosmos, the observation of the multitude of stars in the heavens and a theistic piety.

Here also Kant drew conclusions concerning the extent of the cosmos in space and time. He concluded that the cosmos was infinite, at least potentially, and that it was never complete but always coming into existence. These conclusions, due to their explicit dynamism, contrasted with more static understandings of the cosmos found in traditional metaphysics and theology.[53]

With respect to Kant's cosmogony it is important to note four things. The first is that Kant accepted Newtonian cosmology and Cartesian cosmic geometry, an acceptance which remained unaltered thoughout his subsequent philosophical development. Second, this work reveals a stage in the ascendence of the "dynamic" as a primative characteristic of the cosmos. Galilean and Cartesian mechanics had developed the concept of motion as a state of bodies, a state as fundamental as the condition of rest. In Kant's theory of a developing cosmos, the notion of the primitive character of the dynamic had become more central. Third, in spite of this dynamism Kant retained the more traditional view that this cosmic development was in fact the working out of an external divine plan which served as the internal telos of the universe. Finally, this sort of cosmological speculation stood in sharp relief against what was to become the source of Kant's reknown; namely, his critical analysis of the limits of pure reason. In the light of his later critiques, this cosmogony would be seen as an inevitable product of the human intellect reaching beyond its proper limits and so could not constitute knowledge in a proper sense. It is to Kant's later critiques that attention must now be given.

In what manner does one know the world? What is the relation between the knower and the known? How is conformity between the mind of the knower and the object known obtained? While these were not unprecedented questions, they had gained renewed prominence in the face of the development of the mechanistic world picture. Rationalists following Descartes argued that knowledge of the natural world was largely the result of a proper and active analysis of and deduction from first principles. The empiricists following Locke argued that knowledge was the result of the impression of sensations upon the passive mind of the knower. The question for the empiricists was how did the knowing mind conform itself to the object of knowledge. But as Berkeley, and then more devastatingly Hume, pointed out, sensations were not objects but themselves only ideas. While Berkeley then postulated an immaterialist metaphysic, Hume more modestly proposed a moderate skepticism, a form of metaphysical agnosticism which denied the possiblity of both metaphysical knowledge and scientific realism. It was to develop a more adequate analysis of these issues that Kant entered the epistemological lists.

Kant's critical project was stimulated, he says himself, by David Hume's general attack on metaphysics and in particular Hume's criticism of the concept of causality, the concept that the positing of one thing necessarily entailed the positing of another. However, if causality were nothing more than a way human beings spoke about their habit of associating sequential experiences, as Hume suggested, then serious questions were raised not only for the validity of scientific explanation, which purported to be a description of causal relations, but for a rational morality as well. For ethics requires causality in order that actions may bear moral responsibility.

As a child of his age Kant not only had accepted but had begun his career by explicitly speculating within an uncritical appropriation of the claims of metaphysical knowledge. However, as he stated in an often quoted passage, "I openly confess that my remembering David Hume was the very thing which many years ago first interrupted my dogmatic slumber and gave my investigations in the field of speculative philosophy a quite new direction." Yet, Kant was far from a mere Humean disciple. Kant's aim was to accept the problem which Hume had very effectively raised. But then he was committed to providing a more critical and so more adequate account of the issues involved as well as a proposal for their resolution.[54]

Kant's "First Critique" was an analysis of the limits of what could be called "pure" or *a priori* knowledge. It was an analytic account of the constitution of scientific or theoretical knowledge and at the same time an account of the inevitable appearance of and constitution of metaphysics. The "Second Critique" focused on the rational grounds of morality, given that moral obligation could not be based on empirical experience or knowledge in the proper sense. But did these two critiques then leave two forms of reason? Were science and ethics ultimately isolated from one another? The "Third Critique" was an effort to show how the two fundamentally different domains of reason (theoretical and practical) could yet be related to one another. For present purposes it is Kant's division of the rational domain between the theoretical and the practical, between science and ethics, which is of particular interest.

Kant's approach to the epistemological issues raised by the radical empiricists was to fundamentally reconceive them. He understood his approach to be analogous to that taken by Copernicus. The preface of the second edition of Kant's *Critique of Pure Reason* contains his own description of this analogy. There he wrote:

> Failing of satisfactory progress in explaining the movements of the heavenly bodies on the supposition that they all revolved around the spectator, [Copernicus] tried whether he might not have better success if he made the spectator to revolve and the stars to remain at rest. A similar experiment can be tried in metaphysics, as regards the *intuition* of objects. If intuition must conform to the constitution of the objects, I do not see how we could know anything of the latter *a priori*; but if the object (as object of the senses) must conform to the constitution of our faculty of intuition, I have no difficulty conceiving such a possibility.[55]

By "intuition" Kant meant sensory impression, what the empiricists referred to as sensation or sense data. What Kant was proposing in contrast to previous epistemological analyses was not to ask how the mind conformed to the constitution of the objects of sense experience but instead how objects of experience conformed to the constitution of the mind. For Kant the mind was not to be seen as a passive receptor of sensory impressions but rather as an active shaper of what comprised empirical experience. Prior to any experience the mind had a structure which made such experience possible. Due to this *a priori* structure objects of experience had the form they had. But this meant further that the objects of experience were not simply representations of things-in-themselves. Thus, Kant made a formal and fundamental distinction between phenomena (the objects of experience) and noumena (things-in-themselves). The former were the objects of scientific investigation.

In answer then to the question, "How can we have a knowledge of nature?" Kant replied that such knowledge was possible because the mind participated actively in the formation of empirical experience as sense intuition was shaped by the categories of the understanding. Thus, Kant agreed with

Hume that causality was not simply there in the natural order and then merely perceived by the knower; but at the same time, he disagreed with Hume by saying that the very constitution of the human understanding was such that empirical experience, in order to be experience at all, had to have a causal form.[56] In this way Kant sought to legitimize the products of scientific investigation. Science was the investigation of phenomena, the products of the interaction of the senses and the categories of the understanding.

But what then of noumena, of things-in-themselves? What then of that which is unconditioned by the categories of the understanding? What then of the whole causal nexus of the world? What then of myself as a thinking subject as such? What then of the perfect unity of all objects and qualities, namely, God? What then of the objects of traditional metaphysical attention (the world as a whole, the self and God)?

Kant defined noumena with difficulty and ambiguously.[57] Kant's dilemma was the need to speak of an entity about which nothing could be said, not even that it existed. As he noted, it was that which could in principle be the object of a non-sensory, intellectual intuition. But for Kant the only form of intuition available to the human mind was sense intuition. Thus, noumena could not properly have a positive definition but only a negative one. So, for Kant these were objects beyond experience and so beyond the reach of the understanding. Their existence could not be proved. Yet, it was to the noumenal domain that Kant ascribed such traditional metaphysical objects as the world, the soul (or self) and God. But if these "objects" were noumenal, were we then condemned to silence regarding them?

Kant did not intend to remain silent here. For in his view such ideas as the world as a causal unity, the unified self or soul as an immortal and free agent and God as the perfect unity of all existence, these ideas were necessary as practical conditions for the possibility of seeking knowledge of the world and acting morally. But, he was at the same time determined to exclude these transcendental ideas from the domain of knowledge proper. He sought such exclusion in order to undercut the pretensions of metaphysical dogmatism which he saw as a threat to genuine morality. Thus, he declared: "I have therefore found it necessary to deny *knowledge*, in order to make room for *faith*. The dogmatism of metaphysics, that is, the preconception that it is possible to make headway in metaphysics without a previous criticism of pure reason, is the source of all that unbelief, always very dogmatic, which wars against morality."[58] Kant saw his critical project, then, not simply as an exercise in arcane speculative philosophy but as one addressing the fundamental questions concerning the possibility of moral action given the nature of human knowledge in the light of the human situation.

It was in his "Second Critique," *The Critique of Practical Reason*, that Kant offered an extended analysis of the grounding of morality, and thereby religion, in reason exercised not "to know" but "to do," reason not as a means to understanding but as a guide to human agency.

Kant identified rational beings, in general, and human beings, in particular, as "ends in themselves." This position did not originate with the "Second Critique." Already in his *Foundations of the Metaphysics of Morals* published in 1785 Kant had developed this notion and by means of it had made a fundamental distinction between "persons" and "things."[59] This distinction is very reminiscent of Descartes' ontological distinction between beings with souls (i.e., with the capacity for thought) and things which were merely mechanical.[60] Still, what is of special significance for the present discussion is Kant's placement of the human subject at the intersection of the phenomenal and noumenal worlds, a placement which both emphasized the uniqueness of humanity and the duality of human existence.

At the conclusion of the "Second Critique" Kant expressed the focal character of the human subject in terms which are even more dramatically cosmological and religious when he wrote that

> Two things fill the mind with ever new and increasing admiration and awe, the oftener and more steadily they are reflected on: the starry heavens above me and the moral law within me. I do not merely conjecture them and seek them as though obscured in the darkness or in the transcendent region beyond my horizon: I see them before me, and I associate them directly with the conscious-ness of my own existence.[61]

But here again we are left with a problem comparable to that which plagued Descartes. To assert with Descartes that it is in humanity that the material and the spiritual (or mental or moral) are conjoined or to assert with Kant that rational beings are at the vertex of the phenomenal and the noumenal does not explain how this is the case. Descartes sought a physiological answer to this problem through his analysis of the function of the pineal gland. Kant sought a cognitional answer.

In his "Third Critique," Kant defined the act of judgment as "thinking the particular as contained under the universal."[62] Given this definition, judgment could be seen to operate in two directions: in one direction there was a determinate judgment when a particular was subsumed under a given universal, as for example when the motion of a particular planet was subsumed under the laws of Newtonian mechanics; in the other direction there was a reflective judgment when an unknown universal was sought given only particulars, as when one sought to unify a manifold of natural phenomena under a single natural law or set of laws. It was the latter of these two forms of judgment which was of special interest to Kant for it was by means of the reflective judgment that one was led to a recognition of the principle of the "finality of nature." By this principle Kant meant that though empirical experience led to a multiplicity of natural laws, there was implicit in the search for such laws an *a priori* judgment that nature was a whole and that such laws formed a unified system. This was not a conclusion which derived from empirical experience itself; thus, it was not itself a law of nature. It was, however, the fundamental reflective judgment which made possible the pursuit of empirical laws.[63]

Given the foregoing discussion it is now possible to suggest a summary of the main features which came to characterize the "modern" and "critical" consciousness whose development was bracketed by the works of Descartes and Kant. The first was a cosmic, metaphysical and epistemological dualism. While Descartes' dualism was expressed primarily in cosmological (or metaphysical) terms, Kant manifested a comparable dualism in epistemological terms which while explicitly non-metaphysical in the classical sense was nevertheless quasi-metaphysical in form.

The second was an acceptance of a mechanistic natural order described in Euclidian geometric terms. Descartes' dualism of matter and spirit (body and mind) helped to set the foundations for a view of the cosmos as machine. In addition, he presumed the cosmos to be Euclidian in character. Kant assumed Newtonian mechanics to be the authoritative description of the phenomenal world and in concert with that physics he also assumed that space had the character described for it in the geometry of Euclid.

The third feature was an unquestioned confidence in the power of reason. Both Descartes and Kant shared a confidence in the capacity of reason to identify and explicate the fundamental structure of things, though they had very different ideas as to what that structure was and how reason was to proceed to identify and explicate it.

The fourth was a commitment to analysis as the fundamental methodological approach. Both Descartes and Kant shared a methodological view which held that a whole was to be understood through an analysis of the parts comprising it and their relations.

The fifth feature was a cosmic anthropocentrism. How could a human being be both a mechanical object and a thinking subject? How could human action be both in conformity with determinate natural law and also be autonomous and free as required for moral responsibility? For both Descartes and Kant their analytic success in distinguishing between two cosmic, substantial and epistemic domains mitigated against their being able to consider the world in general or human existence especially as integrated or whole. Thus, both sought in human existence itself a solution which would overcome the problematics created by their dualisms.

The sixth was an explicit critique of the received metaphysical tradition, a critique which itself was dependent upon a revised metaphysic held implicitly. While Descartes' effort was aimed explicitly at overcoming what he saw to be the deficiencies of scholastic Aristotelian metaphysics, his own attempt to deduce a unified science from indubitably known "first principles" was a metaphysical enterprise methodologically linked to his scholastic forebears. Further, although Descartes' explicit metaphysical dualism fell under Kant's critique of the use of pure theoretical reason, Kant's own epistemology reestablished a quasi-metaphysical dualism which profoundly influenced subsequent generations.

Evidence of the power of the thought of Descartes and Kant is found in the fact that, even when those that followed them were explicitly critical of their results, these critics still tended to accept tacitly a "modern" and "critical" cosmological vision. Three developments are of particular significance for they form the immediate contemporary milieu within which a "post-modern" and "post-critical" consciousness is emerging.

One of these developments was logical positivism. The term "positivism" was coined by August Compte in his *Positive Philosophy* written between 1830 and 1842. The development of logical positivism is ordinarily associated with the discussions of the "Vienna Circle" in the first quarter of this century.[64] In general, the logical positivists assumed that the only real world was the world of objects as experienced by the senses. Kant's phenomenal world, described in observational language or language which related observations, was the only reality.[65] Both Descartes' domain of mind (or spirit) and Kant's noumenal domain were removed not only from the arena of knowledge but from that of reality as well. Language which made reference to "noumenal entities" (e.g., the world as a whole, the self and God) was neither true nor false but formally senseless.[66] The logical positivists assumed that observation was merely a matter of looking and seeing and that observational language was simply conventional. It can be said that the logical positivists accepted the division of reality into the material and the mental, the phenomenal and the noumenal, but then ascribed reality only to that which was material or phenomenal.

A second development was existentialism. Existentialism emerged as a criticism of the rationalist orientation of both Cartesian and Kantian (and later Hegelian) thought. While itself critical of the construction of quasi-scientific, rationalist metaphysical systems, it also implicitly accepted the modern and critical dualistic division of existence. Although it rejected an idealistic metaphysic which viewed the "noumenal" or the "mental/spiritual" domain as that of the truly real, existentialism did focus on this domain as that having the greatest significance for human existence.

Soren Kierkegaard was one of the important figures in the formation of the existentialist position. He was not only vigorously critical of the idealist metaphysic of his day (the Hegelian "System"), against rationalists of all stripes he also asserted a fundamental gap between the realm of knowledge and that of faith. For Kierkegaard the domain of faith was central to authentic human existence and that domain was a-rational in character.[67] For existentialists, in general, the natural world as such came to be viewed as having relatively little importance while the world of personal existence was seen as central. Like both Descartes and Kant, the existentialists manifested a formative anthropocentrism. Thus, while not rejecting the reality of nature or the material world, the existentialists tended to disregard it and focused instead on human choice and action as the elements distinctively determinate of human being.[68]

The final development of special interest was Protestant neo-orthodoxy. This theological position is most often identified paradigmatically with the works of Karl Barth.[69] It emerged as a critique of the tendency of 18th and 19th century theological liberalism to accommodate religious doctrine to the findings of the empirical sciences, or, to use more typically Kantian language, the tendency to justify the demands of practical reason on the basis of the categories of theoretical reason. It also drew upon existential views which focused reflective theological attention narrowly on the "noumenal" domain of faith and moral action. At the same time, it manifested a form of positivism (what might be called "revelational positivism") in that it was held that the Christian scriptures contained an indubitable knowledge revealed by God and accessible to any who would but "look and see." Again, while not rejecting the material world, neo-orthodoxy posited a noumenal theological world (the domain of "salvation history") both above, in a value sense, and beyond, in a metaphysical sense, the realm of nature.

While these three developments were not the only ones of significance which emerged in relation to the Copernican/Galilean/Newtonian revolution in physics and the collateral Cartesian/Kantian revolution in philosophy, they were the developments which are most particularly relevant to a consideration of the contemporary relation of cosmology to Christian theology. The mechanistic cosmology of Newtonian physics has now been virtually supplanted by an evolutionary and quantum/relativistic cosmology which has taken form out of the works of Darwin, Einstein, Bohr and others. This shift in astro-physical cosmology has been accompanied by a broader shift in philosophical cosmology and epistemology.

One can reasonably claim that, on balance, the Modern (and Critical) worldview continues to form the dominant perspective in contemporary Western and Christian culture. It is found in the popular understanding of science as an impersonal, detached and objective search for the facts of nature. Yet, the hegemony of this philosophical and related theological tradition is on the wane. In large part the decline is due, first, to developments which have occurred within the sciences themselves and, second, to philosophical developments growing out of reflection on that scientific activity. The newly emerging era may be far from midday, but it is well past dawn.

Beginning as early as the 17th century and continuing today another movement is underway. It can be identified as "post-modern". It has initiated yet another transformation of the tacit Western understanding of the cosmos.

This movement has been occurring along two axes. Along the first axis attention has been focused on biological phenomena. Along the other the focus has been on the most fundamental constituents and relations of the cosmos. In recent years these axes have become intertwined. The resulting history of these developments therefore is a rich and complex one. Thus, again, any brief account of it is problematic. Nevertheless, as the character of the modern period was closely tied to the cosmological revolution beginning with Copernicus and reaching its culmination in the classical mechanics of Newton, so the character of the post-modern period can be said to be closely tied to the emergence of a vision of the cosmos as evolutionary, relational and indeterminate.

In 1859 Charles Darwin published *On the Origin of the Species*. It is customary to mark the beginning of evolutionary theory with this work. While such a practice is not inappropriate, it does mask the cultural context which provided the intellectual medium within which Darwin's theory was incubated. As much as Newton, Darwin "stood on the shoulders of giants."

For example, developmental biological theories had existed in pre-Socratic times. As early as about 550 B.C. the philosophers of Miletos proposed a developmental and historical explanation for the origin of the cosmos. Most notable among these was Anaximander of whose works only a few fragments remain. Later the Epicureans, as exemplified in the works of Lucretius, also understood the world as having come to be by means of an historical process. However, these views were overshadowed for the most part by those of the Platonists and the Aristotelians, especially as these latter views were joined theologically with the Hebrew creation myths which were preserved in both the Jewish and Christian scriptures.

Others who provided a foundation for Darwin's work include the Englishman, John Ray (1627-1705), and the Swede, Carolus Linnaeus (1701-1778), both of whom developed concepts of species based on criteria associated with reproductive capacity. Pierre Louis Moreau de Maupertuis (1648-1759) proposed a theory of inheritance which accounted both for the transmission of particular characteristics of parents to offspring and for the variable dominance of those characteristics. Yet Maupertuis' theory was effectively lost to the scientific community of his own day due largely to his being ridiculed in a dispute he had with Voltaire over the direction of the Berlin Academy of Sciences.

More immediately related to the intellectual climate within which Darwin's thought was formed were the works of George Louis Leclerc de Buffon (1707-1788), Jean Baptiste Pierre Antoine de Monet Chevalier de Lamarck (1744-1829), and Georges Leopold Cuvier (1769-1832). Buffon was one of the first to attempt to determine the age of the earth based on experimental evidence.[70] His results, though well below present estimates, pointed to a geological age (c. 75,000 years) well in excess of that determined by calculating from the geneologies found in the Bible (c. 6,000 years). However, while Buffon placed the formation of the earth in a geological history, he denied such an historical process to the biological domain.

In contrast Lamarck proposed a developmental bio-history to account for the origin and diversity of life. Lamarck believed that there was a connection between geo-history and bio-history. However, his contribution to the development of evolutionary theory was not without flaw. Lamarck was so convinced of his general interpretation of biological development that he sought to justify it by proposing a multitude of hypothetical answers. Perhaps his best known proposal was the theory of the inheritability of acquired characteristics.[71] This very multiplication of proposals ultimately had the effect of counting against his broad interpretation.[72]

One of his chief critics was Georges Leopold Cuvier. Cuvier was one of the outstanding taxonomists and paleontologists of his day. Drawing from the work of Buffon, Cuvier developed a catastrophic account of the Earth's natural history. For Cuvier, as for many others in his day, the catastrophes were seen as occasions of divine intervention. The most recent of the long series of such cataclysmic events was identified as the Noachin flood.

With the publication in 1830 of the first edition of *Principles of Geology*, George Lyell became the most prominent advocate of a uniformitarian, as opposed to a catastrophic, interpretation of the earth's geo-history. Lyell was not, however, the first to hold such a position. The pioneer of the uniformitarian view was another Scotsman, James Hutton. In a 1785 paper and in more substantial form in his two volumes, *Theory of the Earth*, published in 1789, Hutton argued that dislocations in the continuity of the fossil bearing strata were evidence of localized phenomena. More broadly the geologic evidence indicated a uniform operation of presently observed natural forces acting over very long periods of time. Hutton held that such processes as wind and water erosion, volcanic activity and sedimentation were sufficient given enough time to account for any particular geological feature.[73]

Lyell, like Hutton before him, challenged catastrophism on two grounds: the first had to do with the status of the evidence for radical discontinuities in the geological record and the second had to do with the logic of the interpretation of such observed discontinuities. In the light of geological evidence drawn from widely separated sources the discontinuities in the strata showed themselves to be highly local in nature. But, secondly, even where local discontinuities were present, they were to be expected since the forces of nature were destructive as well as constructive. Thus, Lyell argued, earlier strata could be eroded away and then replaced by sediments from a much later and environmentally different period. The fossil and geologic record was not one which nature kept with care.[74]

As will be noted shortly, Lyell's *Principles of Geology* was a major direct influence on the development of Darwin's evolutionary theory. Yet, Lyell himself refused to embrace Darwin's theory for a decade. Lyell viewed the idea of successive development or progressive advancement in nature as an expression of a providential (and so exceptional or catastrophic) rather than a natural or uniformitarian explanation of the present state of organic existence. Curiously, while he was prepared to accept that the species had maintained fixed forms from some primordial moment of divine creation, he could accept neither the view that the species appeared as the result of catastrophic events of divine intervention nor that speciation was a progressive working out of a divine creative plan.

Lyell's evolutionary skepticism was well founded. First, surveying the fossil evidence one did not automatically discover a developmental succession of organisms from the simplest to the most complex. For example, some marine genera seemed virtually unchanged over vast periods of time. Second, to use a human activity like selective breeding as an analogy to natural processes (as Darwin did) was, in Lyell's view, to invest nature with a degree of intentionality unwarranted by experience. Third, humanity appeared to be an anomaly for the progressive view both because human beings seemed to be a species of recent origin and because, for Lyell, the difference between a rational human and an instinctual animal was a categorical one.

In summary, then, three things should be noted in this all too brief discussion of the intellectual environment in the midst of which Darwin's theory of evolution appeared. First, the vision of a progressive history of life on earth did not originate with Darwin. Yet, prior to his work, transformational theories lacked a credible model for the mechanism of transformation. Second, the development of a theory of an evolving biosphere rested squarely on the extensive development of a theory of the earth as a developing geosphere. The recognition of the constitutive significance of the action of natural forces over long time was crucial. Yet, given the available evidence, such a recognition of developmental processes in the geological domain did not compel a parallel recognition of such processes in the biological. Finally, the theological storm which was to break over Darwin's hypothesis had already been foreshadowed in the conflict in geology between the catastrophists and the uniformitarians. Traditional theological chronologies could be accommodated by the theories of the former group. The views of the latter group required a fundamental reconsideration of the meaning of the chronologies found in the sacred texts. What all of this points to is the beginning of a transformation in cosmological vision from one in which the world was given, fixed and essentially static from a time of original creation to the present and toward a vision of the world as processional, developing and essentially dynamic. That Charles Darwin (1809-1882) became the focal figure in the early emergence of this shift of cosmic vision may rest in no small part in the flux of his own personal history.

Describing Darwin's scholarly preparation, John Hedley Brooke has written, "The fact that at Edinburgh [Darwin] preferred shooting to medicine, and at Cambridge beatles, botany and dissipation to a dedicated preparation for the ministry, has made him a classic case of the ne'er-do-well whose subsequent achievements far outstripped his promise as a scholar."[75] In a similar vein Toulmin and Goodfield write that

> the love of the countryside which he inherited from his mother and developed in his youth never left him; the standard education bored him; the dissecting-theatres at Edinburgh turned his stomach. Putting aside all ideas of following his father and grandfather into medicine, he inclined toward Holy Orders, and spent some years ostensibly training for the ministry.

> ... after six years of abortive study for two different professions, neither of which had proved to his taste, it finally became clear that Darwin's interests were those of a naturalist, and nothing else; the problem was to find some occupation in which these interests could be usefully exercised. By a happy chance his teacher, Professor Henslow, had the opportunity to recommend him for an appoint-

ment as chief naturalist with the naval survey ship <u>Beagle</u>, which was due to sail for South America.[76]

So at the age of twenty-three Darwin set out on a voyage which was to take nearly five years to complete. As chief naturalist on the survey, he collected a vast body of observations dealing with the flora and fauna of the lands visited by his ship. On the advice of his teacher Darwin took with him a copy of Lyell's *Principles of Geology* and read it during the voyage. It was to play a seminal role in his theoretical construction.

Ironically, although Henslow recommended Lyell's work to Darwin, he himself did not endorse Lyell's views. Henslow was a catastrophist. So was Darwin at the outset of his journey; however, upon reading Lyell, Darwin was converted to the uniformitarian position and this conversion provided him with a developmental framework within which to consider the observations he made during the voyage.

It is significant that Darwin did not set out with a theory already in mind, a theory for which he sought confirming data. Yet at the same time his observations were not recorded in a theoretical vacuum. As he became convinced of the correctness of Lyell's view that the earth had come to its present state due to presently observed natural forces operating uniformly over great time, so he wondered "both how species close in time and space could be so <u>different</u>, and how other species widely separated geographically could be so <u>similar</u>."[77] The problem was: if nature always acted the same way, how was it possible to account for the diversity of living things.

In his effort to develop an adequate theory Darwin also gained insight from two other sources. One source was the essay by Thomas Robert Malthus (1766-1834) entitled "An Essay on the Principle of Population." Malthus postulated the view that population growth was kept in check by such forces as the availability of food, war and disease.[78] Darwin read this essay in 1838 and wrote of it that

> Being well prepared to appreciate the struggle for existence that everywhere goes on from long-continued observation of the habits of animals and plants, it at once struck me [on reading Malthus] that under these circumstances favorable variations would tend to be preserved, and unfavorable ones to be destroyed. The result of this would be the formation of a new species. Here then I had at last got a theory by which to work.[79]

The other source which gave Darwin additional theoretical insight was the practice of domestic breeding. As a sportsman and a naturalist Darwin was familiar with a wide range of breeding activities both in plants and animals. The intent of such breeding was to select certain desirable characteristics and propogate them through succeeding generations. It was this selectivity which provided Darwin with an analogy by means of which to describe the mechanism which brought about the transformation of existing species into new species. Thus, he called this mechanism "natural selection."[80]

For Darwin the comprehensive process by which species were transformed actually involved two mechanisms: the mechanism of variation and the mechanism of selection. First, there appeared in all species spontaneous variations of characteristics.[81] Second, because some of these variations gave the organism possessing them a competitive advantage in adaptation to its environment, such an organism was "selected" for greater success in the struggle for life as were its offspring to which it transmitted the variation. What is important to recognize is that these two mechanisms were decoupled: that is, novel characteristics were not generated to meet the exigencies of the environment.[82] In fact, many variations actually proved to be disadvantageous.[83] The variations were random or indeterminate. The environment was like a sieve through which certain of the variations so generated passed more easily than others.

As is perhaps evident, one of the primary impacts of Darwin's theory was that it fundamentally undercut the concept of design in nature. Previously, natural theologians, notably William Paley (1743 -1805), had argued that the functional unity of the organs of a single creature or, more broadly, the fitness of organisms to their environments stood as testimony to God as the designer of the cosmos. Given a Cartesian/Newtonian model of universe as a great machine, it not suprising that the natural theologians would find a "watch/watchmaker" analogy to be an appropriate one by which to express the relationship between the cosmos and God.[84] But now, on the basis of his evolutionary theory, Darwin could account for fitness either of organs in an organism or organisms in the environment as a consequence of the forces of nature without assuming that such fittedness was a goal which guided those forces. Again, for Darwin, variation and selection were decoupled mechanisms in the comprehensive evolutionary process. They were related in that the former without consideration of the latter provided the raw materials (indeterminate variations) upon which the latter operated in a selective manner.[85] Thus, Darwin's world was not simply given. Nor was it merely the temporal working out of a pre-established divine plan. Instead, it was a radically historical world in which the convergence of specific circumstantial factors were ontologically constitutive.

It should be noted further that the evolutionary position undercut an essentialist understanding of nature. That is, that group of individuals which could be identified on given taxological criteria as a species was not a set of beings ontologically separate from all other such groups in some primordial period. Rather, a species was a grouping of unique historical individuals sharing a common descent whose identity as a group depended upon the categorical interests of the taxonomist. Put another way, in an evolving world all living things formed a seamless fabric in which patterns of relatedness (e.g., species) were in no small way in the eye of the beholder.[86]

These notions of the wholeness or interconnectedness of existence and the dependence for an understanding of reality on the standpoint of the observer have been reinforced along the second axis upon which the contemporary cosmological perspective has been developing. Along this axis there has been an effort to understand the most fundamental relationships which constitute the cosmos at the extreme macro and micro scales. It is in this effort that both relativity theory and quantum theory have emerged. As in the story of the development of the theory of biological evolution, here also there have been a host of characters each of whom made a significant contribution to what has become the contemporary vision of the cosmos.[87] However, there are three figures of exceptional prominence: Albert Einstein (1879-1955), Niels Bohr (1885-1972) and Werner Heisenberg (1901-). From the imaginations of these three issued the special and general theories of relativity, quantum theory and the principle of uncertainty. In order to sketch the current state of cosmological theory at both the very large and the very small scales, it is necessary to give a brief summary of this set of theoretical developments.

In 1905 Einstein published three papers: on heat, on electricity and on light. The first offered a mechanical interpretation of heat phenomena, the second used the quantum hypothesis developed by Max Planck (1858-1947) to provide a theoretical explanation of the photoelectric effect (and also introduced the notion of the photon as a quantum of light) and the third, "On the Electrodynamics of Moving Bodies," was Einstein's first paper on special relativity.[88]

Two assumptions underlay Einstein's development of special relativity. The first was that the laws of nature took the same form for all unaccelerated observers. This assumption seemed reasonable enough. It was not unlike the uniformitarian assumption that the laws of nature operate uniformly throughout the cosmos both in space and in time. Einstein's second assumption was rather less reasonable: it was that light has a constant velocity regardless of the velocity of its source. This assumption violated the "common sense" of Newtonian mechanics in which the velocity of an emitted object was effected by the velocity of the source of emission.[89] Yet, this assumption was not merely a conjecture.

In 1881 by himself and again in 1887 with Edward Morely, Albert Michelson (1852-1931) had carried out a series of experiments which measured the velocity of light.[90] He was intent upon providing experimental evidence of the motion of the earth through the aether, that theoretical medium which was assumed to be at absolute rest and within which electromagnetic waves were understood to be propogated.[91] Much to Michelson's suprise, however, the measured velocity of light remained essentially constant regardless of the direction in which it was measured, whether in the direction of the earth's motion about the sun or perpendicular to that motion. For Einstein the reason was clear. Light had a constant velocity regardless of the motion of its source.

Yet, this conclusion led to even stranger conclusions. Principally, it indicated that the notion of simultaneity was dependent upon the frame of reference within which the temporal relation of the occurrence of two events was to be measured.[92] But, if the judgment of simultaneity was so dependent, then the notion of absolute time, which was explicitly a part of classical Newtonian mechanics, was fallaceous. And not only absolute time but absolute space also. For Einstein was able to demonstrate theoretically that just as measurements of time were dependent upon the velocity of the frame of reference of the observer, so also were measurements of space.[93]

What emerged from Einstein's 1905 papers was a vision of a world radically different from that imagined by Newton. For the latter there was an absolute frame of reference within which absolute determinations of spatial distance and temporal duration could be made. It was possible to imagine, in effect, a "God's-eye-view" of the universe. For Einstein, on the contrary, every observation whether of distance or of duration was relative to the motion of the frame of reference of the observer. Thus, in principle, what could be meant by a "God's-eye-view" became highly problematic.

It is one of the quirks of the way in which shifts of cosmological perspective become infused in popular culture that many people identify Einstein's theory of relativity with the formula, $E=mc^2$. This is not entirely inappropriate because this expression does appear as one outcome of the analysis of energy relations within the context of special relativity. However, understanding the meaning of the formula as a mathematical expression does not require a collateral recognition that its cosmological meaning cuts as sharply across the grain of "common sense" (i.e., Newtonian) physics as does the variability of time and space. Yet it is these notions taken together and subsequently supported experimentally which reveal a universe significantly different from the one envisaged by Newton: a universe in which space and time are not independent but form a continuum; a universe in which dynamic relatedness is constitutive of reality. In Newton's mechanical universe things moved without undergoing essential change. In Einstein's cosmos motion effected the substance of things.

Einstein went on to generalize his theory for all frames of reference in order to extend it to non-inertial frames (i.e., those which were accelerating with respect to one another). It was in this context that he expressed his "principle of equivalence;" namely, that no absolute distinction could be made between one's experience of gravity and one's experience of uniform accelera- tion. The two phenomena were equivalent.[94] Further development of this general theory of relativity led to the discovery that the world was most adequately modeled (for cosmological purposes) not in the terms of Euclidean geometry but instead in non-Euclidean terms; that is, terms by which the curvature of space/time could be expressed. In the general theory of relativity the "force of gravity" was no longer conceived as some mysterious force acting at a distance (a conception which was already problematic within a mechanical cosmology) but rather it was conceived as an acceleration consequent upon the curvature of space/time.

In the discussion thus far, relativity theory would appear to describe the cosmos primarily at the macro or large scale. However, the theory also has bearing at the micro or atomic and sub-atomic levels. For it is at this very small scale that the velocities of the objects under investigation are significant fractions of the speed of light and thus relativistic phenomena are more pronounced. Yet, it was not Einstein but Neils Bohr with his initial develop- ment of quantum theory who laid the foundation for the contemporary understanding of atomic structure.[95]

Bohr was fascinated by a problem which arose from a consideration of Ernest Rutherford's planetary model of the atom.[96] If one applied classical Newtonian mechanics to this model, one was led to the curious conclusion that atoms should "rundown;" that is, the electrons should lose their energy. However, this was contrary to observation. Atoms were remarkably stable entities. In an act of creative synthesis Bohr constructed an explanation for this apparent anomaly by combining with the Rutherford model the notion that, just as radiant energy came in "clumps" or quanta (as described by Max Planck in 1900), the mechanical energy of an electron could also be described in quantum terms. In 1913, two years prior to Einstein's paper on general relativity, Bohr published his quantum theory of the atom in a paper entitled, "On the Constitution of Atoms and Molecules."

In Bohr's theory the electron was conceived as a particle, an object, an exceedingly small substantial thing. However, in 1924 Louis de Broglie developed a quantum atomic model in which electrons were conceived not as particles but as waves. In 1926 the Austrian physicist, Erwin Schrödinger, generalized de Broglie's model to include any "particles" moving in a field of force. Schrödinger's equations were shown to be capable of producing the results obtained from Bohr's quantum theory and in addition were able to address questions which Bohr's theory had been unable to answer.

Schrödinger's approach, however, assumed that it was possible to completely quantify sub-atomic phenomena. Yet, also in 1926, Werner Heisenberg published a paper on quantum theory utilizing matrix mathematics which challenged this assumption. Heisenberg's formulation of quantum theory assumed that quantum phenomena were unanalyzable. From his perspective one could know the beginning states and the end states of quantum phenomena but could only speculate about what happened in between. At first, the coincidence of the results of two radically distinctive approaches to the characterization of sub-atomic phenomena caused great consternation in the physics community. But it was Schrodinger himself who demonstrated that the two theoretical approaches were mathematically identical, the one being simply another form of the other.

Still, an important question remained unanswered. What were sub-atomic "particles?" Were they small bits of stuff or were they waves? But, if waves, waves of what? Actually, there were two questions here. First, was the material world constituted of particles (little bits of stuff) or of waves (undulations in some medium)? Second, what was that stuff or medium? Bohr's answer to the first question was, "Yes!" The material world could be adequately described neither exclusively in terms of particles nor in terms of waves. The two modes of description were complementary.[97] If this answer seemed troubling, the answer to the second question was even more so. What was it that constituted the world be it particles and/or waves; what was the "stuff" of the universe? The answer was nothing or, more accurately, "no thing." The cosmos was not constituted of stuff at all but of dynamic potentiality.[98]

As noted earlier Heisenberg based his development of quantum theory on the principle that sub-atomic phenomena were unanalyzable, that they could not be described in explicit detail. In 1930 he published his account of why such analysis could not in principle be done. This was the presentation of his "uncertainty principle."[99] The principle of uncertainty undercut the modern and critical rationalist presupposition that the world could in principle be described completely in explicit terms.[100] According to Heisenberg the absolute determination of the state of a sub-atomic particle in space and in time was not possible. This inability to make such a determination was due neither to the clumsiness of the instruments of observation nor an inadequacy in the techniques of measurement. Instead, quantum uncertainty was due to the very relational character of particular attributes of reality. Thus, for example, one could determine the location of an electron with relative certainty but only at the expense of determining its velocity and vice versa. This coupling of variables also applied to such relations as time and energy, angular momentum and angular position, and inertia and angular velocity. In each case the accuracy of the determination of one term could be increased only by also increasing the uncertainty of the determination of the other term. Milic Capek has suggested that Heisenberg's principle might better have been called the "principle of indeterminacy" rather than that of uncertainty.[101]

It is in relation to the foregoing developments in quantum theory that particular epistemological issues arose. Did quantum theory describe the world or was it simply a very effective mathematical means by which to correlate certain experimental observations? As Heisenberg himself expressed the problem, "the transition between the 'possible' and the 'actual' takes place during the act of observation. If we want to describe what happens in an atomic event, we have to realize that the word 'happens' can only apply to the observation, not to the state of affairs between two observations."[102] What quantum theory indicated, given its interpretation by Bohr and Heisenberg (what has come to be called the "Copenhagen Interpretation"), was that in the nature of things there is no absolute distinction to be made between an object to be observed and the observing subject. Again, as Heisenberg put it:

> we have to remember that what we observe is not nature in itself but nature exposed to our method of questioning. Our scientific work in physics consists in asking questions about nature in the language we possess and trying to get an answer from experiment by the means that are at our disposal. In this way quantum theory reminds us, as Bohr has put it, of the old wisdom that when searching for harmony in life one must never forget that in the drama of existence we are ourselves both players and spectators.[103]

It is important to note that this position does not imply some form of subjectivism, much less one of solipsism. On the other hand, it does indicate that the classical dualism (in the Cartesian/Kantian sense) between subject and object, knower and known, mind and matter, realism and idealism are inadequate distinctions either in terms of the world as it is known or in terms of the means by which the world is known.[104]

One of the major historical conflicts of scientific interpretation has been that between Einstein's understanding of the meaning of quantum theory and those of Bohr and Heisenberg. Einstein was deeply troubled by the probabilistic indeterminacy of the "Copenhagen Interpretation." At heart Einstein was a determinist and a realist in the tradition of Newton and the "classical" mechanists.[105]

In the past two decades physicists have sought to combine relativity and quantum theories to form a unified vision of the origin and structure of the cosmos. Particularly through the efforts of Murray Gell-Mann, Stephen Weinberg, Abdus Salam and Sheldon Glashow progress has been made toward the development of "grand unification theories," commonly referred to as GUTs.[106] GUTs are theories which seek to provide in a single formalization a unified account of the four basic forces which seem to constitute the cosmos: the weak force associated with radioactive decay, the strong force which binds the atom together as a stable entity, electromagnetic force and gravitational force. Thus far, the first three of these have been formally unified. GUTs have yet to include the gravitational force. The GUTs are constructed from an integration of relativity and quantum theories. They also represent a wedding of physics with evolutionary theory in that they provide a cosmogeny, a theoretical but historical account of the earliest stages of the formation of the cosmos.

In such a cosmos, then, one in which existence is constitutively indeterminate, one in which basic determinations of distance and duration are relative to the motion of observer and observed, one in which the act of observation is itself constitutive of what is observed, — in such a universe questions concerning the character of the universe as a whole are problematic in the extreme. Of course, such questions are not strictly speaking empirical ones on any account for there is no place "outside" the cosmos where one could stand to "see" the cosmos as a whole.[107] At the same time, some vision of the nature of the cosmos as a whole orients the way in which a community and more broadly a culture understands itself. Within modern/critical culture, for example, the orienting vision is a dualistic one in which there is the phenomenal domain of the cosmic machine, on the one hand, and the noumenal domain of mind or spirit or God, on the other.

An explicit post-modern and post-critical cosmology is still coalescing in both the sciences proper and in speculative philosophy. Therefore, the formation of such a vision at the tacit or cultural level is still very tentative. Nevertheless, the British physicist, David Bohm, has described one possibility for such a vision.[108]

What Bohm proposes is that the cosmos be conceived not as a thing but as a movement. He makes this proposal by distinguishing between what he calls the "explicate order" and the "implicate order." For Bohm this distinction parallels one made between a "mechanistic" cosmic vision and a "holistic" one. From the mechanistic viewpoint the cosmos is perceived as comprised of relatively autonomous entities (particles) which interact externally with one another. In contrast, from a holistic perspective, "individual" entities are explications of a more fundamental implicate order in which everything is enfolded into everything else. The following extended quotation provides a summary of Bohm's position:

approaching the question in different ways, relativity and quantum theory agree, in that both imply the need to look on the world as an undivided whole, in which all parts of the universe, including the observer and his instruments, merge and unite in one totality. In this totality, the atomic form of insight is a simplification and an abstraction, valid only in some limited context.

The new form of insight can best be called Undivided Whole-ness in Flowing Movement. This implies that flow is, in some sense, prior to the 'things' that can be seen to form and dissolve in this flow....

The proposal for a new general form of insight is that all matter is of this nature: that is, there is a universal flux that cannot be defined explicitly but which can be known only implicitly, as indicated by explicitly definable forms and shapes, some stable and some unstable, that can be abstracted from the universal flow. In this flow, mind and matter are not separate substances. Rather, they are different aspects of one whole and unbroken movement.[109]

Bohm calls this "undivided wholeness in flowing movement" the "holomovement." Of it he writes that

in its totality, the holomovement is not limited in any specifiable way at all. It is not required to conform to any particular order, or to be bounded by any particular measure. Thus, the holomovement is undefinable and immeasurable.

To give primary significance to the undefinable and immeas-urable holomovement implies that it has no meaning to talk of a fundamental theory, on which all physics could find a permanent basis, or to which all the phenomena of physics could ultimately be reduced. Rather, each theory will abstract a certain aspect that is relevant only in some limited context, which is indicated by some appropriate measure.[110]

As will be seen below, Bohm's conclusions seem to form interesting parallels with Ludwig Wittgenstein's reflections on the relation of language to the world, Thomas Kuhn's analysis of the growth of scientific knowledge and Michael Polanyi's description of the tacit foundation of all explicit knowing.

This then ends the survey of those developments over the past 150 years which have been leading to a fundamental shift in the cosmological perspective of Western culture. However, it must be acknowledged again that this survey is by no means exhaustive and this for at least two reasons. First, many aspects of this broad development have gone unmentioned, as for example, specific developments in mathematics, in chemistry and bio-chemistry, in the social and human sciences and even in other areas of biology and physics (e.g., thermodynamics). But second, this survey cannot be exhaustive because the transformation being described here is not complete either in the explicit or in the tacit sense. Nevertheless, I would assert here that the broad outlines of the terminal form of this transformation can be discerned. To demonstrate this, however, it is necessary to bring together individual thinkers whose positions may appear at odds and who in some instances explicitly challenge one another's intellectual projects. Yet, I would hold that those who appear in the following discussion form a company of "tacit colleagues" whose individual philosophical contributions form major elements of the intellectual mosaic which gives meaning to the terms post-modern and post-critical.[111]

Among those who have given shape to the emerging post-modern and post-critical perspective, Ludwig Wittgenstein is an inter-paradigmatic figure. His philosophical sensibilities were shaped both by the cosmological shift occurring within the sciences (particularly mathematical physics) and the dynamics of cultural flux in turn-of-the-century Vienna.[112] It could be said that Wittgenstein's philosophical program initially took on a modern and critical form but that it ultimately issued in a position which is central to a post-modern and post-critical understanding of the nature and function of language. But it must be acknowledged that, in so saying, a relationship is asserted which Wittgenstein himself might well have denied.

To the English speaking world Wittgenstein has been something of an enigma. On the one hand, he has appeared to be a philosopher with an exceptional capacity for logical analysis. On the other hand, he has been seen as an individual whose personal characteristics bordered on (if not resided fully within) the eccentric. As Stephen Toulmin recalls, "We [students] saw him as a divided man, as an English-speaking philosopher with a uniquely original technical genius, who just happened also to adhere personally to an extreme moral individualism and egalitarianism."[113] In spite of, or perhaps because of, this initial impression Toulmin along with Alan Janik has sought to provide a cohesive interpretation of Wittgenstein and his work which overcomes this apparent bifurcation. In this effort they have given primary attention to the historical, cultural and intellectual environment within which Wittgenstein was nurtured and to his first published work, the *Tractatus Logico-Philosoph-icus*.[114] While they themselves acknowledge that their argument for this interpretation is largely circumstantial and is therefore not conclusive, it does appear persuasive in the context of the general analysis of this present study.

The more common "received interpretation" of the *Tractatus* identifies Wittgenstein's effort there as an attempt to address issues of logic raised in the works of Gottlob Frege and Bertrand Russell.[115] In this account the *Tractatus* has been seen to represent a philosophical position in sharp contrast with that found in Wittgenstein's later writings.[116] It is a part of Toulmin and Janik's project to suggest that the typical division of Wittgenstein into "earlier" and "later" is not only unnecessary but also misleading. They contend that an adequate interpretation of the *Tractatus* requires an appreciation of the philosophical themes which Wittgenstein developed more extensively in his subsequent writings. In particular, they argue that at the heart of such an interpretation is an understanding of Wittgenstein, the person, (rather than Wittgenstein, the logician) embedded in a particular family which was itself embedded in Viennese culture (art, politics, literature, philosophy, science, etc.) in the first decades of this century. In short, they hold that Wittgenstein came to the logical problems associated with the work of Frege and Russell already possessing philosophical concerns stimulated by the works of Kant, Schopenhauer and Kierkegaard, concerns which were essentially ethical and personal rather than logical.[117]

The works of these three philosophers exhibit a progressive widening of the conceptual distance between fact and value. For Kant, value was related to the domain of the noumena while fact was restricted to the domain of phenomena. Issues of value were addressed by means of the critical exercise of the practical reason while issues of fact were addressed by means of the critical exercise of theoretical reason.

For Schopenhauer the foundation of value lay beyond reason in any form. It lay instead in the domain of feeling. He saw morality as a restraint of egoism in response to a compassionate feeling for others.

For Kierkegaard the ground of morality was still further beyond reason in the realm of the absurd. No exercise of reason or form of rational analysis could lead to a determination of the authentic moral action. Instead what was required was an act of commitment, a "leap of faith," which was discontinuous with reason.

This movement by which the ethical became farther and farther separated from the rational also represented a shift of the center for ethical deliberation from the public domain to the private, from the social to the individual. In so doing this movement effectively removed discourse on value from the arena of the logical and the empirical. This shift is reflected in what for many is the enigmatic conclusion of the *Tractatus* where Wittgenstein wrote:

> My propositions serve as elucidations in the following way: anyone who understands me eventually recognizes them as nonsensical, when he has used them — as steps — to climb beyond them. (He must, so to speak, throw away the ladder after he has climbed it.)

> He must transcend these propositions, and then he will see the world aright.

> What we cannot speak about we must pass over in silence.[118]

It is ironic that these final statements in the *Tractatus* have been taken by some philosophers, most notably those identified with the logical positivism of the Vienna Circle, to count against the significance of that about which nothing could be said. However, Paul Engelmann has suggested that such a conclusion is a gross misconstrual of Wittgenstein's intention. He has written that

> A whole generation of disciples was able to take Wittgenstein as a positivist, because he has something of enormous importance in common with positivists: he draws a line between what we can speak about and what we must be silent about just as they do. The difference is only that they have nothing to be silent about. Positivism holds — and this is its essence — that what we can speak about is all that matters in life. *Whereas Wittgenstein passionately believes that all that really matters in human life is precisely what, in his view, we must be silent about.* When he nevertheless takes immense pains to delimit the unimportant [i.e., the scope and limits of ordinary language], it is not the coastline of that island which he is bent on surveying with such meticulous accuracy, but the boundary of the ocean.[119]

To be sure, Wittgenstein believed that metaphysical discourse was a mistake, a misuse of language. In this he echoed Kant's concern about treating the noumenal as though it were phenomenal. At the same time, he views these mistakes as important ones. Thus he wrote, on the one hand, that "The essential thing about metaphysics: it obliterates the distinction between factual and conceptual investigations."[120] On the other hand, almost immediately he followed this judgment with the further conclusion that "In a certain sense one cannot take too much care in handling philosophical mistakes, they contain so much truth."[121]

For Wittgenstein the central philosophical error was to view language as representational, as pointing to some feature of the world. Instead language was best understood as a form of action, a way of doing something, through which the world showed. Wittgenstein saw in philosophy a tendency to hypostatize language, to treat concepts as though they were things. In so doing the sense of langauge as an activity embedded in life was lost. In contrast, he asserted that "to imagine a language means to imagine a form of life."[122] In the context of a form of life language is comparable to a game — an activity governed by rules to accomplish a purpose. There could be as many language-games as there could be purposes toward which to act. Thus, Wittgenstein wrote:

> how many kinds of sentences are there? Say assertion, question, and command? — There are countless kinds: countless different kinds of use of what we call "symbols", "words", "sentences". And this multiplicity is not something fixed, given once and for all; but new types of language, new language-games, as we may say, come into existence, and others become obsolete and get forgotten. (We can get a rough picture of this from changes in mathematics.)

> Here the term "language-game" is meant to bring into prominence the fact that the speaking of language is part of an activity, or of a form of life.[123]

A parallel can be seen between this view of the dynamic potentiality of language and the view of the cosmos as indeterminate, the view which emerged in physics in the early decades of this century. It is often forgotten that, though Wittgenstein gained recognition principally as a philosopher, he was educated as an engineer. In particular he was drawn to the work in theoretical mechanics of Heinrich Hertz and Ludwig Boltzmann. The work of the latter theoretician was especially significant. It provided a conceptual model within which the relation of language to the world could be understood as one in which, given a statistical array of possible ways of ordering the world, one particular order (e.g., language-game or theoretical model) was actualized. In this light Wittgenstein, writing of notation and signification, did not discuss questions of correspondence. Instead he wrote that

> Although there is something arbitrary in our notations, this much is not arbitrary — that when we have determined one thing arbitrarily, something else is necessarily the case....

> A particular mode of signifying may be unimportant but it is always important that it is a possible mode of signifying. And that is generally so in philosophy: again and again the individual case

turns out to be unimportant, but the possibility of each individual case discloses something about the essence of the world.[124]

It is important to note that for Wittgenstein explicit knowledge, the knowledge about which we speak (in this instance scientific knowledge), was to be understood as a construction. Much of his analysis in the *Tractatus* was related to how we "picture" the world to ourselves. Unfortunately, the use of this "picture" metaphor turned out to be especially troublesome. Many of those who saw themselves following Wittgenstein's lead focused their philosophic attention on questions about the correspondence between elements in the picture and facts in the world. Wittgenstein himself was initially caught up in such a focus and developed an "atomic theory of language."[125] However, it became clear to him that it was not so much the particular picture itself and issues of representation or correspondence but the making of the picture, the building of the conceptual model, the creating of a language-game out of a form of life that was of central significance and interest.

Thus, Wittgenstein found the effort to identify adequate "grounds" for knowledge to be uninteresting at best and more likely fruitless. This position, however, stands in rather sharp contrast with the way in which the philosophical task has often been understood. For much of the practice of philosophy has been devoted precisely to the search for grounds. This search has been at the heart not only of traditional metaphysical reflection but also of the positivist search for criteria for the verification of propositions. The question has been: what are the absolute grounds in reason or experience which justify the validity or truthfulness of a statement? But, such a question is not only epistemological, it is also inherently metaphysical. For Wittgenstein the effort to answer such a question seemed futile. This was because justification, in actual practice, was functional in relation to a particular context and thus relative rather than absolute in character. He wrote:

> Giving grounds, ... justifying the evidence, comes to an end; — but the end is not certain propositions striking us immediately as true, i.e., it is not a kind of seeing on our part; it is our acting, which lies at the bottom of the language-game.
>
> If the true is what is grounded, then the ground is not true, nor yet false.[126]

Grounds are not found in indisputable, atomic facts. To be certain is not to be in possession of an irreproachable truth. Instead, to have grounds is to act in a context of ultimately unjustified presuppositions (like axioms in geometry). To be certain is to engage in such action with confidence.[127]

Wittgenstein's position concerning grounds had implications both for the practice of philosophy and for that of science. On the one hand, philosophical reflection could not be said to be aimed at uncovering the ultimate grounds of being or knowing or anything else. The task of philosophy was to make clear how language was used so that errors in language use could be overcome and so that the meaning of language might be disclosed through attention to its function in particular domains of human activity or forms of life. To believe that philosophy contributed to knowledge was to make an error in judgment.[128]

On the basis of this sort of understanding of philosophy traditional metaphysical systems are not unimportant, but they are instead significant examples of intellectual bewitchment. As noted earlier, the positivists shared Wittgenstein's anti-metaphysical inclination; however, they still wished to ground all knowledge in facts, empirically determined and operationally defined. Most traditional philosophy (and theology) was meaningless, according to the positivists, because it had no "factual" referent in the world. On the other hand, the deliverances of the empirical sciences were held to be free from such a disability. The sciences, they argued, were grounded precisely in ostensive references to the world.[129]

There is irony here. For although Wittgenstein did provide the positivists with a basic logical model by which to describe the world in terms of "atomic facts" and "unit propositions," he himself later came to conclude that it was precisely this objectivist imagery which suggested an erroneous relationship between language and the world. Unlike what was implied by his "picture theory" of language found in the *Tractatus*, Wittgenstein came to hold that the relation of language to the world was not a logical one. Nor was it illogical. It was instead outside the domain of logic. The error of the positivists was that they failed to be anti-metaphysical enough. While denying the meaningfulness of metaphysical systems produced in other forms of life, they manifested a dogmatic crypto-metaphysics in their own philosophy of science.[130]

In this way Wittgenstein's position raised the issue of the meaning of scientific objectivity. Since the meaning of words and sentences were not derived, according to Wittgenstein, from representational correspondence but rather from their function in a language-game manifesting a form of life, then all statements (even the statements of science) were ultimately self-referential; that is, what constituted the meaning of any statement was its function in relation to the context or form of life within which the speaker was a participant. The propositions of science, therefore, were not simply statements about the world but more primitively statements revealing a way of construing the world within a particular context of human activity.

In summary, Wittgenstein's writings show a dynamic movement from attitudes on representation shaped by the modern and critical viewpoint toward a new perspective developed in a changing cultural context; one in which fundamental theoretical changes in the physical sciences were calling attention to the probablistic and so indeterminate nature of scientific modeling. In comparison, the positivists might be said to have manifest a form of secularized scholasticism which sought to establish the absolute ground of meaning in a logical analysis of extrinsic observable relations. In contrast Wittgenstein came to view meaning as relative to the function of language in particular contexts of human living. It is interesting to note, however, that while his own thought exhibited development, a shift in language-games, Wittgenstein himself gave virtually no attention to the processes by which language-games originate, change and are superceded. Further, although many of those with whom he was in philosophical conversation were especially concerned about the development of scientific knowledge, Wittgenstein himself did not explicitly pursue the implications of his philosophy of knowledge for the history and philosophy of science.

However, as Wittgenstein challenged the modern and critical presuppositions of the positivists with respect to the nature and function of language, there have been others who in a somewhat parallel fashion have challenged positivist, and more generally modern and critical, understandings of the nature of scientific knowledge and method. How does scientific knowledge come into existence? What is the character of such knowledge? Is scientific knowledge a representation of reality? Among those, whose explicit considerations of these and similar questions have made a significant contribution to the formation of a post-modern and post-critical perspective, are Karl Popper, Thomas Kuhn and Stephen Toulmin.

Popper's challenge to positivism is clear in that he assumes responsibility for being the cause of the demise of the positivism developed within the Vienna Circle.[131] Popper discussed the "fundamental mistakes" he believed the positivists made in detail in a book published in 1934 under the title *Logik der Forschung*.[132] What is especially ironic about Popper's critique of the positivists is that with them he shared a confidence in the critical power of explicit reason to serve as the only adequate ground for knowledge in general and philosophy in particular.[133] Nevertheless, Popper's critique was telling in that it effectively challenged the positivist assertions that all genuine knowledge could be absolutely justified or verified in principle, that knowledge was grounded in sense data, and that knowledge was built up by means of an inductive process moving from sensory experience to generalized laws of nature.

Popper notes that an incisive analysis of the grounds of knowledge leads to an apparent "trilemma." If dogmatism is to be avoided then scientific statements require rational justification. Yet such justification requires further statements which themselves stand in need of justification. Thus, one comes upon an unsatisfactory infinite regress of justifying statements which need justification. The alternative is to ground the justification of scientific statements not in other statements but instead in sense experience where such experience is understood to be a means of "immediate knowledge."[134] Popper states that positivism holds that "Science is merely an attempt to classify and describe this perceptual knowledge, these immediate experiences whose truth we cannot doubt; it is the systematic presentation of our immediate convictions."[135] However, Popper points out that this position is dependent upon a prior assumption that universals (e.g., statements of scientific law) can be derived inductively from particular sense experiences. But such an assumption is seriously flawed, as David Hume had indicated in the 18th century, because it presumes a logical connection between particular and general statements where there is none.

Thus, the validity of a scientific statement cannot be established by showing its logical derivation from a set of observation statements. But, in addition, neither can a scientific statement be justified with absolute certainty by any amount of confirmatory empirical evidence. What then is the normative relationship between a scientific statement and experience. For Popper the relationship is the possibility of falsification. The mark of a scientific statement, contra the positivists, is not that it can be justified but rather that it can be falsified (at least in principle). Falsification, then, is Popper's "criterion of demarcation" between science and metaphysics.[136] But, if scientific statements cannot simply be justified by reference to experience and if they cannot even be derived inductively from experience, an important question remains. What is the source of scientific statements? In response to this question Popper "grounds" science in the creative human imagination.[137]

Yet to acknowledge a non-logical source for hypotheses leads neither to subjective relativism nor to metaphysical idealism according to Popper. For him science is a descriptive discipline attending to an objective reality. Its object is truth and neither simply conviction nor utility. Here truth is to be understood as correspondence in some sense between statement and reality. Yet such truth remains ever a goal and never an absolute attainment.[138]

The image of science which Popper espouses is one in which there is an interaction between the indeterminate (i.e., the non-logical emergence of hypotheses) and the necessary (i.e., the logical requirements of empirical testability). The epistemological pattern which appears in this description is similar to the pattern of interaction between variation and natural selection found in Darwin's evolutionary description of the emergence of species.[139] Thus, it seems appropriate to identify Popper's epistemology as an "evolutionary" one. However, although he steadfastly affirms the dynamic progressiveness of scientific knowledge, the focus of Popper's interest and concern is on those elements of scientific process which he views as a priori or ahistorical (e.g., his criterion of demarcation or the logical requirements of empirical testing). In general, Popper's epistemology is a rationalistic one and as such retains one foot firmly planted in the modern and critical milieu with its grand estimate of the power of human reason to objectify the world. Still, at the same time, he explicitly rejects the naive modern and critical (and, he argues, positivist) expectation that scientific knowledge can be logically certain. Popper began his career challenging the overly confident modern and critical assumptions of the positivists concerning the logical foundations of scientific knowledge. At the end of his career, however, he has become critically engaged against an historicization of scientific knowledge even more radical than his own. For Popper this particular epistemological move erroneously subjectivizes and relativizes scientific knowledge. His focal adversary on this issue has been Thomas Kuhn.[140]

As a graduate student in physics Kuhn became interested in the history of science. His initial investigations in this field led him to philosophical questions concerning the nature of change in scientific knowledge. His first exposition of his conclusions on this topic, *The Structure of Scientific Revolutions*, has become a contemporary classic in the philosophy of science. Briefly, Kuhn's thesis is that the categories of logical analysis are fundamentally inadequate to an explanation of the actual history of conceptual change in the sciences. In his view only an historical model can provide an adequate account of such change.

Science should not be viewed as a rational cummulative process by which truth is approached asymptotically, according to Kuhn. Quite the contrary, scientific process is best likened to a political revolution. In his own words, "scientific revolutions are taken ... to be those non-cumulative developmental episodes in which an older paradigm is replaced in whole or in part by an incompatible new one."[141] As this statement makes clear, the notion of "paradigm" plays a central role in Kuhn's model of scientific development.

Before considering Kuhn's definition of a paradigm it is worth noting also that it is the incompatibility between paradigms which accounts for the revolutionary character of a shift from one paradigm to another. Because of this incompatibility the movement from a preceding to a succeeding paradigm requires a non-rational transformation in conceptual orientation. To illustrate this point Kuhn has called attention to a number of instances in which a scientific pioneer in one paradigmatic period failed to accept an important conceptual change which led to a later period.[142]

Returning now to the question of what constitutes a paradigm, Kuhn states that a paradigm is an "achievement" marked by two characteristics: first, it is "sufficiently unprecedented to attract an enduring group of adherents away from competing modes of scientific activity," and second, it is "sufficiently open-ended to leave all sorts of problems for the redefined group of practitioners to resolve."[143]

"Normal science" is the expression by which Kuhn refers to the practice of science within an established paradigm. Normal science is precisely the effort of practitioners to resolve the problems left open within the paradigm. The investigation of such problems leads to the identification of "anomalies," occasions either when the expectations for experience generated by the paradigm fail to be realized or when there are problematic experiences which persist as unamenable to explanation within the paradigm. At some point the intellectual pressure exerted by such anomalies spurs some practitioners (perhaps a single practitioner) to engage in what Kuhn calls "extraordinary science;" that is, a fundamental reconsideration of the paradigmatic structure itself. Those who engage in extraordinary science usually experience resistance to their efforts from within the ranks of normal science.[144]

A shift between paradigms, then, involves neither a step by step process of logical deliberation nor a mere reinterpretation of empirical evidence, data which itself remains unchanged. As Kuhn puts it:

> No ordinary sense of the word 'interpretation' fits [the] flashes of intuition through which a new paradigm is born. Though such intuitions depend upon experience, both anomalous and congruent, gained with the old paradigm, they are not logically or piecemeal linked to particular items of that experience as an interpretation would be. Instead, they gather up large portions of that experience and transform them to the rather different bundle of experience that will thereafter be linked piecemeal to the new paradigm but not to the old.[145]

The idea expressed here, that experience itself is transformed in the process of a paradigmatic shift, further shows why Kuhn choose to use the term "revolution" to characterize the process of conceptual change in the sciences. This idea indicates that a revolution in science actually involves a move from one world of experience into another. Having undergone such a shift, the proponent of a new paradigm will be, in Kuhn's view, unintelligible to those continuing to exist conceptually and experientially in the previous paradigm.

More recently, Kuhn has identified the incommensurability between paradigms as resting on a difference in languages, where languages are manifestations of "different cognitive commitments, suitable to different worlds."[146] One
might describe the linguistic shift which Kuhn is indicating as a shift between
"language-games."

To summarize Kuhn's position: in contrast with Popper he argues that
the growth of scientific knowledge is not a direct result of critical rational
activity in any respect. Reason may be exercised to help identify and clarify
the anomalies which arise within a given paradigm. But, according to Kuhn,
to suggest that paradigmatic change is to be identified as some form of rational
activity fails to do justice either to the spontaneity of the insight by which a new
paradigm is made possible and, more especially, it fails to account for the
opposition, and at times hostility, with which a fundamental conceptual change
is initially greeted in the community of science.

However, Kuhn's model, while it is more historically adequate than
Popper's, tends too easily toward the sort of relativistic interpretation of which
Popper and Imre Lakatos, among others, have been critical.[147] The historical
record does indicate instances of disciplinary disruption. Yet even in the most
severe of these the social enterprise of science has not been absolutely
overthrown or abandoned and there is a persistent affirmation within the
community of science that there is an ongoing, if dynamic, corpus of scientific
knowledge. This bespeaks of a considerable continuity within the intellectual
and social enterprise which is science. While the emergence of a new
theoretical insight does appear to manifest imaginative processes which are
beyond logical analysis, rational standards are brought to bear in the evaluation
of alternative theoretical proposals even though such standards are never
conclusive in determining the judgment of the scientific community on an issue
of paradigmatic allegiance.

A third post-modern and post-critical model of the development of
scientific knowledge has been offered by Stephen Toulmin. This model, like
that of Kuhn, is rooted in reflection on the history of science and has been
refined in critical relation to the proposals of both Popper and Kuhn. In contrast
with Popper's model of rational conceptual development and Kuhn's model of
conceptual revolutions, Toulmin describes an "ecological" model. Its advantage, he holds, is that

> it allows us to attack the central problems about the rationality of
> collective concept-use in a way that involves no appeal (such as
> Popper makes) to an arbitrary, *a priori* demarcation-criterion, as the
> definition of 'science'. Again, instead of leaving us wandering (as
> Lakatos does) in an abstract world of 'methodological research

programmes' whose very names are inherited from the arguments of the formal logicians, it requires us to focus directly and in detail on the historically-developing problems and strategies with which our rational enterprises are concerned. At the same time, it gives us the means of distinguishing between actual conceptual choices in fact made by professional scientists ... and those which the genuine needs of the specific problem-situation would — if accurately judged — have demanded of them; so that we can acknowledge the proper roles of professional elites or 'reference groups', without running the risk (as Kuhn does) of bowing absolutely to the judgments of the currently authoritative groups.[148]

Toulmin's model maps a developmental model from biology into the epistemological field. In so doing he is asserting that both fields are essentially historical in nature. As the process of speciation does not manifest radical discontinuities in biological history, so also in the history of ideas there is persistent continuity. As speciation is characteristically a process by which contingent novelty in a biological population is actualized and propogated into future generations, so also in the life of an intellectual community (like that of the sciences) there is the realization and perpetuation of genuinely novel ideas. Finally, as species become extinct in the face of environmental pressures, so also ideas which fail to meet the tests of current problems fade from the collective memory.[149] Here again, as was already seen in Popper's model, there is described an interaction between creative innovation and environmental selection.

It is important to note in this account, however, that conceptual innovation never occurs in the abstract. Kuhn has already argued that such innovation always occurs in relation to some problem, an anomaly. Toulmin states this contextuality more explicitly as follows:

Scientific possibilities are always 'possible ways of tackling such-and-such problems'; and the context of discussion implicitly shows what specific problems the suggestions are directed at, and how the proposed innovations will help to deal with them. Unless this minimum condition is satisfied, such innovations — however formally consistent — do not even acquire the tentative status of 'possibilities'.[150]

Still, one new idea, even if it speaks to a specific problem, does not a conceptual "revolution" make; just as an individual genetic variation in a biological population does not make a new species. What is required is a mechanism by which innovations can be propogated into future generations (either of off-spring or of scientists).

Without direct evidence for such a mechanism Darwin assumed that there was an inheritability factor at work in the organic world. It was the genetic studies of Mendel which provided experimental evidence for such a mechanism and contemporary microbiology and biochemistry are still describing the genetic mechanism in detail. Similarly, in relation to conceptual change there is need for a mechanism by which conceptual variations and innovations are propogated. In Toulmin's view this mechanism is found in the forums of professional discussion.[151] Of particular interest here is the relationship between individual insight and community response, an interaction which makes possible the long term impact of specific conceptual innovations. Summarizing his discussion of these factors Toulmin writes that

> One can, perhaps, generalize roughly about the balance between them, by saying, 'The social factors are necessary, but the intellectual ones are crucial.' Wherever men have the chance to speculate freely and critically in an organized way, they will find some aspects of their experience that are ripe for reflective attention. Intellectual considerations thus focus the theorizing which social incentives make possible. On the other hand, if the institutional, social or ideological conditions are unfavorable, even the most scandalous outstanding problems may remain long unsolved; there was no intrinsic reason, for example, why the transition from Ptolemy's Almagest to Copernicus's De Revolutionibus should have taken well over 1,000 years. The sheer amount of intellectual innovation going on in any situation thus reflects, first and foremost, its overall social and institutional character, and only secondarily the specific disciplinary considerations of the time.[152]

There is one further point to note in Toulmin's development of an "ecological" epistemology. It is his insistence that rationality be understood in terms broader than logicality.[153] The recognition that the ideas which provide both explicit and implicit orientation for a culture form a developing "conceptual population" (like a species) opens the way for a broader understanding of rationality. No longer is rationality simply the proper realization of formal logical criteria. It is more the exercise of a disciplined cross-cultural and cross-historical comparative judgment in service to the solution of current problems and to the accomplishment of intended goals. In such endeavor the exercise of rationality is not a haven for the cautious but a challenge to those who would be responsible.[154]

In the development of his "ecological" epistemology Toulmin has been especially critical of those who adopt an orthogenetic understanding of evolutionary process. This understanding couples genetic mutation with ecological selection such that evolutionary process, taken as a whole, is viewed as teleological. One of those he criticizes on this matter is Pierre Teilhard de Chardin. Another is Michael Polanyi.[155] Polanyi is also seen by the proponents of Popper's general views, such as Imre Lakatos, as a champion along with Kuhn of an epistemology of subjective relativism.[156] However, it is my view that Polanyi is neither a relativist nor a subjectivist . Instead, I would identify him as a "tacit colleague" with Toulmin in the expression of a post-modern and post-critical epistemology.

In a distinctive way Michael Polanyi also developed an "evolutionary" epistemology which emphasized the non-formal character of the foundations of human knowing. He was particularly concerned to show the interaction between the individual and the community in the formation of human knowledge. Polanyi quite explicitly identified his epistemological reflections as tending toward a "post-critical philosophy". Thus, he wrote of his endeavor

> When I gave this book [*Personal Knowledge*] the sub-title 'Towards a Post-Critical Philosophy' I had this turning point in mind. The critical movement, which seems to be nearing an end of its course today, was perhaps the most fruitful effort ever sustained by the human mind. The past four or five centuries, which have gradually destroyed or overshadowed the whole medieval cosmos have enriched us mentally and morally to an extent unrivalled by any period of similar duration. But its incandescence had fed on the combustion of the Christian heritage in the oxygen of Greek rationalism, and when this fuel was exhausted the critical framework itself burned away.
>
> Modern man is unprecedented; yet we must now go back to St. Augustine to restore the balance of our cognitive powers. In the fourth century A.D., St. Augustine brought the history of Greek philosophy to a close by inaugurating for the first time a post-critical philosophy. He taught that all knowledge was a gift of grace, for which we must strive under the guidance of antecedent belief: *nisi credideritis, non intelligitis*. His doctrine ruled the minds of Christian scholars for a thousand years. Then faith declined and demonstrable knowledge gained superiority over it....
>
> ... All belief was reduced to the status of subjectivity: to that of an imperfection by which knowledge fell short of universality.
>
> We must now recognize belief once more as the source of all knowledge. Tacit assent and intellectual passions, the sharing of an idiom and of a cultural heritage, affiliation to a like-minded community: such are the impulses which shape our vision of the nature

of things on which we rely for the mastery of things. No intelligence, however critical or original, can operate outside of such a fiduciary framework.[157]

It is important to note here that the "fiduciary framework" to which Polanyi refered was not some particular faith system or particular system of beliefs or dogma. Rather his reference is to faith as that act necessary to the possession of any explicit knowledge whatsoever. Further, this act is faith in that which is, in principle, unspecifiable. The "that" which is unspecifiable is the tacit dimension of all human knowing, that from which we attend in order to know something. It is the "ground" of knowing for which "explicit grounds" cannot be given. For Polanyi truth could not be established by some determination of correspondence, for at the root of all explicit statements there was an indeterminacy for which the objectifying notion of correspondence was inappropriate.[158] But does this then mean that truth is simply based upon one's own conviction? Is there no extrinsic standard by which the truthfulness of human claims to knowledge can be assessed?

If what is sought in such a standard is some explicit methodology by which a definitive judgment can be rendered on the truthfulness of an assertion, then Polanyi would deny access to any such standard. Yet, he also steadfastly refused to bow to the charge of subjectivism. Why from his perspective were claims to true knowledge not merely subjective assertions? It was because Polanyi held that the claim by an individual to be in possession of true knowledge bore with it a "universal intent" and so also a risk.[159] This leads to his understanding of the role of the community in the establishment of "truth."

For Polanyi truth was neither objective nor yet subjective but was instead intersubjective. The scientist labors within a community committed to the quest for a truthful understanding of a reality which in some sense stands beyond the community. It is to that community that the scientist bears the fruit of his or her endeavor so that what is universally intended in it (i.e., what ought to be held as true) will be confirmed. But is such a turn to the social context merely the avoidance of individual subjectivism at the cost of substituting an intersubjective or cultural relativism? Simple experience makes it clear that all human communities do not share a single vision of what constitutes the "truth."

Polanyi acknowledged the variability of such visions. Writing of language as a medium by which the tacit cosmology of a society or culture is transmitted he wrote that

Different languages are alternative conclusions, arrived at by the secular gropings of different groups of people at different periods of history. They sustain alternative conceptual frameworks, interpreting all things that can be talked about in terms of somewhat different allegedly recurrent features. The confident use of nouns, verbs, adjectives and adverbs, invented and endowed with meaning by a particular sequence of groping generations, expresses their particular theory of the nature of things. In learning to speak, every child accepts the culture constructed on the premises of the traditional interpretation of the universe, rooted in the idiom of the group to which it was born, and every intellectual effort of the educated mind will be made within this frame of reference.[160]

Polanyi's point was that there was no privileged or conceptually neutral perceptual stool upon which one could stand to see the world-as-it-is. All standpoints are firmly set in some cultural context which mediates to every "looker" tacit judgments as to what there is to "see." Yet, there is another aspect of the tacit dimension which qualifies the social relativity of the quest for truth.

The capacity to seek the truth rests in a tacit apprehension of reality as hidden, though open to the possibility of discovery.[161] There has been a tendency on the part of some of Polanyi's interpreters to treat this apprehension as a kind of "unconscious" knowing of an objective reality. The process of knowledge acquisition takes on a quantitative image as though discovery amounted to taking finite shovels full of knowledge from an infinite and obscure reservoir of the real. However, such a substantive image of the process of knowing was far from Polanyi's intent. Rather than a cumulative process, Polanyi adopted the image of "breaking out" to characterize the discovery of fundamentally new knowledge.[162] Polanyi expressed an understanding of conceptual change as transformative. Such an understanding finds collateral expression in Kuhn's description of paradigm change as a form of conversion. The image of "breaking out" is a far cry from those images which would characterize knowledge acquisition as a logical step by step process of cognitive accumulation.

It might be thought that Polanyi's reference to passion as a condition for knowledge would again lend itself to a subjectivist interpretation of the process of knowing. It is, however, but another way in which he sought to indicate that the concept of knowledge as "personal" transcended the customary dychotomy between objectivity and subjectivity.[163] Personal knowing is neither detached nor is it whimsical. It has an objective quality. It emerges from a tacit indwelling in the real and is explicitly related to a normative community through universal intent. Its subjective-like qualities rest in the condition that all knowledge requires commitment, assent and responsibility.

More could be said here to describe Polanyi's "triadic structure" of personal knowing but perhaps one final point is sufficient for present purposes.

Unlike any of those who have been cited thus far, Polanyi gave direct attention
to religious knowledge. However, in so doing his approach was neither metaphysical nor revelational. Far from being concerned with demonstrating how
doctrinal systems or confessional statements could be representative of objective theological realities, Polanyi was concerned instead to show how it was
that religious knowledge emerged like all knowledge as an integration of
subsidiaries in a focal meaning. On the one hand, ritual acts and symbols used
in worship provide the subsidiaries from which one attends, by dwelling in
them, to God. Yet in another sense, the term God is also meaningful in relation
to the whole of human experience. In both of these respects, however, what
Polanyi offered was in no way an ontological argument for the existence of
God. As he himself wrote:

> God is ... not a being whose existence can be established in some
> logical, scientific, or rational way before we engage in our worship
> of him. God is a commitment involved in our rites and myths.
> Through their integrative, imaginative efforts we see him as the
> focal point that fuses into meaning all the incompatibles involved
> in the practice of religion. But, as in art — only in a more whole and
> complete way — God also becomes the integration of all the
> incompatibles in our lives.
>
> These incompatibles include not only all the false starts and
> stops in our lives, the blind alleys, the unfinished things, the loose
> ends, the incompatible hopes and fears, pains and pleasures, loves
> and hates, anguishes and elations, the memories, the half-memo-
> ries, the forgotten moments that meant so much to us at the time, the
> disjointed "dailiness" of our lives — in a word, all of our inchoate
> memories and experiences — but also all the incompatibles that
> make up the whole stance of our lives: the hope that we may be able
> to do or achieve what we know we must do but which we also know
> we have not the power to do.[164]

Now while holding Polanyi's understanding of the nature of religious
knowledge in mind, consider the following quote.

> The wisdom of the subjective aim prehends every actuality for what
> it can be in such a perfected system — its sufferings, its sorrows, its
> failures, its triumphs, its immediacies of joy — woven by rightness
> of feeling into the harmony of the universal feeling, which is always
> immediate, always many, always one, always with novel advance,
> moving onward and never perishing. The revolts of destructive
> evil, purely self-regarding, are dismissed into their triviality of
> merely individual facts; and yet the good they did achieve in

individual joy, in individual sorrow, in the introduction of needed contrast, is yet saved by its relation to the completed whole. The image — and it is but an image — the image under which this operative growth of God's nature is best conceived, is that of a tender care that nothing be lost.

The consequent nature of God is his judgment on the world. He saves the world as it passes into the immediacy of his own life. It is the judgment of a tenderness which loses nothing that can be saved. It is also the judgment of a wisdom which uses what in the temporal world is mere wreckage....

.... God's role is not the combat of productive force with productive force, of destructive force with destructive force; it lies in the patient operation of the overwhelming rationality of his conceptual harmonization. He does not create the world, he saves it: or, more accurately, he is the poet of the world, with tender patience leading it by his vision of truth, beauty and goodness.[165]

The distinctive rhetoric of this passage marks it as coming from the hand of Alfred North Whitehead.

It may seem strange to include a speculative philosopher among those who have been shaping the post-modern and post-critical perspective, not the least because all of the philosophers discussed thus far are at best dubious of the value of metaphysical speculation.[166] Yet the religious sentiments expressed above by Whitehead seem commensurate with those evident in Polanyi's vision of God as the integration of the "incompatibles of our life." Still, there is an apparent difference between the approach of Polanyi and that of Whitehead. Polanyi made no ontological claim, at least not explicitly. Whitehead, on the other hand, understood God to be the paradigmatic instance of his cosmological vision; that is, everything else is as God is. But, even accepting this difference, the question remains: is speculative philosophy inherently antithetical to a post-modern and post-critical perspective? Although this question cannot be explored in depth in this present survey, several observations can be made which may suggest the direction in which an answer to this question might be found.

While many of those who contributed to the formation of the modern and critical perspective understood themselves in the image of rational St. George slaying traditional metaphysical dragons, in the place of such beasts they frequently installed philosophical chimera no less formidable in their dogmatic ferocity and equally threatening of a comprehensive appreciation of human existence. The development and propogation of a modern and critical dualism

first metaphysically separated spirit (mind) from matter and then epistemologically separated value from fact. This dualism finally issued in a positivist denial
of the meaningfulness of the spirit/value pole and so a reduction of its
significance. Those who nurtured this dualistic movement were no less
confident in what could be definitively known through the exercise of reason
than were their scholastic forebears. In one respect the emergence of the post-
modern and post-critical perspective is due to a severe attack of philosophical
modesty. Thus, those giving shape to this latter movement have been very
hesitant about making any kind of ontological claim especially about the nature
of reality as a whole.

Nevertheless, among those who have been considered in the preceding
paragraphs, both Michael Polanyi and more recently Stephen Toulmin have
indicated the need to engage in conversation about that whole which is the
cosmos.[167] In this regard it seems appropriate to include Whitehead among
those giving form to the post-modern and post-critical perspective in particular
because of his understanding of his own philosophical enterprise.

Whitehead's "summa" is *Process and Reality.* Yet this work for all its
careful reasoning is not an attempt to do metaphysics as such; that is, to
delineate the necessary structure of any particular reality or of being as such.
Instead, it is an attempt to offer a description of the particular reality in which
we live in the most general and so most comprehensive terms. Thus,
Whitehead sub-titled this work, "An Essay in Cosmology."

But there is a second way in which Whitehead manifested the sort of
philosophical modesty which has been characteristic of those previously
discussed. For Whitehead "speculative philosophy" was not simply a looking,
seeing and reporting of the general structure of the cosmos. Rather, such a
philosophical endeavor was a constructive activity, an act of "framing,"
anchored in "everything of which we are conscious, as enjoyed, perceived,
willed, or thought ...."[168] The product of speculative philosophy was thus not
some detached objectification of the way things are but instead an artifact of
personal reflection on the whole of experience.

In a very personal way Whitehead's philosophical modesty was also
manifest in the way in which he wished his philosophical legacy to be handled.
At his request, upon his death, all of his unpublished papers were destroyed.
According to Victor Lowe this request was not simply that of a man scrupulous
about his privacy even in death. Rather it reflected the philosophical sensibility
of one who "idealized youth and wanted young thinkers to develop their own
ideas, not spend their best years on a *Nachlass.*"[169]

What these observations suggest is that it may be possible to engage in a speculative attempt to provide a comprehensive "picture" of the cosmos as a whole which is compatible with a post-modern and post-critical perspective. For such compatibility to hold, however, the contextual limits of the philosophical task must be appreciated and the product which issues from that task must be understood to be an artifact of personal construction. It is clear from his own published writings that Whitehead held such a view of the nature of speculative philosophy.

In *Process and Reality* Whitehead exhibited an understanding of the philosophical task which was conscious of its limitations.[170] In his discussion of "speculative philosophy," Whitehead indicated both the transience of philosophical systems and at the same time the tendency of philosophers to err by way of overstatement.[171] These views resonate with some of those found in the works of Toulmin.[172]

One of the sources of Whitehead's modesty concerning the possibility of stating the ultimate logical principles, derives from the impact of Gödel's Proof on the logical system presented by Whitehead and Bertrand Russell in *Principia Mathematica*.[173] This latter work was an effort to express the general logical ground of all mathematics. In 1931 Kurt Gödel demonstrated that such a system could in principle be either consistent or complete but not both. In a sense, Gödel was expressing in the domain of mathematics and logic a principle similar to Heisenberg's "uncertainty principle" in physics.

In addition, it is important to emphasize the two sources of error by which Whitehead believed philosophy fell into overstatement. The first is to mistakenly take as actual our concepts of the actual which are constructive abstractions from the actual. Though it should be an obvious error, there is a great tendency to take the story of an event for the event itself. Here there is an echo of Kant's distinction between things-in-themselves and empirical knowledge of things. The second error is the failure to see philosophy as a hypothetical discipline whose value is determined not on the basis of dogmatic claims to the certainty of its first principles but by its success in helping to provide conceptual coherence to actual experience. In this sense, Whitehead understood philosophy to be an "experimental" discipline. Still, given these cautions Whitehead was far from being an irrationalist. The exercise of reason both as a means of analysis and in the effort to synthesize general systems was for him a great adventure.[174]

Given this brief summary of Whitehead's understanding of the philosophic task, a survey of his cosmological system indicates how his thought reflected a recognition of the fundamental significance of dynamic relatedness. The primacy of such relatedness has already been discussed above in the consideration of developments in biology and physics. The notion of dynamic relativity is central to Whitehead's cosmology.

At the core of this cosmology is the concept of "creativity." It is the most fundamental notion in Whitehead's system. The centrality of creativity is an acknowledgement of the ultimate dynamism of the cosmos. Creativity also identifies the source of novelty. For Whitehead creativity replaces Aristotle's notion of 'primary substance.'[175] In the process, however, the notion of 'substance' itself is transformed. The cosmos is not, in Whitehead's view, comprised of things. It is instead instances of creativity, occurrances, happenings, actual entities, occasions of experience. To be something is to be an event.[176]

Further, as conceived by Whitehead, such events have a quantum character; that is, there are no partial events.[177] Still, though an actual entity was, for Whitehead, the fundamental constituent of the actual world and can not be sub-divided into still more fundamental elements, the becoming of an event can be analysed in terms of temporal process. Thus, though it is inappropriate to speak of the parts of an actual entity one could speak of phases of its actualization or, to use Whitehead's term, its concrescence, its becoming concrete. Such an analysis, however, does not result in the identification of still more fundamental facts but rather shows how an actual entity is itself comprised of actual entities. As Whitehead himself described this process: "in the becoming of an actual entity, the potential unity of many entities in disjunctive diversity — actual and non-actual — acquires the real unity of the one actual entity; so that the actual entity is the real concrescence of many potentials."[178] "The many become one, and are increased by one."[179]

In this process of actualization novelty emerges. Though each entity had implicated in it the totality of all past occasions in the actual world, it also draws upon non-actualities or pure potentialities. These potentialities are what Whitehead called "eternal objects" or forms of definiteness. Yet care must be taken here not to hypostatize these. The domain of "eternal objects' is not one of things but instead one of ordered potentiality. These "Pure Potentials for the Specific Determination of Fact" are similar to though not identical with the "ideal forms" of Plato.[180]

One final element of Whitehead's cosmological system needs to be indicated. Since the cosmos is comprised of happenings rather than things, the notion of persistent existence through time requires some explanation. How is it possible to account for the apparent enduringness of elements in the actual world when the fundamental facts of the world are quantum-like events? Whitehead's answer to this question was expressed in his notion of the "enduring object."[181] Such an object is a serial order of actual entities in which the concrescence of each occasion in the series actualizes a complex eternal object shared by all the other actual entities in the series.[182] However, since the enduringness of the object is dependent upon the actual concrescence in each occasion of the same common form of potentiality, the essence of the object is contingent rather than necessary and there is an openness to fundamental ontological novelty in each occasion of the series constituting the enduring object. Here in most general language and applied to the cosmos as a whole is a statement of the evolutionary hypothesis which takes into account the possibility of inheritability and also the openness to fundamental change.

As this all too brief summary of Whitehead's cosmology suggests, he sought to do justice to a vision of the cosmos in which the constitution of entities was directly consequent upon their dynamic relatedness. In addition, by identifying the fundamental facts of the world not as things but as events, it would be less appropriate to say that the cosmos as a whole is a thing which has history than that it is history itself.

Given, then, this review of the development of an emerging cosmological paradigm in the sciences and collateral developments in philosophy, an attempt can be made to identify the general features which are coming to characterize a post-modern and post-critical perspective. In summary, the post-modern and post-critical philosophical perspective which has been taking form out of the contributions of such as Wittgenstein, Popper, Kuhn, Toulmin, Polanyi and Whitehead (in response to the cosmological revolution spurred by such as Darwin, Einstein, Bohr and Heisenberg) can be said to manifest features which contrast sharply with those characterizing the modern and critical perspective.

First, rationality is understood to be broader than the logicality. Mathematics and geometry are no longer taken as the paradigms of rationality. They are instead special cases. Rationality is taken to have dimensions which are explicitly social, related to the solution of human problems and the pursuit of human goals in community. For example, both Popper and Kuhn argue that the growth of knowledge is finally dependent upon a rational (though not irrational) processes. Further, Kuhn describes these processes as being more like a conversion than like a deduction or induction.

A second feature is the view that even the most rational of knowledge is beyond complete explicit articulation. Polanyi argued that all explicit knowledge is dependent upon tacit elements which can never be articulated fully. Wittgenstein argued that even logic can not be stated explicitly but only "shown" and Gödel showed that the most logically rigorous axiomatic systems can be either complete or consistent but not both.

A third feature is the affirmation that <u>wholes are greater than the sum of their parts</u>. Though this synergistic principle has become almost trite, it nevertheless expresses a central post-modern and post-critical position. Reductionistic analysis, though a useful tool for identifying the constituents of a whole, cannot of itself provide an explanation of the whole. Wittgenstein came to hold that language can not simply be reduced to "atomic" units of meaning, to grammar and definitions. Polanyi argued that the emergent character of the world as an evolving reality constitutes a form of hierarchical structuring which precludes explaining higher order realities simply in terms of lower orders.

Fourthly, following on this anti-reductionist stance, there is also an affirmation of <u>a fundamental holism</u>. This position is perhaps most clearly expressed in Bohm's description of the "holomovement" but it is also present in the emphasis on context in Wittgenstein's reflections on meaning in language and in Toulmin's and Polanyi's considerations of the nature of truth in the sciences. Meaning in language is not derived by some one-to-one form of correspondence between the word and the world. Likewise, truth is not measured by some determination of correspondence between statement and reality. Instead language is meaningful in the context of a form of life, within an holistic experience. Similarly, the truth of a scientific statement is a judgment made in the context of the life of a whole community of scientists.

This holism leads to a fifth feature. <u>The cosmos is "seen" as an indeterminate dynamic relativity</u>. It is an event constituted of events. It is not a thing constituted of things. Further, these events are contingent. Though containing determinate elements (for implicated in each event is the actual past), each event is open to novelty and so indeterminate as a whole. Whitehead's speculative cosmology most explicitly expresses this pattern of dynamic relativity but it is also found clearly in the epistemological positions of Kuhn, Toulmin and Polanyi.

Sixth, from a post-modern and post-critical perspective there is <u>a more modest appraisal of the "place" of humanity in the cosmic scheme</u>. While there is an appreciation of the uniqueness of human beings (a uniqueness possessed by every entity or class of entities), there is generally no sense that humanity is either the ontological center of the cosmos or the spearhead of cosmic history. Toulmin is, perhaps, most explicit in his expression of this view in *The Return to Cosmology*.

Finally, there is <u>a cautious affirmation of the importance of metaphysical questions along with an affirmation that metaphysical answers are human artifacts which are hypothetical at best</u>. Those shaping the post-modern and post-critical perspective are especially sensitive to the abuses wrought on the human intellect by dogmatic philosophies. Yet, there is also the recognition that all human discourse occurs within a framework of presuppositions which are metaphysical in character. Thus, metaphysical questions are important even if unanswerable. It is this two-fold appraisal of metaphysics which links such apparently disparate positions as that of Wittgenstein and that of Whitehead.

NOTES

1.   R. Hooykaas argues in favor of the former view in *Religion and the Rise of Modern Science* (Grand Rapids, MI: William B. Eerdmans, 1972), while N. Max Wildiers, *The Theologian and His Universe* (New York: The Seabury Press, 1982) argues for the latter.

2.   See *Cosmology and Theology*, Vol. 166, David Tracy and Nicholas Lash, eds. (Minneapolis, MN: Winston Press, 1983).

3.   Wildiers, *The Theologians and His Universe*, p. 25f.

4.   For a discussion of this contrast see Hooykaas, *Religion and the Rise of Modern Science*, pp. 1-13. An example of the Biblical perspective is found in Psalm 8.3-8.

5.   Cuthbert A. Simpson suggests that it is unlikely that the Priestly authors, given their strong sense of religious identity, would have simply co-opted the Babylonian cosmology even for their own purposes. Rather, he argues the similarity between Genesis 1:1-2.4a and *Enuma Elish* is more likely due to the prevalence throughout the Middle East of the cosmological scheme embodied in the latter myth. Simpson also proposes that the Yahwist author also drew upon a version of the *Enuma Elish* cosmogony. However, since J was written prior to direct contact between Israel and Babylon, the source is more likely Canaanite and this again supports an argument for the pervasiveness of the Babylonian cosmology over a long period of Middle Eastern history. Cuthbert A. Simpson, "Genesis," *The Interpreter's Bible* (Nashville, TN: Abingdon Press, 1952), p. 450f.

6.   F. M. Cornford, "Pattern of Ionian Cosmogony," *Theories of the Universe*, Milton K. Munitz, ed. (New York: The Free Press, 1957), p. 29f.

7.   Ironically, the Pythagoreans proposed a cosmological system in which the earth moved about a central celestial fire. The revolution of the earth about the fire while always maintaining its inhabited area away from that fire was equivalent geometrically to having the earth rotate on its axis. This model, which implied a two-fold motion for the earth, was set aside in the development of Western natural philosophy in favor of the Platonic-Aristotelian scheme which imagined the earth to be the motionless center of the cosmos. This latter view was compatible with the implicit cosmological geocentrism of the Bible and prevailed until a resurgence of Pythagorean views in the 16th century. For a discussion of the Pythagorean cosmology see Theodor Gomperz, "The Development of the Pythagorean Doctrine," in Munitz, *Theories of the Universe*, pp. 32-40.

8.   Though the number of spheres were not consistent between the two philosophers, the general structure of the scheme was quite similar. For the most part Aristotle's system was more detailed. While Plato was satisfied with placing the earth at the cosmic center and surrounding it with eight spheres (the first seven providing for the moving planets and the eighth for the fixed stars), Aristotle included in his system four earthly spheres for the four basic elements (earth, water, air, fire); seven spheres containing the observable planets, the moon and the sun (all in the same order as Plato); plus fifty-five intermediate spheres rotating in opposite directions to account for the "apparent" non-concentric, non-regular motion of the planets. In addition to the four basic elements, Aristotle also identified the "stuff" from which the stars and the celestial spheres were made; namely, the quintessence or ether.

9.   Plato, *The Timaeus*, 30C-31A, John Warrington, ed. and trans. (London: J. M. Dent and Sons, Ltd., 1965), p. 20.

> "... the world resembles most closely that Living Creature of which all other living creatures, severally and in their families, are parts. For that embraces and contains within itself all the intelligible living creatures, just as this world contains ourselves and all other creatures that have been fashioned as visible things. For the god, desiring to make it closely resemble that intelligible thing which is best and in all respects complete, constructed it as a single visible living creature, containing within itself all living things whose nature is of the same order."

10.   Aristotle, *Metaphysics*, XII, viii.17-21, Hugh Tredennick, trans. (Cambridge: Harvard University Press, 1977), pp. 161-163.

> "if we are to suppose that one motion is for the sake of another, the latter too must be for the sake of something else; and since the series cannot be infinite, the end of every motion must be one of the heavenly bodies which are moved through the heavens....
>
> A tradition has been handed down by the ancient thinkers of very early times, and bequeathed to posterity in the form of a myth, to the effect that these heavenly bodies are gods, and that the Divine pervades the whole of nature. The rest of their tradition has been added later in a mythological form to influence the vulgar and as a constitutional and utilitarian expedient; they say that these gods are human in shape or are like certain other animals, and make other statements consequent upon and similar to those which we have mentioned. Now if we separate these statements and accept only the first, that they supposed the primary substances to be gods, we must regard it as an inspired saying ...."

11.   Of special note among the heirs of Plato is Plotinus whose Neo-Platonism intuited three levels of divinity within the Godhead. Plotinus' influence on Christian thought is found not only in the Church Fathers, particularly Augustine, but also in the works of the medieval theologians

including Thomas Aquinas.

12.   This work came to be known commonly as *The Almagest* during the medieval period. This title was a corruption of the Arabic expression "Al-megiste" meaning "the greatest," an expression which Islamic natural philosophers had associated with the text.

13.   See, Wildiers, *The Theologian and His Universe*, pp. 27-58.

14.   The litany of theologians whom Wildiers identifies over this nine century period include: Ambrose, Irenaeus, Basil, Lactanius, Gregory of Nyssa, Maximus the Confessor, Isidore of Seville, Bede the Venerable and John Damascene among the Christian Fathers; non-Christian philosophers and theologians such as Plotinus, Boethius and Prophyry; such pre-scholastic theologians as Rhabanus Maurus, John Scotus Eriugena and those of the "School of Cratres" (Magister Theodoricus, William of Conches and possibly Bernardus Silvetris). Others whom he cites as immediate contributors to the formation of the medieval worldview were Peter Lombard, Roger Bacon and Albert the Great. Albert, it should be noted, was very instrumental in the revival of Aristotelian science in the face of the prevailing Platonism. Albert was also the mentor of Thomas Aquinas.

15.   Augustine, *De actis cum Felice Man.*, 1, 10.

16.   J. L. E. Dreyer, "Medieval Cosmology," in Munitz, *Theories of the Universe*, p. 133.

> "Though Aquinas was deeply convinced that revelation is a more important source of knowledge than human reason, he considers both to be two distinct and separate ways of finding truth; and in expounding Aristotle he therefore never lets himself be disturbed by the difference between his doctrine and that of the Bible, but assumes both to be ultimately derived from the same source."

17.   According to Wildiers the elements comprising this cosmology included:

> "that the earth is surrounded by seven spheres carrying the planets which greatly influence birth, death, and all phenomena in the sublunary world; that the earth stands immovable in the center of the cosmos; that above the spheres of the planets there is a higher sphere still, or rather, three spheres, the lowest of which carries the fixed stars; that the whole cosmos is completely round; that the planets move in a circular orbit; that macrocosm and microcosm are perfectly attuned to each other and constructed according to the same plan; that there are four elements - earth, water, air, and fire - each of which strives after its due place; that, in a word, the whole cosmos has been perfectly arranged by the Creator."

Wildiers, *The Theologian and His Universe*, p. 38.   He summarizes the cosmology of the Middle Ages by indicating that for the medieval theologian "the world was a perfectly ordered whole"; that that order was hierarchic; and that it was also anthropocentric, "all things were created for man and ... the entire cosmic order was aimed at him." Ibid., p. 57f.

18.   For a discussion of these elements of the Ptolemaic system see R. Hooykaas, "The Impact of the Copernican Transformation," in *The Conflict Thesis and Cosmology* (Milton Keynes: Open University Press, 1974), pp. 59-60.

19.   Heraclides (c. 388-310 BC) had allowed for the motion of the earth and Aristarchus of Samos (c. 310-230 BC) had held that the earth possessed an annual revolution about the sun and a daily rotation on its axis. See Milton K. Munitz, ed., *Theories of the Universe* (New York: The Free Press, 1957), p. 6f.

20.   From *Copernicus: On the Revolutions of the Heavenly Spheres*, A. M. Duncan, trans. (Newton Abbot: David and Charles, Ltd., 1976), p. 22.

21.   Brahe's motives for retaining a geocentric model were in no way reflective of a commitment to Aristotelian physics. He himself was a severe critic of Aristotle. Rather, he was anchored in his view by a commitment to a literal reading of the Christian scriptures. See Hooykaas, *The Conflict Thesis and Cosmology*, pp. 72-73.

22.   In *The Circles of God* (Edinburgh: Scottish Academic Press, 1985), Harold Nebelsick argues that the identification of the circle with divine perfection, reflecting metaphysical and theological commitments, was a major impediment to the development of the heliocentric cosmology.

23 .   This quip was made by Derek deSolla Price in the George Sarton Memorial Lecture at the 1984 national meeting of the American Association for the Advancement of Science held in Detroit, Michigan. This address was later published but without the quip as "Sealing Wax and String," *Nature*, Vol. 93 (January 1984), pp. 48-57.

24.   An empirical demonstration of the movement of the earth about the sun depended upon the ability to detect that motion relative to the "fixed stars." This is known as the measure of the stellar paralax. Although Galileo could identify this avenue of "proof" (he did so in the personna of "Filippo Salviati" in his *Dialogue Concerning the Two Principal Systems of the World*) and anticipated its eventual acquisition, such measurement was not actually obtained until 1838. It is evidence of the "theoretical" heart of science that in the more than two hundred years after Galileo's trial and condemnation, the Copernican model of the world became the established authoritative physical cosmology quite apart from crucial empirical support.

25.   For an extended discussion of "ideals of natural order" see Stephen E. Toulmin, *Forsight and Understanding* (Indiana University Press, 1961), pp. 44-82.

26.   Both Luther and Calvin had reservations concerning the Copernican cosmology. However, these reservations were rooted neither in commitments to a literalist interpretation of scripture nor to convictions that the Ptolemaic cosmology was theologically sanctioned. They were, however, both men of their time and so began with Ptolemaic cosmological presuppositions which appeared to be congenial with though not in particulars required by the

cosmic picture implicit in scripture. At the same time, both Protestant reformers were committed to Biblical interpretation which rested in the plain or clear meaning of the text. On this point they were distinguishing themselves from forms of allegorical interpretation which had been common place among Biblical commentators from the patristic period and upon which many of the practices of medieval Catholicism were dependent for sanction. Still, Calvin openly adopted a "principle of accommodation" as a hermeneutical tool whereby it was understood that the Divine word was present in scripture in such a way as to accommodate to the understanding of those who received it. For a summary of the views of Luther and Calvin see John Dillenberger, *Protestant Thought and Natural Science* (Nashville, TN: Abingdon Press, 1960), pp. 29-39. There has been considerable debate among social historians as to the reasons why the Protestant and, specifically, the Calvinist communities proved especially hospitable to the "new science" of Copernicus and Galileo. One of the foremost analyses of this relation is Robert K. Merton, "Science, Technology and Society in the Seventeenth Century," *Osiris*, No 4 (1938). For a summary critique of Merton's analysis see R. Hooykaas, "Puritanism and Science," *Scientific Progress and Religious Dissent* (Milton Keynes: The Open University Press, 1974), pp. 5-25.

27.   Ibid., p. 84f.

28.   This distinction can be found in a letter apparently to Cornelis von Hogelands (August 1638) commenting on Johannes Commenius' *Conatuum comeniorum Praeludia* and is found in *Descartes' Philosophical Letters*, Anthony Kenny, ed. and trans. (Oxford: Clarendon Press, 1970), p. 60.

29.   This is a position which Thomas Aquinas, the pre-eminent medieval theolgian, would have supported. Descartes' position reveals the degree to which he, the founder of "modern" thought, was still deeply influenced by his medieval heritage. In the application of Aristotelian philosophy as a framework within which to express Christian theology, Aquinas distinguished between knowledge of the physical, the metaphysical and the supernatural worlds. The two former domains were accessible to reason through the senses and analogy. But knowledge of the supernatural world was accessible only by means of revelation. Reflection on the physical and metaphysical worlds could lead to a knowledge of God's existence, but only through revelation could the attributes of God (e.g., God as creator, the Trinity), as expressed in the dogmas of the Church, be known. See, Thomas Aquinas, *Summa Theologiae*, Ia 12,13. Thus Aquinas could argue that the existence of God could be made evident, apart from revelation, by the natural exercise of reason. *Summa Theologiae*, Ia 2,2. But, on the other hand, he could argue that the existence of the world as the non-eternal creation of God could be known only by means of revelation. *Summa Theologiae*, Ia 46,2. Aquinas took great pains to show contrary to the Averroists that while the doctrine of the creation of the world could only be known through revelation, such a position was not inconsistent with a rational

consideration of the nature of the world, especially as found in Aristotle's cosmology.

30.   René Descartes, *The Philosophical Works of Descartes*, Elizabeth S. Haldane and G. R. T. Ross, trans., Vol. I (Cambridge: Cambridge University Press, 1983), p. 3.

31.   Ibid., p. 7.

32.   Ibid., p. 8.

33.   Ibid.

34.   Ibid., p. 14.

35.   Ibid.

36.   Ibid., p. 101.

37.   Ibid., 109f.

38.   Ibid., p. 192.

39.   Two such developments in the early history of Christian thought were Gnosticism and Manicheaism. While different in significant ways they each held a strong dualistic view of the relationship between the material and the spiritual. Although both positions were judged to be "heretical" due in large part to their extreme dualism, nevertheless they manifested a strand of Christian theological sensibility which has persisted within the tradition. Thus, the notion of the "immortality of the soul" has been a persistent element of popular Christianity as contrasted with the orthodox affirmation of the "resurrection of the body." For a discussion of these views see George Widengren, *Mani and Manichaeism*, trans. Charles Kessler (New York: Holt, Rinehart and Winston, 1965) and Kurt Rudolph, *Gnosis: The Nature and History of Gnosticism*, trans. and ed. Robert McLachlan Wilson (San Francisco: Harper and Row, 1983).

40.   Aristotle identified a variety of powers of the soul: vegetative, sensitive, appetitive, locomotive and intellective. Together these marked off the domain of the living or animate from that of the inanimate. In addition, by means of these an order within the kingdom of life could be determined. Thus, the vegetative powers which governed growth and nutrition were present in all living things: plants, animals and human beings. The sensitive powers which governed sensation and were indispensible to the appetitive and locomotive powers were held to be restricted to animals and human beings. The intellective powers bestowed understanding on human beings alone. See Aristotle, *De Anima* II, 3.414a29-32 and Aquinas, *Summa Theologiae*, Ia 78,1.

41.   Descartes, *Works*, p. 264.

42.   Ibid., pp. 229-230.

43.   Ibid., p. 262f.

44.   For a more detailed discussion of the following see John Hedley Brooke, "Newton and the Mechanistic Universe," *Towards a Mechanistic Universe* (Milton Keynes: Open University Press, 1974), pp. 85-87.

45.   The primary concepts considered here are Newton's three laws of motion 1. that a body at rest will remain at rest or a body in motion will remain in motion in a straight line unless acted upon by an external force; 2. that force

is to be defined as the mass of a body times the derivative with respect to time of its velocity; 3. that for every action there is an equal and opposite reaction) and his law of universal gravitation (that the gravitational force exerted by a body varies directly with its mass and inversely with the square of the distance from it).

46.   Brooke, *Towards a Mechanistic Philosophy*, pp. 59-65. Brooke explores the "historian's problem" which is involved in any attempt to characterize the tacit cosmology of an age by reviewing R. S. Westfall's characterization of the "mechanical philosophy" found in *The Construction of Modern Science* (John Wiley and Sons, Inc., 1971). The specification of the general features of that philosophy listed here are those which Brooke abstracts from Westfall. Brooke especially points out that Pierre Gassendi and Robert Boyle both took exception to the notion that nature was completely transparent to reason. However, the period, in general, reflected the confidence of Descartes that the right use of reason (plus empirical observation and experimentation) could uncover the truth of the natural order.

47.   Pierre Simon, Marquis de Laplace, *A Philosophical Essay on Probabilities*, Frederick Wilson Truscott and Frederick Lincoln Emory, trans. (New York: Dover Publications, Inc., 1951) p. 4.

48.   This anecdote is very possibly apochryphal. Although it is widely quoted in histories of science, I have yet to discover it footnoted. One example is found in Stanley Jaki, *The Relevance of Physics* (Chicago: University of Chicago Press, 1966), p. 433.

49.   To encompass the epistemological positions of Descartes, Locke and Berkeley in one paragraph is exceedingly inadequate. However, the purpose here is not to deal with their positions in even a summary way but rather merely to indicate the constellation of reflection on the nature of knowing which was stimulated by the new cosmological perspective and out of which the "critical" position of Kant was eventually to emerge.

50.   Reid's basic argument is found in his first major work, *The Inquiry Into the Human Mind on the Principles of Common Sense*, which was published in 1764. In addition to its importance as one of the premier works of the "Scottish Enlightenment," Reid's "common sense" philosophy and rational justification of a theological positivism became the central epistemological foundation for the development of Calvinist orthodoxy in the 18th and 19th centuries and of 20th century Protestant fundamentalism. For an extended discussion of this work see Norman Daniels, *Thomas Reid's Inquiry* (New York: Burt Franklin and Co., 1974). For a discussion of the Scottish "common sense" school and in particular its impact on American theology see Sydney E. Ahlstrom, "The Scottish Philosophy and American Theology," *Church History*, Vol. 24, No. 3, (September 1955), pp. 257-272.

51.   Ironically, this work never came on the public market because its publisher went bankrupt while it was in press and his warehouse was sealed.

See Ernst Cassirer, *Kant's Life and Thought* (New Haven: Yale University Press, 1981), p. 40.

52.   Immanuel Kant, *Universal Natural History and Theory of the Heavens* in Munitz, *Theories of the Universe*, p. 238.

53.   Ibid., p. 240 and p. 243.

54.   Immanuel Kant, *Prolegomena To Any Future Metaphysics That Will Be Able To Come Forward As Science*, James W. Ellington, trans. (Indianapolis, IN: Hackett Publishing Co., 1977), p. 5. The *Prolegomena* was published after Kant's "First Critique," and he understood it as a more accessible summary of the main lines of his argument. See, Ibid., p. 6. However, though the *Prolegomena* is considerably shorter that the "First Critique," it is not obvious that it is less obscure than its predecessor.

55.   Immanuel Kant, *The Critique of Pure Reason*, Norman Kemp Smith, trans. (New York: St. Martin's Press, 1929), p. 22.

56.   It should be observed that the notion that empirical experience as such was dependent in part upon the constitution of the human mind had already been anticipated in the "common sense realism" of the "Scottish Enlightenment." See, n. 37 above.

57.   Kant, *The Critique of Pure Reason*, p. 268.

58.   Ibid., p. 29.

59.   Immanuel Kant, *The Critique of Practical Reason*, Lewis White Beck, trans. (Chicago: University of Chicago Press, 1949), p. 85f.

60.   See ns. 36 and 37 above.

61.   Kant, *The Critique of Practical Reason*, p. 258f.

62.   Immanuel Kant, *Critique of Judgment*, James Creed Meredith, trans. (Oxford: Clarendon Press, 1928), p. 18.

63.   Ibid., p. 20ff.

64.   The "Circle" was formed initially under the leadership of Moritz Schick. Its earliest members were Otto Neurath, Friedrich Waismann, Edgar Zilsel, Bela von Johos, Felix Kaufman, Herbert Feigl, Victor Kraft, Philipp Frank, Karl Menger, Kurt Godel and Hans Hahn. Rudolph Carnap later became one of its most influential members. Ludwig Wittgenstein, Karl Popper and A. J. Ayer participated in the discussions of the "Circle" though they were not formally members of it and reached very different conclusions concerning the views developed within it.

65.   A. J. Ayer, *Language, Truth and Logic* (New York: Dover Publications, Inc., 1952), p. 120f.

66.   Ibid., p. 31.

67.   For example see Soren Kierkegaard, *Fear and Trembling* with *Sickness Unto Death*, Walter Lowrie, trans. (Princeton: Princeton University Press, 1954).

68.   Two 20th century exemplars of the existentialist position were Martin Heidegger and Jean Paul Sartre. Heidegger's existentialism was influenced both by Kant and Kierkegaard as well as the phenomenology of

Husserl. Sartre was in turn influenced by Heidegger. The diversity among existentialists can be seen in the varying ways in which they individually dealt with the issue of theism.

69.   See especially, Karl Barth, *The Epistle to the Romans*, 6th ed., Edwyn C. Hoskyns, trans. (London: Oxford University Press, 1933), and his summa, *Church Dogmatics*, 4 vols., var. eds. and trans. (Edinburgh: T. and T. Clark, 1936-1962). Ibid., p. 39.

70.   Buffon's calculations were based on experiments which measured the cooling rates of spheres of various sizes. He extrapolated from this data to incorporate the planets and adjusted his results to account for solar heating. Unfortunately, he assumed that the primary source of surface temperature was internal heat residual from the first formation of the planets. In fact, solar radiation is the overwhelming source of surface temperature for the earth. As a consequence his calculations produced figures several orders of magnitude below present estimates of the earth's age.

71.   This theory can be summarized as follows: change in a succession of organisms is related to changes in the environment; these changes produce felt behavioral needs in the individual organism; the development attained by structures in an organism is directly proportional to the use of those structures; all acquired structural changes are transmitted to the next generation. For a more thorough discussion of Lamarck's developmental theory see John Hedley Brooke, "Precursors of Darwin?" *The Crisis of Evolution*, Block 5, *Science and Belief: from Copernicus to Darwin* (Milton Keynes: Open University Press, 1974), pp. 32-35.

72.   For a discussion of this problem see Stephen Toulmin and June Goodfield, *The Discovery of Time* (Chicago: University of Chicago Press, 1965), p. 180f.

73.   Hutton was aware that the provision of sufficient time required the abandonment of the theological cosmology which assumed a recent creation of the earth. This factor as well as the uniformitarian challenge to the belief in the Noachin flood as a global catastrophe led many of Hutton's contemporaries to associate his views with the aggressive anti-clerical atheism which was a part of the French Revolution. Ironically, Hutton himself believed that the operation of diverse forces over long periods of time to form a fit habitat for human beings was evidence of the wisdom of a divine Creator. Thus, well before the controversy surrounding Darwin's works there was already a theological dispute concerning the interpretation of geo-history. For a more detailed discussion of Hutton's work see Ibid., pp. 155-158.

74.   Ibid., pp. 167-168.

75.   John Hedley Brooke, "Darwin," *The Crisis of Evolution*, p. 59.

76.   Toulmin and Goodfield, *The Discovery of Time*, p. 197f.

77.   Ibid., p. 200.

78.   The specific nature of Malthus' influence on Darwin is disputed. This is in part because Darwin interpreted Malthus' position in a distinctive

manner, in a way different from many of Malthus' contemporaries or even Malthus himself. Malthus had written his essay as a critique of the utopian speculations of his day. He saw the divergence between population growth and food production as a divinely ordained prod to overcome human sloth. A contemporary, William Paley, understood Malthus' "checks" on population growth within a broader natural theology which viewed nature as divinely "balanced." For Darwin, however, Malthus' mathematical treatment of population growth and environmental checks heightened his appreciation of the selective forces of nature and reinforced in him a competitive image of the selective process. For a more extended discussion of the relationship between Darwin and Malthus see Brooke, *The Crisis of Evolution*, pp. 46-50 and 67f.

79.   Charles Darwin, *The Autobiography of Charles Darwin and Se-lected Letters*, Francis Darwin, ed. (New York: Dover Publications, 1958), p. 42f.

80.   This analogy was problematic because, as Lyell noted, it implied an intentionality operating in nature determining those characteristics which were to be propogated. While this implication allowed some natural theologians to embrace Darwin's theory by identifying that intentionality with the divine, such an implication was far from the meaning with which Darwin himself invested the expression, "natural selection." For an example of the approach of the natural theologians see Asa Gray's citation of the Rev. Charles Kingsley in *Darwiniana* (New York: 1986), p. 282. Darwin, however, was not alone in his discovery of this mechanism. On June 18, 1858, Alfred Russell Wallace (1823-1913), who was engaged in biological studies in the Malay Archipelago, wrote Darwin describing a principle of "natural selection" by which to account for the development of species. Some of Wallace's language was almost identical to that which Darwin had been using in his painstaking development of his own theory. Although there is little doubt of Darwin's precedence on the basis of his correspondence with others of his contemporaries, Darwin and Wallace joined in the first public presentation of this evolutionary position in papers before the Linnean Society of London on July 1, 1858. For an account of Wallace's career with special reference to evolutionary theory see Henry Lewis McKinney, *Wallace and Natural Selection* (New Haven: Yale University Press, 1972).

81.   Darwin was never able to identify an adequate mechanism by which to account for variation. In 1866 Gregor Johann Mendel, an Augustinian monk, published a statistical theory of heredity based on his studies of the common garden pea. But this work was virtually ignored by the scientific community of his day. It was not until 1900 that this work was "discovered" simultaneously by Hugo de Vries (a Dutchman), Karl Correns (a German) and Erich Tscher-mak (an Austrian). Ironically, the revived Mendelian genetics was viewed initially as an alternative to the Darwinian theory of evolution. However, in the mid-1930's Sir Ronald Fisher, J. B. S. Haldane and Sewell Wright were able to show that the Darwinian and Mendelian theories were supplementary. See

J. B. S. Haldane, *The Causes of Evolution* (New York: Harper and Brothers, 1932). This union was then combined with paleontology and population genetics in the works of such persons as Theodosius Dobzhansky, A. S. Romer, George Gaylord Simpson, E. H. Colbert and Ernst Mayer to form what is now called "the modern synthetic theory of evolution." See Theodosius Dobzhansky, *Genetics and the Origin of the Species* (New York: Columbia University Press, 1937) and George Gaylord Simpson, *Life of the Past* (New Haven: Yale University Press, 1953).

82.   Toulmin, *The Return to Cosmology* (Berkeley: University of California Press, 1982), pp. 144-146; also, *Human Understanding* (Princeton: Princeton University Press, 1972), p. 338f.

83.   Darwin was morally and theologically troubled by what he observed as the massive waste of life which was the result of the interaction of these two mechanisms. For example see the letter to Asa Gray (May 22, 1860) in Darwin, *Autobiography*, p. 249.

84.   Paley's primary exposition of the teleological argument for the existence of God, or the argument from design, is found in *Natural Theology: or Evidences of the Existence and Attributes of the Deity, Collected from the Appearances of Nature* (Fornborough, GB: Greg International, 1970). It is in this work that Paley developed the "watchmaker" analogy whereby the functional unity of the organs both individually (e.g., the eye) and collectively as forming a whole creature or the fitness of an organism to its environment were likened to a watch found on a deserted beach. According to Paley, just as the functional unity of the watch requires a watchmaker, so functional unity in nature requires a divine "watchmaker."

85.   It is clear that this decoupling is what Darwin expressed in his naturalistic theory, even though he was troubled by the apparent conclusion that this effectively removed the Creator from the history of the development of creation. Today, however, without contradicting Darwin's basic insight a number of factors complicate the interpretation of "natural selection." These include: environmental impact on variation (e.g., environmental factors effecting gene mutation), the dynamism of the ecosystem such that "the environment" itself varies in relation to the nexus of species which comprise it at any particular moment, and the impact of intentional human actions which either deliberately or indirectly affect the selection process.

86.   For further discussion of "species" as conceptual artifacts see Toulmin and Goodfield, *The Discovery of Time*, pp. 214-215.

87.   A partial list of this cast of characters would include: Michael Faraday (1791-1867), Lord Kelvin (1824-1907), James Clerk Maxwell (1831-1879), Ludwig Boltzman (1844-1906), J. J. Thomson (1856-1940), Marie Curie (1867-1934), Lord Ernest Rutherford (1871-1937), Max Born (1882-1970), Erwin Schrödinger (1887-1961), Louis de Broglie (1892-), Enrico Fermi (1901-1954) and Paul Dirac (1902-). These persons encompass fields

ranging from the study of electricity and electromagnetism to thermodynamics to radiation studies to sub-atomic physics.

88.   Special relativity is "special" because it limits its concern to phenomena in which all observers are in inertial frames of reference, that is, frames of reference which are not accelerating relative to one another. A clear and concise discussion of special relativity can be found in Frank Durham and Robert D. Purrington, *Frame of the Universe* (New York: Columbia University Press, 1983), pp. 169-174. As they themselves note, Einstein's own popular account of relativity theory is also quite readable; see Albert Einstein, *Relativity*, R. W. Lawson, trans. (New York: Crown, 1961).

89.   Within the framework of classical Newtonian mechanics an object emitted from a moving source has its velocity either increased or decreased depending on the direction in which the source moves. This interpretation assumed an "absolute space" in relation to which all motion could be measured.

90.   For a thorough though somewhat technical discussion of the Michelson-Morley experiment and its pre-relativistic interpretations see Barry M. Casper and Richard J. Noer, *Revolutions in Physics* (New York: W. W. Norton and Company, 1972), pp. 299-315.

91.   The concept of the aether was in one sense a Cartesian substantialization of the Newtonian concept of absolute space.

92.   This conclusion was demonstrated by means of Einstein's "thought experiment" in which two events are observed by two individuals one of which is on a train moving at a constant velocity with respect to the other who is standing beside the tracks. What this "experiment" showed was that events which were simultaneous for one observer were not so for the other. For a more detailed discussion of this "experiment" see Einstein, *Relativity*, pp. 25-27.

93.   Ibid., pp. 28-29, 35-37, 79-89.

94.   For an extended discussion of the "principle of equivalence" see Casper and Noer, *Revolutions*, pp. 407-411 and Einstein, *Relativity*, pp. 66-70.

95.   For a brief survey of the history of quantum theory see Werner Heisenberg, *Physics and Philosophy* (New York: Harper and Row, 1958), pp. 30-43.

96.   This is the model which is perhaps most familiar to non-physicists today. It describes the atom as a planetary system where electrons orbit the nucleus much as the planets orbit the sun.

97.   Ibid., pp. 48-50.

98.   As Milic Capek has written,

"... wave mechanics associated a kind of periodical process with 'material corpuscles.' At first there was a hope of interpreting the associated vibrations as vibrations of some hypothetical material or quasi-material medium. Because this medium would in the last analysis consist of particles, it would be possible to recover the concept of permanent corpuscular entity, enduring through time, in a finer microphysical, 'subaetheral' level. But these hopes were not fulfilled; the 'waves of probability' replaced the 'waves of subaether.' The associated vibrations are not vibrations of something; they are inherent in material entities themselves; or, better, the material 'particle-events' are constituted by them."

Milic Capek, *The Philosophical Impact of Contemporary Physics* (Princeton: D. van Nostrand Company, 1961), p. 285.

99.   Werner Heisenberg, *The Physical Principles of Quantum Theory*, Carl Eckart and Frank C. Hoyt, trans. (Dover Publications, 1930), pp. 13-54. Jacob Bronowski has suggested an alternative nomenclature:

"the Principle of Uncertainty is a bad name. In science or outside it, we are not uncertain; our knowledge is merely confined within a certain tolerance. We could call it the Principle of Tolerance. And I propose that name in two senses. First, in the engineering sense. Science has progressed step by step ... because it has understood that the exchange of information between man and nature, and man and man, can only take place with a certain tolerance. But second, I also use the word passionately about the real world. All knowledge, all information between human beings can only be exchanged within a play of tolerance. And that is true whether the exchange is in science, or in literature, or in religion, or in politics, or even in any form of thought that aspires to dogma."

Bronowski, *The Ascent of Man*, p. 365.

100.   See Laplace Note above.

101.   For an extended discussion of the relations between uncertainty, indeterminacy and contingency see Capek, *Philosophical Impact*, pp. 289-332.

102.   Heisenberg, *Physics and Philosophy*, p. 54.

103.   Ibid., p. 58.

104.   John A. Wheeler has offered a more homespun illustration of this point which I quoted here at length:

"What is the difference between a 'participatory' reality and a reality that exists 'out there' independent of the community of perceivers? A homely example may illustrate a little of the difference. Edward Teller and I, and a dozen other guests, were sitting in the living room of Lothar Norheim in Durham after dinner. From general conversation we moved on to the game of twenty questions. One, chosen as victim, was sent out of the room. The rest of us agreed on some implausible word like 'brontosaurus.' Then the victim was let back into the room. To win, he had to discover the word with no more than twenty yes/no questions. Otherwise, he lost.

"After we had played several rounds, my turn came and I was sent out. The door was closed, and was kept closed for the longest time. I couldn't understand at all why they were taking so long. Moreover, when at length they let me in, every one had a grin on his face, sure sign of a joke or trick. However, I went ahead innocently asking my questions. 'Is it animal?' 'No.' 'Is it vegetable?' 'No.' 'Is it mineral?' 'Yes.' 'Is it green?' 'No.' 'Is it white?' 'Yes.'

"As I went on with my queries I found the answerer was taking longer and longer to respond. He would think and think. Why? That was beyond my understanding when all I wanted was a simple yes or no answer. But finally, I knew, I had to chance it, propose a definite word. 'Is it cloud?' I asked. My friend thought for a minute. 'Yes,' he said, finally. Then every one burst out laughing.

"My colleagues explained to me that when I was sent out of the room, they agreed not to agree on a word. There was no word in the room when I came in! What is more, they had agreed that each respondent was permitted to answer my question as he pleased — with one small proviso: if I challenged him, he had to have in mind a word compatible with his own and all previous answers! The game, in other words, was just as hard for my colleagues as for me.

"What is the symbolism of the story? The world, we once believed, exists 'out there,' independent of any act of observation. The electron in the atom we once considered to have at each moment a definite position and a definite momentum. I, entering, thought the room contained a definite word. In actuality the word was developed step by step through the questions I raised, as the information about the electron is brought into being by the experiment that the observer chooses to make; that is, by the kind of registering equipment that he puts into place. Had I asked different questions or the same questions in a different order I would have ended up with a different word as the experimenter would have ended up with a different story for the doings of the electron. However, the power I had in bringing the particular word 'cloud' into being was partial only. A major part of the selection lay in the 'yes' and 'no' replies of the colleagues around the room. Similarly, the experimenter has some substantial influence on what will happen to the electron by the choice of experiments he will do on it, 'questions he will put to nature'; but he knows there is a certain unpredictability about what any given one of his measurements will disclose, about what 'answers nature will give,' about what will happen when 'God plays dice.' This comparison between the world of quantum observations and the surprise version of the game of twenty questions misses much, but it makes the central point. In the game, no word is a word until that word is promoted to reality by the choice of questions asked and answers given. In the real world of quantum physics, <u>no elementary phenomena is a phenomena until it is a recorded phenomena</u>."

John B. Wheeler, "Bohr, Einstein and the Strange Lesson of the Quantum,"

Mind in Nature, Richard Q. Elvee, ed. (San Francisco: Harper and Row, 1982), pp. 19-21.

105.   As Capek notes, Einstein's position in this regard was ironic in the light of his own challenge to the classical mechanical concepts of absolute space and time:

> "It is interesting ... to see Einstein hesitating to apply Occam's razor to classical determinism, although he had previously boldly used this razor in eliminating the empirically unverifiable motionless aether.... Einstein's reluctance to depart from determinism was due to certain unconscious or semi-conscious metaphysical predilections. This explains why Einstein, who was a fairly consistent phenomenalist in his theory of relativity, was much less so in his attitude to quantum phenomena, although at present classical determinism is as unverifiable as absolute space or absolute motion."

Capek, *Philosophical Impact*, p. 297f. Elsewhere Capek also notes Einstein's positive contributions to the development of quantum theory which are found in Einstein's quantum analysis of the kinetic theory of matter. Ibid., p. 278. In addition see Wolfgang Pauli, "Einstein's Contribution to Quantum Theory," *Albert Einstein: Philosopher-Scientist*, Paul Arthur Schilpp, ed. (Evanston, IL: Library of Living Philosophers, 1949), pp. 153-156.

106.   For a popular treatment of this development see Stephen Weinberg, *The First Three Minutes* (New York: Basic Books, c1977).

107.   As will be noted in a moment, modern and critical epistemologies are rooted in a pre-modern form of naive realism in which knowing is assumed to be analogous to a common sense model of visual perception, a process of "looking and seeing" facts. From a post-modern perspective the social and cultural context has a constitutive bearing upon what one actually sees as for example in the Wheeler parable.

108.   An example of the incompleteness of the current cosmological shift and its embedding as a tacit cultural presupposition is that Bohm's views themselves manifest a sharp internal tension. While ascribing the most fundamental dynamism to the cosmos, he also seeks to overcome the apparent indeterminism and so contingency of the cosmos (as given in the Copenhagen Interpretation of quantum physics) by means of a "theory of hidden variables." Such a theory holds that the apparent lawlessness (or indeterminacy) of quantum phenomena can actually be given a lawful account from a deeper or broader level of physical understanding. For a detailed discussion of this position see David Bohm, *Causality and Chance in Modern Physics* (London: Routledge and Kegan Paul, 1957). For a summary comparison of the Copenhagen Interpretation of quantum theory and the interpretation of quantum phenomena from a perspective of "hidden variables" see David Bohm, *Wholeness and the Implicate Order* (London: Routledge and Kegan Paul, 1980), pp. 65-110.

109.   Bohm, *Wholeness*, p. 11.

110.   Ibid., p. 151.

111.   There is as yet no broad consensus as to the specification of the terms "post-modern" and "post-critical." What follows then is one possible specification which is itself a personal construction and not simply a report on or description of an extrinsic intellectual system.

112.   The discussion of Wittgenstein's work presented here is primarily dependent upon the interpretation of Wittgenstein's intellectual project found in Alan Janik and Stephen Toulmin, *Wittgenstein's Vienna* (New York: Simon and Schuster, 1973). This interpretation is in some contrast with the "received interpretation" of Wittgenstein and his work in that it attempts to show that Wittgenstein's intellectual project was embedded in and was formed primarily in response to the historical and cultural environment in which he was born, grew up and lived rather than being simply a response to particular problems in analytic philosophy.

113.   Janik and Toulmin, *Wittgenstein's Vienna*, p. 22.

114.   Ludwig Wittgenstein, *Tractatus Logico-Philosophicus*, D. F. Pears and B. F. McGuinness, trans. (London: Routledge and Kegan Paul, 1961).

115.   For examples see G. E. M. Anscombe, *An Introduction to Wittgenstein's Tractatus* (London: Hutchinson University Library, 1959) and Max Black, *A Companion to Wittgenstein's Tractatus* (Ithaca: Cornell University Press, 1964).

116.   The distinction between the "early" and the "later" Wittgenstein is often identified paradigmatically with a comparison between the *Tractatus* and Wittgenstein's *Philosophical Investigations*, G. E. M. Anscombe, trans. (New York: Macmillan Publishing Co., 1968). This latter work was completed shortly before Wittgenstein's death in 1951 and first published in 1953. In addition to the *Tractatus* the only other writing by Wittgenstein published during his lifetime was an article, "Some Remarks on Logical Form," PAS Supp. Vol. 9 (1929), pp. 162-171, with which he expressed dissatisfaction. A large number of his other writings have been published since his death. These others were originally in the form of notebooks (e.g., *Notebooks 1914-1916*), lectures (e.g., *Lectures and Conversations on Aesthetics, Psychology and Religion*) and incidental writings collected together after his death and ordered, usually thematically, by his editors (e.g., *On Certainty* and *Zettel*). The contrast between an "earlier" and a "later" Wittgenstein is often taken to parallel one between "modern" and "post-modern" or between "critical" and "post-critical." For example see Jerry Gill, *On Knowing God* (Philadelphia: The Westminster Press, 1981), especially pp. 34-39 and 79-83.

117.   For Schopenhauer's views see his *The Fourfold Root of the Principle of Sufficient Reason and On the Will in Nature*, E. F. Payne, ed. (LaSalle, IL: Open Court, 1974) and his *On the Basis of Morality*, E. F. Payne, trans. (New York: Bobbs-Merrill, 1965). For Kierkegaard's views on the grounding of morality see especially *Fear and Trembling* with *Sickness Unto Death*,

Walter Lowrie, trans. (Princeton: Princeton University Press, 1954).

118.   Wittgenstein, *Tractatus*, 6.54-7.

119.   Paul Engelmann, *Letters from Ludwig Wittgenstein, With a Memoir*, B. F. McGuinness, ed., L. Furtmuller, trans. (Oxford: Basil Blackwell, 1967), p. 97 cited in Janik and Toulmin, *Wittgenstein's Vienna*, p. 43.

120.   Wittgenstein, *Zettel*, G. E. M. Anscombe and G. H. von Wright, ed., G. E. M. Anscombe, trans. (Berkeley: University of California Press, 1967), p. 458.

121.   Ibid., 460.

122.   Wittgenstein, *Philsophical Investigations*, 19.

123.   Ibid., 23.

124.   Wittgenstein, *Tractatus*, 3.3421-3.343. Wittgenstein later exemplified this relation between the arbitrariness of signification and the essential significance of the possibility of a particular form of signifying when he wrote of Newtonian mechanics that it

"imposes a unified form on the description of the world. Let us imagine a white surface with irregular black spots on it. We then say that whatever kind of picture these make, I can always approximate as closely as I wish to the description of it by covering the surface with a sufficiently fine square mesh, and then saying of every square whether it is black or white. In this way I shall have imposed a unified form on the description of the surface. The form is optional, since I could have achieved the same result by using a net with triangular or hexagonal mesh. Possibly the use of the triangular mesh would have made the description simpler: that is to say, it might be that we could describe the surface more accurately with a coarse triangular mesh than with a fine square mesh, (or conversely), and so on. The different nets correspond to different systems for describing the world.

"... the possibility of describing the world by means of Newtonian mechanics tells us nothing about the world: but what does tell us something about it is the precise <u>way</u> in which it is possible to describe it by these means. We are also told something about the world by the fact that it can be described more simply with one system than with another.

"Mechanics is an attempt to construct according to a single plan all the <u>true</u> propositions that we need for the description of the world."

Ibid., 6.341-6.343.

125.   This is the language theory found explicitly developed in the *Tractatus*; see especially 1-3.

126.   Ludwig Wittgenstein, *On Certainty*, G. E. M. Anscombe and G. H. von Wright, ed., Denis Paul and G. E. M. Anscombe, trans. (New York: Harper and Row, 1969), 204-205.

127.   Ibid., 193-196.
128.   So Wittgenstein wrote,
"... we may not advance any kind of theory. There must not be anything hypothetical in our considerations. We must do away with all _explanation_, and description alone must take its place. And this description gets its light, that is to say its purpose, from the philosophical problems. These are, of course, not empirical problems; they are solved, rather by looking into the works of our language, and that in such a way as to make us recognize those workings: _in despite of_ an urge to misunderstand them. The problems are solved, not by giving new information, but by arranging what we have always known. Philosophy is a battle against the bewitchment of our intelligence by means of language." Wittgenstein, _Philosophical Investigations_, 109. Or again, "Philosophy may in no way interfere with the actual use of language; it can in the end only describe it. For it cannot give it any foundation either. It leaves everything as it is."
Ibid., 124.

129.   An "ostensive reference" is one derived by "pointing to" something in the world. To refer ostensively is to refer by pointing. For the positivists one pointed either to the "facts" of empirical observation or the operations by which such "facts" were observed.

130.   For a helpful summary of the development of positivism in relation to the _Tractatus_ and the distance which grew between positivism and Wittgenstein's own philosophical work see Janik and Toulmin, _Wittgenstein's Vienna_, pp. 212-219.

131.   In an autobiographical sketch he writes:
"Every body knows nowadays that logical positivism is dead. But nobody seems to suspect that there may be a question to be asked here — the question 'Who is responsible?' or, rather, the question 'Who has done it?' ... I fear that I must admit responsibility. Yet I did not do it on purpose: my sole intention was to point out what seemed to me a number of fundamental mistakes."
Karl Popper, "Autobiography of Karl Popper," _The Philosophy of Karl Popper_, Paul Arthur Schilpp, ed. (LaSalle, IL: Open Court, 1974), p. 69.

132.   This work was published in English in 1959 with revised editions in 1960 and 1968 under the title, _The Logic of Scientific Discovery_ (New York: Harper and Row). Subsequent citations will be made from the 1968 edition.

133.   Ibid., p. 70.
134.   Ibid., p. 93f. This statement of the issue is derived by Popper from J. F. Fries' analysis of experience.
135.   Ibid.
136.   Ibid., p. 40f.
137.   Ibid., p. 280.

138.   Ibid., p. 278.

139.   It should be noted, however, that, while in Darwin's theory there was a fundamental separation between the two interacting factors, in Popper's epistemological model conjectures which lead to new hypotheses are stimulated by current empirical experience which is itself related to the testing of existing hypotheses. Still, contemporary insight into the impact of environmental factors on gene mutation suggests that Popper's epistemological theory and contemporary evolutionary theory form a closer parallel than might be initially thought.

140.   For a lively presentation of the debate between Popper and Kuhn see Imre Lakatos and Alan Musgrave,eds., *Criticism and the Growth of Knowledge* (Cambridge: Cambridge University Press, 1970), pp. 1-23, 51-58 and 231-278.

141.   Thomas S. Kuhn, *The Structure of Scientific Revolutions (Chicago: University of Chicago Press, 1962), p. 91.*

142.   Ibid., p. 150. In particular Kuhn notes unwillingness of Joseph Priestly to accept the oxygen theory of combustion and of Lord Kelvin to accept electromagnetic theory. In this context Kuhn quotes Max Planck's statement that "a new scientific truth does not triumph by convincing its opponents and making them see the light, but rather because its opponents eventually die, and a new generation grows up that is familiar with it." Max Planck, *Scientific Autobiography and Other Papers*, F. Gaynor, trans. (New York: Philosophical Library, 1949), pp. 33-34. Kuhn then goes on to comment that

> "These facts and others like them are too commonly known to need further emphasis. But they do need re-evaluation. In the past they have most often been taken to indicate that scientists, being only human, cannot always admit their errors, even when confronted with strict proof. I would argue, rather, that in these matters neither proof nor error is at issue. The transfer of allegiance fom (sic) paradigm to paradigm is a conversion experience that cannot be forced. Lifelong resistance, particularly from those whose productive careers have committed them to an older tradition of normal science, is not a violation of scientific standards but an index to the nature of scientific research itself."

Kuhn, *The Structure of Scientific Revolutions*, p. 150. Also, Thomas S. Kuhn, *The Essential Tension* (Chicago: University of Chicago Press, 1977), p. 208f.

143.   Kuhn, *The Structure of Scientific Revolutions*, p. 10. Much debate has occurred concerning the adequacy of Kuhn's definition of "paradigm." For example see Lakatos and Musgrave, eds., *Criticism and the Growth of Knowledge* especially the article by Margaret Masterman, "The Nature of a Paradigm," pp. 59-89. Subsequent to that criticism Kuhn has sought to clarify his use of the term. For example see Kuhn, *The Essential Tension*, pp. 297-319.

144.   Kuhn, *The Structure of Scientific Revolutions*, p. 64.

145.   Ibid., p. 122.

146.   Kuhn, *The Essential Tension*, p. xxii. This focus on language suggests a parallel between Kuhn and Wittgenstein. For the latter different language-games were appropriate to different "forms of life." For Kuhn a paradigmatic shift is not simply a conceptual change, it is also a transformation of scientific practice.

147.   See Karl Popper, "Normal Science and Its Dangers," Lakatos and Musgrave, *Criticism and the Growth of Knowledge*, especially p. 56ff. In the same work also see Imre Lakatos, "Falsification and the Methodology of Scientific Research Programmes." pp. 91-196.

148.   Toulmin, *Human Understanding*, p. 480.

149.   Toulmin writes

> "What makes it worthwhile to extend ecological terminology from organic to intellectual evolution is, simply, the extensive parallels between the ecological account of organic change and the disciplinary account of intellectual development. Within intellectual history, any actual problem-situation creates a certain range of opportunities for intellectual innovation. The nature of these opportunities depends, of course, as much on the character of other coexisting ideas as it does on purely 'external' features of the social or physical situation. We may study the resulting conceptual changes either qua processes, by looking to see simply what historical courses they took, or alternatively qua achievements, by asking how far those changes exploited the intellectual opportunities in the current situation. As in the organic case, the relationship between concepts and opportunities is a complex and reciprocal one. Earlier populations of scientific concepts can differentiate in such a way that they generate novel disciplines (say) only where suitable intellectual opportunities present themselves; meanwhile, the character of those opportunities is powerfully affected by the other conceptual populations already in existence .... The disciplinary account of scientific change accordingly studies the opportunities to be exploited in any problem-situation, analyses the demands created by those opportunities, and appraises the achievements resulting from the conceptual changes by which scientists actually responded to those demands."

Ibid., p. 316f.

150.   Ibid., p. 208.

151.   Ibid., p. 209.

152.   Ibid., p. 221.

153.   In Toulmin's words

> "... a preoccupation with the systematicity of geometry and formal logic makes a universal, quasi-mathematical absolutism in our intellectual methods and standards appear the only alternative to outright historico-cultural relativism; ... this opposition leads, in

turn, to a seemingly-inescapable choice between uniformitarian and revolutionary theories of conceptual change; and ... the arguments that impose these distasteful choices on us both rest on the assumption that 'rationality' is primarily a matter of 'logicality' — i.e., that the tests and/or criteria for judging the rationality of intellectual methods and positions primarily involve questions about coherence, entailment, consistency, and other such formal characteristics....

"The moment we stop assuming that ideas of any milieu form static 'proposition systems', and recognize that they constitute historically developing 'conceptual populations', we are free to abandon the philosophers' traditional assumption that rationality is a sub-species of logicality."
Ibid., pp. 485-486.

154.   Ibid., pp. 502-503.

155.   Toulmin, *The Return to Cosmology*, pp. 113-126, especially p. 119f; also see *Human Understanding*, p. 339, n. 1. For a comprehensive presentation of the view Toulmin is criticizing see Pierre Teilhard de Chardin, *The Phenomena of Man* (New York: Harper and Row, 1959).

156.   See Lakatos and Musgrave, *Criticism and the Growth of Knowledge*, pp. 92 (n. 2), 115, 163 (n. 2), 178.

157.   Michael Polanyi, *Personal Knowledge* (New York: Harper and Row, 1962), pp. 265-266.

158.   Polanyi indicated the relation of grounds to the truth of our knowledge in the following way: "we cannot ultimately specify the grounds (either metaphysical or logical or empirical) upon which we hold that our knowledge is true. Being committed to such grounds, dwelling in them, we are projecting ourselves to what we believe to be true from and through these grounds. We cannot therefore see what they are. We cannot look at them since we are looking with them. They therefore must remain indeterminate." Michael Polanyi and Harry Prosch, *Meaning* (Chicago: University of Chicago Press, 1975), p. 61.

159.   For example, in the practice of science
"[T]he scientist, having relied throughout his inquiry on the presence of something real hidden out there, will justly rely on that external presence also for claiming the validity of the result that satisfies his quest. As he accepted throughout the discipline which the external pole of his endeavor imposed on him, he expects that others — if similarly equipped — will also recognize the presence that guided him. By his own command, which bound him to the quest of reality, he will claim that his results are universally valid. Such is the universal intent of a scientific discovery.

"I do not speak of established universality, but of universal intent, for the scientist cannot know if his claim will be accepted....

To claim validity for a statement merely declares that it ought to be accepted by all."
Michael Polanyi, *The Tacit Dimension* (Garden City: Doubleday and Company, 1922), p. 78.
160.   Polanyi, *Personal Knowledge*, p. 112.
161.   Polanyi, *The Tacit Dimension*, p. 22f.
162.   Polanyi, *Personal Knowledge*, p. 196.
163.   Ibid., p. 300f.
164.   Polanyi and Prosch, *Meaning*, p. 156.
165.   Alfred North Whitehead, *Process and Reality*, corrected ed., David Ray Griffin and Donald W. Sherburne, eds. (New York: The Free Press, 1978), p. 346.
166.   For example, Wittgenstein, *Tractatus*, 6.53. Popper, Toulmin and Polanyi all recognize the inescapability of metaphyiscal presuppositions but also the potential for error when particular presuppositions are taken to be inviolate. For example see Popper, *The Logic of Scientific Discovery*, pp. 198, 277-278, 314; Toulmin, Ronald W. Hepburn and Alasdair Macintyre, *Metaphysical Beliefs* (New York: Schocken Books, [1957] 1970), pp. 3-71; and Polanyi and Harry Prosch, *Meaning* (Chicago: University of Chicago Press, 1975), pp. 189-190.
167.   See Polanyi, *Personal Knowledge*, pp. 381-405; and Toulmin, *The Return to Cosmology*, especially pp. 255-274.
168.   Whitehead, *Process and Reality*, p. 3.
169.   Victor Lowe, "A. N. W.: A Biographical Perspective," *Process Studies*, Vol. 12, No. 3 (Fall 1982), p. 137f.
170.   Whitehead, *Process and Reality*, p. 17: "Philosophy destroys its usefulness when it indulges in brilliant feats of explaining away. It is then trespassing with the wrong equipment upon the field of particular sciences. Its ultimate appeal is to the general consciousness of what in practice we experience. Whatever thread of presupposition characterizes social expression throughout the various epochs of rational society must find its place in philosophic theory. Speculative boldness must be balanced by complete humility before logic, and before fact. It is a disease of philosophy when it is neither bold nor humble, but merely a reflection on the temperamental presuppositions of exceptional personalities."
171.   Ibid., pp. 7-8:
"In its turn every philosophy will suffer a deposition. But the bundle of philosophic systems expresses a variety of general truths about the universe, awaiting coordination and assignment of their spheres of validity. Such progress in coordination is provided by the advance of philosophy; and in this sense philosophy has advanced from Plato onwards. According to this account of the achievement of rationalism, the chief error in philosophy is overstatement. The aim at generalization is sound, but the estimate of success is

exaggerated. There are two main forms of such overstatement. One form is what I have termed, elsewhere, the 'fallacy of misplaced concreteness'. This fallacy consists in neglecting the degree of abstraction involved when an actual entity is considered merely so far as it exemplifies certain categories of thought. There are aspects of actualities which are simply ignored so long as we restrict thought to these categories. Thus, the success of a philosophy is to be measured by its comparative avoidance of this fallacy, when thought is restricted within its categories.

"The other form of overstatement consists in a false estimate of the logical procedure in respect to certainty, and in respect to premises. Philosophy has been haunted by the unfortunate notion that its method is to dogmatically indicate premises which are severally clear, distinct, and certain; and to erect upon those premises a deductive system of thought.

"But the accurate expression of the final generalities is the goal of discussion not its origin. Philosophy has been misled by the example of mathematics; and even in mathematics the statement of the ultimate logical principles is beset with difficulties, as yet insuperable. The verification of a rationalistic scheme is to be sought in its general success, and not in the peculiar certainty, or initial clarity, of its first principles."

172. For example see Toulmin, *Human Understanding*, pp. 485-486.

173. Alfred North Whitehead and Bertrand Russell, *Principia Mathematica* (Cambridge: Cambridge University Press, 1910-1913).

174. Whitehead, *Process and Reality*, p. 9.

175. Ibid., p. 21. For discussions of how Whitehead's understanding of creativity differs from Aristotle's notion of 'primary substance' see Ibid., pp. 30, 50.

176. One of the difficulties encountered by Whitehead in the presentation of his cosmological system was that Western languages have inherent to them a substantialist orientation. Thus, to express oneself in English is already to have invoked a subject/predicate, substance/quality form of discourse. Consequently, Whitehead's language often seems strained as he attempted to mold his language to the vision he sought to express. David Bohm has proposed the development of a form of English which is inherently dynamic, a form based entirely on transitive verbs. For a discussion of this proposal see Bohm's discussion of the "rheomode" in *Wholeness and the Implicate Order*, pp. 27-47.

177. Whitehead, *Process and Reality*, p. 18.

178. Ibid., p. 22.

179. Ibid., p. 21.

180. Whitehead saw his philosophical work, and in fact the whole European philosophical tradition, as a continuation of reflections initiated by

Plato, or as he put it as "a series of footnotes on Plato." Ibid., p. 39. For a discussion of the differences between Whitehead's notion of "eternal objects" and Plato's of the "ideal forms" see Ibid., pp. 43-46.

181.   Ibid., pp. 34-35.

182.   Ibid., p. 39.

What Ever Happened to Immanuel Kant?
A Preliminary Study of Selected Cosmologies

Langdon Gilkey

The Divinity School
University of Chicago
Chicago, Illinois

Part I

This paper is deliberately circumscribed. Although the implications of our topic are immense for the entire field of science and religion, still we shall confine our attention to a small area, and in that area raise only certain sorts of questions. The area is current cosmologies—of which a few, and only a few, have been sampled[1]—and the questions I shall raise about them are neither scientific nor theological but philosophical in character. Since I am really not a professional in either cosmology or current philosophy, this will be at best an amateur effort. But perhaps in this day of specialization and thus of uninhabited and unpatrolled "no person's land" between fields, a bumbling amateur may in his or her innocence raise some useful questions. I hope so. Readers familiar with my thoughts on science will perhaps expect from me religious or theological criticisms of science: for its intellectual or spiritual hubris, its dogmatism, its unawareness of its status as established, its naive mythologies, its utopianism, etc. Such criticisms, instructive as they may be, will not appear here. I am interested—as I was in most of *Religion and the Scientific Future*—in the points where both science and religion meet on a philosophical common ground—or should do so—namely, in the necessary epistemological and in the ontological/metaphysical middle ground between scientific theory and theology. For having gone through a goodly number of cosmologies, I am now assured that it is in what might now be better called the philosophical "middle wasteland" that many, though surely not all, of the misunderstandings and problems in the relation of science and religion lie. In any case, I am convinced that both sides: the scientific and the religious, can in our day only profit by more exposure to the issues and principles lurking in this currently deserted philosophical middle ground.

This came, I must admit, as a surprise. Having done my homework in current philosophy of science, I was as aware as anyone not only of the demise in philosophy of science of Logical Positivism, and even of "scientific empiricism" but even of the birth of what has been welcomed as the "new philosophy of science"[2] What is more, it was evident that those philosophers of science who have presided over the heir's birth, were also conscious of the new relevance to the understanding of science of hermeneutics, a mode of philosophical understanding appropriate not only to the humanities—its "home ground"—but even to religious understanding as well. In principle, therefore, the philosophical problems of the interrelation of scientific theory to theology and so of scientific knowledge to religious disclosures, seemed resolved. On the level of philosophical discussion, this rapprochement is no illusion. Nevertheless, from my limited reading of scientific cosmologies, it appears that word of this new breakthrough in the philosophy of science seems not to have reached most of the "working cosmologists". In a sense, then, this paper represents elements of the viewpoint of that new philosophy of science now applied critically to selected cosmologies; however, my references will be more inclusive than that, for I am interested really in the relation of modern cosmology to the rich, varied—but perhaps now long forgotten—philosophical tradition from Kant on known as critical philosophy.

This is not to say that contemporary cosmologies are not exceedingly impressive works. I have found Pagels, Sagan, Weinberg, Dawkins, and Barrow and Tipler learned, intelligent, enthralling and surprisingly charming. They appear (to a lay person) to know exactly what they are talking about— even if much of it remains incomprehensible to me—and each of them is astoundingly able to synthesize clearly and helpfully (if in quite different ways) very disparate realms of scientific theory. And, finally, what contemporary science can legitimately claim to "know" about the vast physical universe is a continuing and enthralling astonishment, even "wonder", to an amateur like myself. What I did find, however—and this is my point here—is that none of them seems to be conscious of the important philosophical (epistemological and metaphysical) problems that hovered inevitably over or in the background of their entire work. It was as if these questions concerning the possibility and status of our knowledge, even of our scientific knowledge, were simply not there; or, if they were aware of them, had once been raised in a quite different cultural matrix than our own—say, in ancient China. If they had heard of them (and many referred to Whitehead, even to Kant), these authors did not seem to feel that these problems were relevant in any way to what their scientific colleagues were saying or to the cosmologies which they themselves were writing. Apparently—and this is a most important point in my argument—the relevance of philosophical questions and discussions to the possibilities, the limits and the validity of cosmology never occurred to them, even though—as I shall try to show—these philosophical issues are crucial to the intelligibility of what they are writing. I wish, therefore, to be very clear that it is the philosophy of science implicit in these cosmologies, not the science with which these books explicitly deal, about which I am raising questions here. The question "Whatever happened to Kant?" has occurred to me before, especially when I listen to my good friend, Ralph Burhoe. But it is only with these cosmologies that the critical problem has moved center stage in my mind. So let us begin: what is it about these cosmologies that makes me think they have long forgotten Immanuel Kant?—and in fact, along with him, most of the points emphasized in the "new philosophy of science"?

$$* \ * \ * \ * \ *$$

I shall introduce my theme by listing and then describing—with a few references—four propositions about science and its knowledge which seem assumed by these cosmologies. It is not irrelevant that these four are also characteristic of an older, now frequently repudiated, "objectivist" understanding of science and therefore challenge directly the new understanding of science. As will be evident, on most important issues these propositions also represent the kind of naive realism, "the Fallacy of Misplaced Concreteness,"[3] which critical philosophy from Hume through Kant to Whitehead and Polanyi (not to mention Lonergan and Tillich) has sought to challenge.

1. Science—in this case physics—is about to answer satisfactorily its own most important questions, resolve fully its deepest puzzles, and thus in effect to bring about, through this virtual apotheosis, its own end. Not all the cosmologies I read uttered these surprising almost eschatological predictions; but Pagel's book is full of them, and he quotes some impressive authorities for this view. Let me cite a sampling: "Today scientists confront the universe as a puzzle with scattered clues to its solution. Challenging as it is, many believe they will solve it some day. That day may be closer than many people think." (PS 10) "Some day. . . the physical origin and the dynamics of the entire universe will be as well understood as we now understand the stars. The existence of the universe will hold no more mystery for those who choose to understand it than the existence of the sun. Steven Hawking (in his Plumean lecture). . . said that the major problems of the universe may be solved in several decades." (PS 367-8) Thus. . ."the end is in sight for theoretical physics." (PS 373)

Quotations like these are frequently cited in current philosophies of science (much as medieval or Reformation dogmatic statements are cited!) in order to illustrate the kind of objectivist realism familiar at the end of the last century in the classic physics before the revolution of quantum and relativity theory appeared. With that 'revolution'—so current philosophy of science assures us—there was evident a new sense of the mystery of the objects of physical science, of the perspectival character of every inquiry, even new ones, of the consequently symbolic character of human conceptuality, and so of the non-identity of our concepts with actuality.[4] Added to this was the now evident fact that observations depended on observers and were affected by the latter-so that the results of inquiry were always "infected" by the aims, assumptions, instruments and locus of the inquirers. As we shall see in a moment, recent philosophy of science has increased the weight of the perspectival, relative aspect of inquiry. It was, therefore, a great surprise to encounter these sentences with their undeniably objectivist assumptions. For to predict a. that the deepest puzzles of actuality will soon be "solved," and thus b. that inquiry on that level may well cease, is (1) to regard actuality and theory as potentially completely congruent if not identical, so that actuality is completely "available" to theory; (2) to deny any perspectival or relativistic aspects of even the best theory; and so (3) as a consequence to regard theory as in principle totally ahistorical, in fact almost eschatological in character. As we shall see, thesis 2 intensifies this interpretation of science.

2.   There are no effective presuppositions to scientific inquiry and so to adequate scientific judgments; such judgments on the contrary are purely empirical, based on objective evidence alone and thus influenced not at all by the locus, perspective or "pre-understanding" of the inquirer. One of the major thrusts of the new understanding of science has been the emphasis on its "theory-laden" character. Evidence and facts, so many now argue, take shape only as a result of prior theories; arguments in scientific disputes hinge on the "paradigms" (Kuhn), the "ideals of natural order" (Toulmin) which the then current science assumes; and, finally, every scientific inquiry and scientific conclusion makes sense against a "background of order," a "metaphysical world view" or "idea of nature", (Collingwood) which only metaphysics can elaborate (Whitehead).[5] The conceptions of presuppositionless facts or evidence, and of scientific judgments based only on objective induction from that evidence represent, therefore, for this viewpoint a vast abstraction, an illusion of logic, in contrast to the actuality of the perspectival, theory-laden and so historically and intellectually relative character of the mind's cognitive power.

Throughout the cosmologies I read, this objectivist, empiricist view of science was assumed. Let me again give a few examples: "Whereas philosophies and theologies appear to possess an emotional attachment to their theories and ideas which requires them to believe them, scientists tend to regard their ideas differently. They are interested in formulating many logically consistent possibilities, leaving any judgment regarding their truth to observation." (APC 15) "In modern science models and descriptions of natural phenomena are taken up and discarded solely according to their transient usefulness, whereas for early scientists they represented not just the model but the very essence of the Universe, the 'thing in itself'." (APC 55) The sense of the empirical, pragmatic objectivity in these passages is clear: no cultural or epochal presuppositions or paradigms undergird, shape or deflect the empirical knowing of science, not to mention any ideological undertow! Other attempts to know may be weighed down by all manner of subjective needs and biases, but not contemporary empirical science. Thus Pagels welcomes the fact that cosmology—and by that he means the inquiry that addresses itself to most of Kant's antinomies (PS 135)—is now "an empirical science" and thus can look forward to exploring once and for all the age old questions about ultimate origins, the "very origin" even of space, time and matter itself, as a manageable empirical discipline. (PS 135 ff.)

3. Scientific criteria of the meaning, the validity or the "usefulness" of a theory or notion are the only criteria of any interest at all to science or to the understanding of science. This is a most interesting proposition, evident in all the books I perused, seemingly innocuous enough—in fact, almost a trivial tautology—and yet redolent with epistemological and metaphysical assumptions relevant to our larger subject.

If there are no presuppositions to scientific inquiry, no ontological or metaphysical—and so epistemological or transcendental—assumptions on which it depends, nor any relevant sociological, physchological, historical or existential bases of science, then science stands so to speak purely on itself: on given "facts" indicative unambiguously of the actuality they represent, and on the objective perceptual and logical power of the inquiring human mind.[6] If that understanding of science be valid, then this proposition makes good sense. For then there are no propositions outside the limits of such empirical inquiry, except questions of logic and of mathematics, which are relevant to the interpretation and understanding of science. But by the same token, if there are presuppositions on which inquiry is dependent, if the inquirer—even with tenure—is a historical, sociological, psychological and even "metaphysical" being, and if facts are always in correlation with cultural and historical paradigms or theories   then propositions about these matters are not only extra scientific, "beyond the limits of science" (since they have to do with the conditions or possibility of science), but also they are important to the interpretation and understanding of science.

For obvious reasons this issue—and the distinction between these two views of science—was not discussed in any of these works. Why should it be, since each assumed that science was self-sufficient: based on evidence, instruments, its own tradition and logic alone? No prolegomenon dealing with these "conditions" of empirical science was, therefore, either needed or possible. For this reason the philosophical questions about the modes of validity, of adequacy, and/or the testing of the presuppositions of science, that is for extra scientific "truth", were, as unasked and because unintelligible questions, left quite unexplored. For this reason the proposition to which this section is devoted was implied but never stated.

Evidence, however, that this proposition above was in fact affirmed—that in fact scientific modes of validation were regarded as the only modes of validation—did appear in indirect ways. I will cite several from ACP. These are interesting because to all intents and purposes they involve philosophical questions (that is of teleology, of ontological reductionism, and of ontological determinism)—which at least historically have been so regarded. That these have been philosophical issues was recognized but dismissed without argument: the only criteria cited as relevant are <u>scientific criteria</u>, "scientific evidence". I suspect that if the question, "how do we know that these metaphysical assumptions necessary for science are true?" were pressed, the same sort of empirical criteria (scientific success or fruitfulness) would be cited for, e.g., the assumption of a universal order, the assumption of universal causality, of temporal and spatial homogeneity, and of the relevance of logic to the exploration of actuality, to name a few of these assumptions. Apparently to these representatives of science, these various "metaphysical assumptions of modern empirical science"[7] are themselves conclusions from (inductions from) scientific inquiry rather than the necessary bases of that inquiry. Not only is Kant forgotten, Hume is as well. But to my quotations:

> "The rather violent hostility with which most scientists regard teleology is partly due to the failure of teleological arguments to account for adaptation in living beings...but it is also due to the paucity of significant scientific advances derived from teleological arguments." (ACP 123—as an explanation of the grounds of the hostility referred to, this sentence leaves much to be desired!)

> "Both Peacocke and Mascall...defend cosmic teleology by arguing that the continuing operation of physical laws needs some teleological justification...This sort of argument is so general that it would be consistent with <u>any</u> scientific result(!) And so, although interesting, it is completely useless." (Clearly, there is no sense here of the different status of arguments concerning the <u>foundations</u> of science from arguments <u>in</u> science, ACP 183)

The clearest example comes, however, in these authors' discussion of "ontological reductionism" and "ontological determinism"—a topic to which we will return in the next section. Although they are well aware of the history of philosophical disputes about "ontological determinism" and "ontological reductionism"—the physicalist and determinist character of actuality "out there"—these are not mentioned. On the contrary, the assumptions of science, the methodological rules of its inquiries, and the character of its theoretical formulations, are taken as quite sufficient to determine the ontological character of the referents in <u>actuality</u> of scientific inquiry. Quite without thinking about it, the rules of scientific method are assumed to determine and validate ontological judgments.

> "Although the final constituents of the world have changed with each successive scientific revolution (?), the fundamental evolution equations for these entities have always been deterministic. Thus there is no evidence whatsoever that the fundamental equations are not deterministic; in fact, to the extent that we believe the fundamental equations to be true, we are forced by the evidence to be ontological determinists." (AP 139)

In short, scientific inquiry assumes as a fundamental heuristic principle the determining patterns of cause and effect; there is therefore and can be no scientific evidence that is not determined (the equations are determined); since science alone adjudicates the ultimate character of reality or actuality (ontological determinism), as a result "the evidence establishes" that actuality is determined, and the same arguments are applied to reductionism or physicalism. Clearly in this strangely circular argument there is presupposed on the one hand an identity of science and its heuristic presuppositions with all truth about reality ("ontological"), and on the other hand an identity between the entities investigated by science and the concepts with which science thinks those objects. In other words, however convoluted and circular these arguments may be, questions about the founding assumptions of science are really scientific and not philosophical questions and so are determined by scientific evidence alone.

4. As our last remarks have intimated, there is presupposed in these writings a "naive realism", namely an unexamined identity of the ontological objects to which scientific inquiry directs itself — what is, to use Lonergan's phrase, "already out there now real"[8] — **with the concepts, formulae and models of science.** Scientific theory thus describes reality directly, immediately and "as it is"; and, as we have seen, for many that description can, now in principle and soon in fact, become so accurate, so isomorphic, that no further descriptions are necessary. As we noted, this realistic identification of objective ontological entity with the concepts and models of physics was frequently exemplified in classical physics; although it is repudiated widely in much of the literature of current philosophy of science, nevertheless it reappears in cosmological literature and is, I suspect, assumed widely throughout the scientific community. One wonders if in fact it was ever seriously questioned in that community on a wide scale. (Much as recent changes in religious understanding to a "symbolic" rather than a "literal" interpretation of doctrines may not be so widely assented to among clergy and laity as we once thought!) Of all the assumptions here delineated, this surely is the most fundamental, and the most significant for the relations of science and religion.

Again it is relevant to give some examples of this most important assumption. Clearly it is the fundamental presupposition of Carl Sagan's widely read book, *Cosmos*. This volume begins: "The Cosmos is all that is or ever was or ever will be" (C1). It proceeds then to tell us how well our race is through science penetrating into the mystery of the Cosmos: "In the last few millennia we have made the most astounding and unexpected discoveries about the Cosmos and our place within it, explorations that are exhilarating to consider." The cosmology that follows, learnedly and charmingly written, delineates for us that exploration through scientific inquiry. There is not the slightest hint that there is any other modality by which humans might explore this mystery. The cosmos is what is real, and the cosmos is described without ambiguity by scientific inquiry.

Naive realism assumes (1) that ontological entity and scientific explanation are isomorphic, (2) that this explanation uncovers the entire "mystery" of the object so that no other explanation is either necessary or possible, and so (3) any alternative explanations on the same plane, unequivocally false, and thus are cancelled out by the "correct" explanation. Were there genuine "distance" between object and scientific explanation, and thus genuine mystery in actuality—for example if scientific explanations represented "constructions" or "abstractions" from the fullness of experience—then an alternative explanation (metaphysical or religious) could be complementary or supplementary and not contradictory. Thus to state that scientific explanations rule out as "false" metaphysical or religious ones is to espouse—though perhaps unconsciously— a naive realist position concerning established scientific theories. This surely is what Dawkins does in the following:

> "The only thing he (Paley) got wrong—admittedly quite a big thing—was the explanation itself. He gave the traditional religious answer to the riddle...the true explanation is utterly different, and it had to wait for one of the truly revolutionary thinkers of all time, Charles Darwin...Paley's argument is made with passsionate sincerity and is informed by the best biological scholarship of his day, but it is wrong, gloriously and utterly wrong... Natural selection, the blind, unconscious, automatic process which Darwin discovered, and which we know now is the explanation for the existence and apparently purposeful form of all life, has no purpose in mind." (BW, pp. 4-5)

Another example of this sense of utter certainty about the <u>whole</u> of the universe—about ontological statements—on the basis of the results of scientific inquiry (in short, the identification of the two sorts of questions—though the tentativeness associated with scientific conclusions is clearly lost when we shift to the ontological level!) comes at the end of Pagel's book when he expresses his approval of a conclusion by another prominent scientist/cosmologist, Steven Weinberg. Weinberg, therefore, spoke for many scientists when he wrote...'The more we know about the universe the more it is evident that it is pointless and meaningless'...This is not the conclusion of pessimistic religion or the raving of an unhappy philosopher, but the only rational inference that emerges from our scientific view of the cosmos." (PS 383) Since science describes exhaustively and accurately the structure of the real world, and since it is such that it can find no meaning or purpose in the "objects" of its inquiries, therefore, the universe as a whole—when known by science—is known to have no meaning or purpose.

It is not irrelevant to point out that all of these books manifest what can only be called an "unyielding dogmatism" on these issues relevant to teleology and religion, i.e., on "ontological" or "metaphysical" issues. Here, clearly, the characteristic tentativeness of scientific statements, which each well represents when scientific theories are under discussion, ceases and utter certainty enters the scene. Paley was "utterly wrong", etc. This is unexpected in scientific writings that intend to be "scientific". However, it is not at all surprising when we realize that these claims have transcended science and have moved, quite unknown to the claimant, out of the range of scientific—and so of empirical and probabalistic—judgments and into the realm of ontological and even theological judgments, where dogmatism (as these authors are very well aware!) finds itself quite at home. One of the problems of the unphilosophical consciousness of many scientists—as is also the case with theologians—is that the former become as rigid and dogmatic as have religionists on subjects that transcend science and so are essentially unprovable, and yet, thinking they are still speaking in the discourse of science, the scientists claim the authority of science—in fact, as we have noted, much more authority than real science ever claims![9]

Naive realism, as we have seen, identifies unequivocally the ontological object with the scientific explanation or description of that object. One of the clearest cases of this is found in the interesting and rather radically unconventional volume on the Anthropic Principle by Barrow and Tipler. This volume is unconventional in its insistence on a fundamental correlation between cosmos and mind, and it sets out to explore—within the parameters of the assumptions we are here delineating—that fundamental correlation. Nevertheless, this volume also makes an unequivocal affirmation of naive realism in its discussion of "ontological reductionism" and "ontological determinism":

"Ontological reductionism claims that the "stuff" comprising the
world can be reduced ultimately (sic.) to the particles and forces
studied by physics; the vast majority of biologists (and we ourselves) are ontological reductionists...Ontological determinism
claims that the evolution equations which govern the time development of the ultimate (sic.) constituents of the world are deterministic; that is, the state of those constituents at a given time in the
future is determined uniquely by the state of those constituents now
[shades of La Place!]. All theories of physics which have ever been
proposed as fundamental...even quantum mechanics—all of these
are ontologically deterministic theories...In fact, to the extent we
believe the fundamental equations to be true, we are forced by the
evidence to be ontological determinists." (APA 138-9)

Equations and entities are here radically identified; if the first are
deterministic, so are the ontological entities: this is the essence of realism.

There is little question in this quotation (1) that it is the "ultimate"
constituents of the real world that are here being referred to, and (2) that it is
assumed that scientific desriptions give an accurate, univocal and exhaustive
account of these constituents. What is known through physics, in all its
characteristics as there delineated, is what is real " ontologically"—though how
this squares with the vast changes in physics is not clarified (Cf. 138). This is,
I take it, precisely the error which Whitehead, describing the understanding of
classical physics after Newton, characterized as "the fallacy of misplaced
concreteness", the error of taking the conclusions of science: its models,
entities and theorems, as indicating directly and unambiguously the real
constituents of actuality (SMW 71-70). Not only does this fail to recognize (in
fact, it denies) that there may be other modes through which actuality is
experienced and "known"—that, e.g., of self-awareness (causal efficacy), or
that of moral, aesthetic or religious experience, etc. Even more, it is to identify
what is an abstraction—for all knowledge abstracts in order to become
knowledge—with the richness and mystery of what is concretely actual.
Because of the naive realism of these works, the role of philosophy as "the critic
of abstractions" is left unrecognized; in fact, apparently the fact that philosophy—or anything else— might have that role never even surfaces: science is
adequate, and it is self-sufficient.

To me, however, the definitive example of naive realism in connection
with scientific inquiry appears in Pagels' book. Pagels is understandably
excited with the prospect, imminent in his view, that scientific inquiry can now
at least answer all the traditional puzzles about the coming to be of things, what
he calls "the very origin" of the universe (e.g., PS 24, 135, 355, also 265-8, 375-
6, etc.). As we noted, Pagels is aware of all the strange questions: what

happened before time, where did matter itself come from, etc.? that have accompanied this issue since Augustine; and he is sure that cosmology as an "empirical science" is now equipped—with the help of Einsteinian relativity theory and new instruments—to answer these questions. I will not here go into the details of his projected inquiry. I am inclined to agree with Aristotle that as far as empirical inquiry is concerned, "nothing can come from nothing," so that empiricism must always assume there is something given in order for inquiry to begin.(l0) Pagels, however, seems to feel that modern science can trace the derivation of something from "nothing", at least "from a vacuum" (Cf. 353-9, 365-8, 375-6). To me, Augustine was right—as was Whitehead who denies the possibility of these questions—that questions of the origin of the space-time continuum (the very origin of the universe) are structurally different from questions presupposing that the system is already there and working. In any case, I cite this surprising optimism of his about the capacities of empirical science to answer all questions about actuality as an illustration (l) of his view that science represents the only way all questions about actuality can be asked or answered, and (2) that scientific theory can in principle now, and will ultimately in fact, trace out the principles and the dynamics of every aspect of actuality, even of its origin. No more clear case of unqualified realism is, I think, possible than this claim to describe in empirical terms what has been called "the ultimate ontological question", why is there something rather than nothing.[11]

* * *

The result of our perusal of selected cosmologies—as opposed to a survey of the new philosophy of science—uncovers clear and significant difficulties in science so interpreted for religious understanding, and certainly for any religious understanding based on or associated with a metaphysical interpretation of reality. Clearly, the heart of these difficulties lies in two points: (l) that scientific inquiry represents the only relevant avenue to truth about what is real—with the result that anything, for example either religious or metaphysical, based on grounds other than those probided by empirical science, is merely "subjective".[12] Thus are alternative views, as we have seen, clearly false, the result of projected "needs and wishes" rather than objective evidence (PS ll), and representative of "closed minds" (PS l67).[13] When reality is exhaustively and adequately defined by physical science—and is, therefore, only physical, determined and "meaningless"—there is little "place" for any credible referent for religious language or belief.

Incidentally, the view that scientific and religious affirmations are equivalent (the former, therefore, being true and the latter simply false) is a view shared with the creationists for whom, of course, the religious doctrine of creation is "true" and its equivalent: the cosmology of modern science, false.

In that connection, it is not irrelevant to note that our investigation of modern scientific cosmologies—though not of the scientific theorems on which they are built—tends to justify the creationist complaint that in fact many if not most explications of scientific theory bring inescapably with themselves the sort of cosmology we have described; and, further, that those cosmologies, as we have also shown, have 'religious' overtones, namely, the assertion that all that is arose blindly and pointlessly from material, deterministic origins. As far as I can see, the cosmologists we have read would say to this description of the direct implications of modern science, "Right on!" The problem is that when the theories of science are interwoven as closely as they are with a materialistic, deterministic cosmology—as if the two were one—then the teaching of science so understood is in fact the teaching of atheism. Among other things, moreover, it is this that "breeds creationism" as a reaction. Thus, it can be said that the sorts of cosmologies here described represent part of the cause of creationism—for, let us recall, these cosmologists are more sure and so more categorical about the ontological conclusions they see in science than they are about the theories themselves.

(2) Secondly, it also seems evident from our investigation that this understanding of science renders ambiguous, in fact, practically undiscussible, a number of assertions important to science and yet not amenable to scientific inquiry itself. Each of the scientists cited refers to the assumption of order ingredient in all scientific inquiry, in fact necessary to it. Pagels goes so far as to affirm that the rule of scientific law holds even "in the void" and "prior to space and time" (PS 365 and also 375)—though it is hard to know what such apparent Platonism might mean to him. And all recognize that the uniformitarian principle: events in the past exhibit the same orderly processes as do observable or traceable events around us, is the necessary basis of every scientific theory about origins, proximate or ultimate (Cf. PS 77, 159).

Not surprisingly, the cosmologies here analyzed do not recognize this principle of order, extending out into space, back into time and forward into every relevant future, as a metaphysical insight. Such metaphysical principles, as Whitehead saw, are unprovable because they represent the presupposed grounds of all proof. Such principles, therefore, are based on fundamental intuition and held by what Whitehead terms "faith", a faith peculiar to some cultures and not to others.[14] For this reason the questions of the historical origins and the rational grounds of such faith necessary for science become significant questions. Such questions lie not in science itself but in the history of ideas, in epistemology and in ontology/metaphysics. All this, however, does not arise in these cosmologies where "knowledge" is strictly confined to scientific knowledge. Because the principle of universal order is not seen as a principle, a view of things that develops historically, nor as thus historically contingent, nor as a principle that might be questioned (or wondered at!), it appears here simply as a fact, a fact about the universe like any other fact, a fact presumably not known before science but now known through scientific inquiry. Pagels states it as if it were both obvious and uncontroversial: "Since these properties are universal..." (PS 77), "physical law is universal—it is a fact, never controverted by any observation" (!, ibid., 158-9), and "the fact that the entire universe is governed by simple natural laws is remarkable, profound and on the face of it, absurd" (PS 159)—and then he goes on from there. To view this reduction of a presupposed principle of order to an empirical datum is (to me) seriously confused intellectually and accordingly intellectually vulnerable to criticism. In any case, such confusion about the status and grounds of the fundamental presuppositions of science is another result of the naive realism and the positivism of such cosmologies.

One final and quite minor point in this section. It is both natural and yet also ironic that these books are filled with wonder at the wonder of science. This is natural because the capacity to do science is surely one of the most extraordinary of human powers, and because the knowledge it brings is of the very greatest value to us all—and needless to say, those who practice science well are particularly aware of these its "virtues" and so of the "high" nature of their own calling as scientists. This awareness of the importance of what one does is hardly new: holy men, priests and monks have always seen the religious capacities of humanity as the most sublime of our gifts or of the gifts of grace; correspondingly, philosophers (except perhaps John Dewey!) always regarded philosophical rationality and wisdom as the crown of human achievement and the essence of what is uniquely human. At this point, therefore, modern cosmologists find themselves in a long and certainly a distinguished tradition.

Carl Sagan is particularly rapturous about the human and even the cosmic meaning of his profession. He is, he says, proud of and confident in our species. And to be sure there are varied grounds for this pride: Humanity possesses a host of "excellences". The only one, however, of which he seems to be aware is the ability to know, and to know the cosmos: that is, physical science (compare with the Socratic "Know thyself"!):

> And yet our species is young and curious and brave and shows much promise. In the last few millennia we have made the most astounding and unexpected discoveries about the Cosmos and our place within it, explanations that are exhilarating to consider. They remind us that humans have evolved to wonder, that understanding is a joy, that knowledge is prerequisite to survival. I believe our future depends on how well we know this Cosmos..."(C 1-2)

All this is understandable, if a bit exclusivist, as if to know the cosmos was the paradigmatic human gift. The rapture becomes fairly heavy, however, when he tells us that if there were no changes in our world, "there would be no impetus for science", and if things were utterly unpredictable, "again there would be no such thing as science..." (C 32). Again, not unnaturally, it is the capacity to observe the cosmos and so to understand it scientifically that motivates the interesting Anthropic Principle: how is it that the entire universe developed in such a way as to make possible, and to produce, a being capable of science? All this is, I agree, a wonder. It might be even more of a wonder, however, if scientists wondered at a universe that brought forth an unusually loving mother, an artist, a dependable and responsible colleague, a courageous act of self-sacrifice, an unexpected capacity to love what is unlovable. One gets the feeling from these undialectical effusions about science, that, as for far too many religious saints and wise men of the past, all of these other "virtues" of humanity are regarded as really somewhat lower than the ability to know, now epitomized in the community of scientists. This is, as I said, ironic, because as Dawkins put it, the religious person's identification of human religiousness with the center and purpose of the cosmos was "conceited" and "small-minded" (BW, 143). In any case, let us now turn to our constructive part: what is wrong with the understanding of science and of the world as science describes it in these cosmologies, and how can we provide a better interpretation of science, its conditions and its role than these works provide?

Part II

In our investigation of a selected number of modern cosmologies, we have found them representing an objective scientific empiricism and a direct or naive realism. And, as in the late 19th century, such realistic physical science presents us with a "world" within which religion makes little or no sense. In such a world, if it be the real world, religious experience cannot have any conceivable referent and so cannot be understood save as a human projection grounded in ignorance, fear and fundamental alienation, a projection that can only dissipate as scientific knowledge and reliable techniques advance. There are a number of possibly convincing arguments against this position: it represents a misunderstanding of religion; it is a challenge to the status and value of the humanities—and so to the important aspects of life they represent—as well as to religion; it is based on and reflects a false estimate of the existential and historical human situation—and so on.

The most relevant and fruitful, however, seem to me to be arguments claiming that this view of scientific knowledge and its cosmological results represents a misinterpretation of the character of the knowing process, and thus a misunderstanding of scientific knowledge itself. This is a critique of the philosophy of science which these realistic cosmologies assume and so of the physicalist ontology they proclaim as science; it is not a criticism of the science on which these cosmologies are also based. Such a line of argument is of course philosophical in character; it proposes in effect a different philosophy of science; and in principle it would develop an understanding of scientific knowing which would lead into the beginnings of a more encompassing epistemology, ontology or metaphysics. And its aim in the end would be that of establishing, via epistemology and ontology, the kind of philosophical theology which in its own way and on its own grounds could encompass as well the otherwise excluded sphere of religion. In this second part of the paper I shall suggest a beginning of such a movement of thought. The argument is neither new nor particularly original, except that to my knowledge it has not heretofore been aimed in the direction of contemporary cosmologies such as those of Sagan, Pagels and Dawkins!

It is one of the main themes of the new philosophy of science that all knowing involves a "preunderstanding", that all inquiry is "theory-laden".[15] There are no "facts" or "data" in and of themselves; nor as a consequence are valid theories based on solely objective induction from self-standing evidence. On the contrary, aspects of the manifold experience become "facts" or "data" only when they are discriminated out as important, as "clues", from the whole welter of experience; and that discrimination only arises because prior theory (hypothesis) has joined to prior habitual familiarity (long experience) to organize or order experience in a certain way. Only with such prior organization does experience yield "data"; only in such an ordered "world" is it possible or conceivable to conceive and then to test an hypothesis. Theories, paradigms, "forms of order" accompany the investigation of experience from beginning to end; without experience such forms of thought are empty, but without them experience is blind.

The experience into which the scientist inquires, out of which she shapes her new hypothesis, and in relation to which she tests it, is therefore already organized by more fundamental "forms of thought". The picture then of each hypothesis as simply induced from "pure" data and simply tested "objectively" there, is a false picture. Thus, the "reality" known by the scientist, explicated and organized in and through her structure of theories, is a "reality" in part shaped, even constructed in terms of, the intellectual tradition of the scientific community, the preunderstanding of the scientist herself and the particular hypotheses she is testing. Granted another intellectual tradition, another set of paradigms and forms of order, and therefore different questions asking for different answers, then different sorts of "facts" and "data" would arise—and accordingly tests with different consequences would ensue. This is the point so forcefully argued by Thomas Kuhn with his theory of "paradigms" and "paradigm shifts", by Toulmin with his varying "forms of order", and by Collingwood in his discrimination of different "ideas of nature" in the intellectual tradition of Western science. Since these differing forms of preunderstanding have been themselves influenced and so shaped by their cultural matrix, the "world" created by science is not simply already "out there", objective to human perceiving, knowing, evaluating. On the contrary, the "world" described by science is in part always a historical construct, different as the cultural "minds" of different epochs and places differ. Science itself has a history, and the "world" created by science is itself a function of that cultural history. Reality, whatever it may be, and "scientific reality" are, therefore, not identical: science is not a "mirror" of nature.[16]

The findings of science—and so the cosmologies science produces—are, therefore, <u>historical</u> documents molded by the paradigms of their time and place. This insight into the influence of cultural and historical forces on even the most "objective" sort of thinking is, however, itself grounded in an even deeper influence on inquiry and on thinking. I refer to the essential and so inescapable role of sensible and intellectual consciousness, of perception and of thought, on the knowing process. Here, the constructive role of consciousness itself in the creation of the "world" which is known—the world both as perceived by the senses and as "known" by the cognitive power of mind—comes itself to full consciousness. The thoughts humans think and the inquiries they make are historical, because human consciousness helps to <u>construct</u> the world that is experienced and thought—and human consciousness is itself historical.

Ironically, this modern sense of what the perceiving self <u>adds</u> to experience began with Galileo who showed that the "secondary qualities" of experience were not attributable to the quantitative, mechanical world physics studied, to "primary qualities";[17] thus were these qualities, e.g., color and sound, added by the experiencing mind. Soon this critical analysis was pushed further by Berkeley and Hume: <u>all</u> knowledge, primary and secondary qualities alike, is based on (sense) impressions—and thus no form of our knowing can penetrate through and beyond this screen of impressions to "reality". Kant formalized and ordered this critical view: the manifold of experience is shaped originally by the forms of intuition: space and time; and it is unified and ordered by the categories of understanding: causality and substance. Thus does the entire manifold of experience possess its universal order, thus is it amenable to inquiry by means of mathematical physics, thus is it characterized by an omnipresent determinism: physical science is in this way possible. Nevertheless, that world of ordered sequences governed by necessary law is the <u>phenomenal</u> world, a <u>construct</u> by human sense and the human mind out of the given. As a consequence, the world so constructed, the world even of science, is not the "real" world, the <u>thing in itself</u> or <u>noumenon</u>—which latter (and here another tradition gets its start) we know directly only from the inside in moral experience.[18] Critical philosophy did not completely sunder scientific knowledge and "reality", but it surely distinguished them—and led many to think that the naive realism of pre-Kantian philosophy was at an end.

As is evident from the first half of this paper, the critical philosophy of Kant has apparently had no effect at all on the writers of scientific cosmologies: to them the world known by scientific theory is simply the real "ontological" world, a world uncovered or discovered ("seen") by means of our objective scientific inquiry based solely on observations, hypotheses and experimental testing. If our senses are congruent with the real shapes of the world and our minds characterized by the real world's forms of order, this is for modern cosmology not—as Kant had said—because the known world is a construct by our cognitive faculties, but the reverse, namely because the forms of our experiencing and thinking have—according to tested biological theory— arisen out of the ordered processes of the precedent world. Far from the world of science being an effect of mind, mind itself is simply an effect of the precedent and objective order of the world. As Pagels said wonderingly: "The universality of law is simply a fact," and those laws even characterize the void before the world began—so "already out there real" are they. The "human" sensible shape and the rational order of the world out there pose no problems for modern cosmology; it is simply the way the world really is in itself. This deep gulf or wall of ignorance between critical philosophy and the spokespersons for modern science itself begs for an explanation: why is it that modern cosmologists are not only in disagreement with this major philosophical tradition but seemingly assured of its irrelevance if they are conscious of it at all?[19]

The critical philosophy, albeit like all else significantly transformed, has continued in much important philosophy into our own day. Two very creative philosophers from the first half of the century—Santayana and Whitehead— elaborated and, each in his own way, to me improved on the Kantian distinction between the world of appearance and so of scientific theory on the one hand from "the realm of matter" (Santayana) and from "concrete actuality" (Whitehead) on the other hand. Husserl, Heidegger and Tillich each represented a parallel mode of distinguishing the world of science from what the first called the primordial life world. And in current philosophy, as noted, Richard Rorty and Richard Bernstein continue these motifs. In my brief elaboration of this tradition in its application to the question of scientific knowledge, I shall appeal first to Whitehead and then to Tillich and off and on to Santayana—as giving strong reasons why the naive realism of current cosmologies lacks credibility.

Whitehead is impressed with what he likes to call the "abstract" character of the cosmos as described by modern science. He means by this that world of "vacuous entities", blindly following determined causes, does not fit with, and so cannot be thought to undergird, important and pervasive areas of common experience: social relations, courts of law, literature and art, commerce, morality and so on and on. As he remarked, it is a world that is "quite unbelievable".[20] Moreover, the presuppositions of science: that an order obtains throughout experience, that entities "over there" are real, that there is a unity of effect between past, present and future—in philosophy the "categories" of existence—none of these are either experienced or known, and certainly not established, either via the experiments of science or in the sensory experience (Presentational Immediacy) on which science is based. "The categories are manifested elsewhere."[21] The variety of experience and the possibility of science itself show, therefore, that the sensationalist dogmas that (1) only through sense data is reality known, and thus that (2) science alone gives indication of what is real, are false. There are other more fundamental modes of experiencing, modes that are more directly in touch with actuality. These non-sensory perceptions are multiple; centrally they are the sense of "withness with the body" through which we know ourselves as an organic unity; the sense of continuity with, in fact conformation to, the immediate past; and the sense of aims and of intentions for the immediate future. Here, actuality is itself experienced through our own participation in being the organic society we are; and this level of experience is rich in metaphysical implications. It is, therefore, through non-sensory experience that the reality, the interconnectedness and the order of experience in time are known and thus which, while beyond science (non-sensory), provide the bases or presuppositions of science. These Whitehead calls "experience in the mode of causal efficacy: and it is by metaphysical inquiry, not scientific inquiry, that these modes can be explored and concrete actuality more directly known.

Thus metaphysics provides the theoretical framework (the "rationality") for science which science by itself lacks. It provides a clearer, less abstract, more concrete and direct delineation of what is real and so the bases of our knowledge of the real. Thus as "the critic of abstractions" metaphysics can assess the cognitive value of each special mode of experiencing and knowing: physical science, art, physchology, religion. Above all, it can give a credible account of those factors crucial to all of experience which science, by abstracting from them, tends to overlook, ignore or even deny: the pervasiveness of order, the continuity within time, the appearance of novelty, the importance of aims and values, the reality of purposes and responsibility, the grounds for hope—and the trust that value characterizes even the depth of actuality. These pervasive traits of experience, always there, can never be seen by the empirical method, for they are assumed and so are not noticed: "Experience never takes a holiday from them".[22] Yet civilization is utterly dependent on this "faith" in persuasive order and in value amid transience; if there were no credible grounds or rational articulation for this faith, that confidence would become precarious—even when the science based on that confidence itself flourishes. To Whitehead, then, while metaphysics will temper and limit the claims of the science described in these cosmologies, metaphysics will also provide the rational grounding that science needs. For metaphysics alone can explore through its method the concreteness of actuality from which science abstracts.

Many of these same themes appear in Tillich—in fact the ontologies of these two are remarkably similar. For both thinkers science represents an abstraction from actuality (from "finite being" in Tillich), an abstraction of remarkable if only relative validity; thus is science, if understood correctly in its validity and its limitations, of vast use to civilization. And again, it is ontological inquiry that can uncover and recover the full structure of finite being from which science (technical reason) has abstracted, and thus give a more accurate and inclusive account of what is real.[23]

Tillich begins, as had the whole critical tradition and as had Whitehead, with the influence of the experiencing self on the creation of its "world". Self and world, he says, represent a mutually dependent polarity; the one is essential to the appearance and reality of the other—and this applies to all finite being everywhere.[24] Through modern empirical science we have become aware of how the self arises out of and is dependent on its world: it arises as a part of nature out of nature, its social character is a function of the habits and traditions of its community, its psychological contents come to it entirely from its material and social environment, and its personal character (as "spirit") comes to it in communion with others.[25] This dependence of consciousness and self-consciousness on world is assumed and delineated throughout modern science. But self and world are polar, mutually dependent; thus "world", as experienced and known by rational selves—by science—is throughout dependent on the self, on the self as "reason" and as "spirit".

With the introduction of reason or spirit, says Tillich, what was a mere environment to the organism becomes a "world": a potentially ordered unity, with patterns of similarity and difference, continuity and discontinuity, a potential whole with potentially discriminable parts. As, therefore, the self was in effect a creation of its world, so in a different way this "world," experienced and subsequently known by mind, is a creation of the self. Clearly, as Sagan implied, there could be neither the possibility for, nor the impulse to, science were the manifold of experience, the world, not so constituted as a potential whole of potentially identifiable elements. Tillich's defense of this view is brief but interesting.[26] The shift from environment to world presupposes "distance", a separation of the self from its world so that the latter becomes an object; the objectification of world into a realm to be 'looked at' is the work of consciousness. Further, in order that judgments about that world be possible: this here is this and not that, negation is necessary (see a similar theme in

Whitehead: "The negative judgment is the peak of mentality" PR 7)—which involves even more distance, not only so that objects appear but that novel possibilities, what is not yet, are objects of consciousness. In all this, the self "stands out" from its world, and so the world is "over against" the observer; thus can self or mind look at its world and also at itself. It transcends world and itself and thus makes both an object of itself—which for Tillich is the first sign of its infinite dimension, its relation in experience and cognition to "the infinite ground of reason" (see the similar motif in Rahner).[27] Finally, in its experience of the world as objectified and of the self as self-conscious, the self brings order to each: it has the capacity for language and so for universals; and thus it can "grasp" reality in cognition and in artistic expression. And consequently, it is capable of proposals and projects for its own action in the world, and so it can "shape" reality, the two great capacities of reason. Thus is the world "named": patterns of order and continuities are seen (metaphysical visions, paradigms and so on), and discrimination, identity and definitions are made—and science begins. The self also shapes reality through its projects and on the basis of the order it has discriminated there: language and techne are therefore the first fruits of reason, of the active constructing and reconstructing of its world. In modern life, these are in part represented by empirical science and technology; both are dependent, as this analysis shows, on world as constituted by the rational self, by spirit.

For both of these thinkers, this analysis of the rise of world and of a science of the world, or (in Whitehead's terms) of the appearance of Presentational Immediacy as an abstraction from causal efficacy, represents in human form the pervasive ontological or metaphysical structure applying to all reality everywhere. The self-world correlation (experienced "inside" by us) is, says Tillich, the universal structure of finite being; and the internal relations of entities with one another, experienced by us in causal efficacy, via feelings or prehensions of one another, for Whitehead represent the most fundamental structure of all actuality. Thus for Tillich all of finite being represents an analagous edition of world and self, of order balanced by spontaneity, and analogous forms of the other polarities characteristic of the self in the world: individuation and participation, dynamics and form, and freedom and destiny. Similarly, the categories (space, time, casusality and substance) experienced by us in our being in the world are found, again analogously, to characterize finite being everywhere.[28] And in Whitehead the internal relations of prehension or feeling, the inner experiences of conformation and then of new aims for novelty, which appear in us in conscious and intentional form, are analogously represented in all of actuality, in fact in "the most trivial puff of existence in far off empty space."[29]

While the structure of finite being—the real world behind the scientific cosmology—in each of these ontologies is on many counts different, still the conceptual parallels between them are significantly similar. Above all, to each of them science, while relatively valid and so exceedingly reliable, represents an abstracting, in part a construct, because it is a product of sense, of consciousness and of self-consciousness. Thus to delineate the structure of actuality we must pass through and beyond, without denying, the objectified world of physical science into the richer, "thicker", more mysterious actuality which lives in and through our widest experience. For Tillich this task is accomplished by "ontological reason" and carried through as the work of ontology, philosophy's major task; for Whitehead it is "speculative reason", an analogue of science but dealing with the whole of experience. For both, this metaphysical or ontological task seeks for those pervasive and universal structures that characterize all that is insofar as it is.[30] In proposing that the sensed and human world, and so the science based on that world, is a "construct" in correlation with a given which is prehended or felt, both are in the Kantian tradition; in affirming that a metaphysical analysis is nevertheless possible beyond the range of scientific empirical inquiry, these two are non-Kantian.

The most important conclusion of this discussion for our purposes is that world and mind are inextricably correlated or mutually dependent. World does not originate from mind, as idealism has stated; but by the same token, the world as it is known by science is not independent of mind, *a se* so to speak, and thus to be considered, as cosmology certainly considers it, the mindless origin of mind. This correlation of self and world, of mind and universe has fascinated thought, both religious and philosophical/scientific, since the beginning, illustrated alike in myths, in early philosophical speculation and in the science that has supplanted the latter. As Collingwood has shown, for the Greeks nature was permeated with mind; for early modern science mind came before nature's mechanism as its necessary designer. For modern cosmologies as we have shown, mind has largely been removed from the cosmos which is regarded as throughout governed by necessary and determining law and in principle capable of reduction to the objects of the inquiries of physics. We have here been in the process of challenging this exclusion of mind: mind, we have argued, is there in the creation or construction of that world as it is <u>viewed</u> by science. Interestingly, the cosmologists seem to sense this; they rejoice, as we have noted, in the "observer" who inquires and understands. But the weighty contribution of the latter in the construction of the world as it is known is overlooked—and no grounds are given for that omission.

This is one reason the appearance of speculation and debate about the Anthropic Principle is so fascinating. For "this principle has sought to relate mind and observership to the phenomena traditionally within the encompassment of the physical sciences", (ACP 1), and "the Anthropic Principle seeks to link aspects of the global and local structure of the Universe to those conditions necessary for the existence of living observers." (ACP 13) I find this stubborn reappearance of mind within modern cosmology interesting and reassuring. I have, however a question about the way mind is here being brought back in. For as I understand it, the propounders of the Anthropic Principle accept a reductionist and determinist ontology, and they thus depend entirely on scientific data, scientific evidence and scientific theorems to establish and describe the "link" between the world of science and observing mind which they seek to find.

Our argument has been that mind is correlated to universe prior to scientific inquiry as the latter's precondition; thus mind actively reshapes the "given" in the construction of cosmology, of the developing physical process as science understands and pictures that process. In this case the role of mind, the link between the two, is uncovered by epistemological, ontological or metaphysical analysis, by the analysis of a "reality" which is more concrete and so more full than the abstracted material sequences of physics. It is in that richer actuality—for Whitehead and Tillich—that mind, purpose, aims and novelty reside and thus that through ontology both the possibility of spirit and the role of teleology are to be understood and interpreted. Here mind and purpose appear as conditions of science itself as a human capacity, not as conclusions of scientific investigation. Hence science and its conclusions, as the results of mind and purpose, i.e., of the scientist or observer herself, can hardly exclude either one from the real world.

If on the contrary the world science portrays is taken as primordial, real and self-sufficient in its own right—a se in the classic sense—and if scientific inquiry is taken as the only mode of knowing what is real, then neither mind nor purpose (nor the conditions of science) can appear at all. In such a situation mind and purpose are understood as only epiphenomenal products of a process void of both; and if the role of each is established and tested by scientific criteria alone, neither one will or can be found. The method of the physical sciences rightly excludes consciousness, self-consciousness and purpose from the objects it recognizes; this is its genius and should not be challenged. Its world is by the canons or rules of its method reductionist and determined. The mistake, as Whitehead said, is to take that world not as a construction of sense and of mind—an abstraction—but as the only real world. And this mistake is continued in the current discussions of the Anthropic Principle. For they seek to establish the link between mind and universe scientifically, as an inference from scientific data and as implied by scientific theories and formulae; they look to the conclusions of science for that link rather than to the conditions of science. For the point is that, granted the heuristic requirements of physical science as reductionist and determined, that link can only be established by an analysis of the character of experiencing, of consciousness and of teleology, an analysis that must be carried deeper by metaphysics and ontology if it is to be carried on at all. Then what is uncovered about the conditions of knowing can be correlated with what is found by the scientific inferences thus made possible. In short, unconsciously (?) a movement has been made from a methodological requirement to an ontological affirmation.

* * *

We have in this argument espoused a modified or perhaps "soft" critical philosophy, emphasizing the role of mind—or better "spirit"—in providing some of the essential conditions of science and thus in shaping, in fact structuring, the picture of reality which science presents to us. As we have noted, one important consequence of this constructive role of mind is that reality, what is really there, remains obscure at best and quite unknown at worst. A view which rejects naive realism and stresses the constructive activity of mind itself faces the problems of relativism and skepticism in general; and specifically, in limiting the absolutist claims of science, it seems to put itself in danger of granting in the end no validity to scientific knowledge at all. In a scientific and technological culture, however, where willy-nilly we all partici- pate in the results of science (I shall return by plane), it is hypocritical and inconsistent so to think about our knowing process as to leave to science no validity. One thing the continuously accurate and reliable results of science in technology, medicine and agronomy (to name only some examples) show is that science in its effort to know "reality" is somehow on the right track. The only question is in each case whether its pictures, models, theorems and formulae give us either the entire or the final knowledge of what is there. How then are we to understand the positive relation of our knowing to the realities that are known if the simple realist picture is denied?

If sensory experience and the science based on it are not isomorphic with the actualities so experienced and known, then at the least they can be said to be _analogical_. Sense experience as Whitehead reminded us, abstracts from the real relations and the internal dynamics of actuality; it objectifies those relations into necessary, determined and external relations, and it ignores the inward spontaneity of what it observes. (After all, as Whitehead notes, sensory experience presents to us a _past_ and so an _objectified_ world, shorn of its immediacy, its inwardness, its subjectivity.) Hence the objects of science represent an invariant, determined pattern of physical relations, a sequence of material events that are "vacuous and empty"—and so subject to the exact formulae and equations of mathematical science. That this is not identical with the "ontological character" of process, the rest of our experience affirms—as Whitehead said, "it is unbelievable" (SMU 77-8)—and science so understood cannot, as we have shown, account for itself. But that this abstracted account is analogical to the reality it portrays, the success of science more than verifies. And that success has taken two quite specific forms, which have given to science its prestige far beyond the bounds of the scientific community, and make it inane to question the sciences' general reliability and validity.

These are (1) the power, well illustrated in the physical sciences, of prediction. As is evident the ability to predict on the basis of an hypothesis does not indicate that all that can be known is known—another factor might regularly be at work. Nevertheless prediction does entail necessarily that aspects of invariant relations are known, and thus that the hypothesis in question is probable. It shows an analogous reading of reality that is reliable for practice, and that itself permits further inquiry into fruitful directions. For one consequence of our understanding of science as abstracted is that no formulae or theories at a given time are final; thus there is always "more" in the mystery from which the abstraction has been made to be uncovered—or to disclose itself.

(2) Closely linked to prediction is, of course, the power successfully to reshape reality, the power of technology. Knowledge implies, said John Dewey, a plan of action, a program of planned activity which will resolve a felt problem, and knowledge is validated when that plan of action works. Technology reshapes the reality within which we live, and it does so by building instruments and tools and applying them to the environment around us. Knowledge here is power, power to manipulate through understanding the forces that control us and that control our environment; and by redirecting those forces as our aims dictate. Insofar, therefore, as knowledge results in such power and such redirection, that knowledge is tested and validated. (The deepest ambiguities of technology arise from the ambiguity of the aims that direct it rather than the fallibility of the knowledge it uses.) Again, validation is not complete; pragmatic success indicates only that we have understood and controlled aspects of the mystery of dynamic actuality. Nevertheless, the steady success of technology in achieving our aims, i.e., our control—in relation to the actuality within and around us certainly qualifies radically the relativism and the skepticism inherent in a critical view of scientific knowledge. To use Santayana's metaphor: Sense reproduces in our language the movements of matter outside of us; our sounds are not its motions, but a translation into another tongue. And translations work—"They are not misleading as signs."[31]

Sense experience and science then are "analogical"; "The babble of our innocent organs under the stimulus of things" and "A sensation or a theory, no matter how arbitrary its terms (and all language is perfectly arbitrary), will be true of its object, if it expresses some true relation in which that object stands to the self, so that these terms are not misleading as signs, however poetical they may be as sounds of pictures". "The terms of astronomy are essences no less human and visionary than those of mythology; but they are the fruit of a better focussed, more chastened, and more prolonged attention to what actually occurs".[32]

These analogies, then, or signs in human vocabulary, are checked, and subsequently refashioned or improved, by their predictive power and their technological or practical fruitfulness into signs that are "less and less misleading". (Note the interesting relation to Popper's insistence on falsification.) This seems enough. Nevertheless, our "acquaintance with reality", our sense of participation in knowing and so in truth, and thus our confidence in our knowledge—and in science—seem more deeply and more surely based than this practical, manipulative, instrumental interpretation of signs would warrant were it all we have. Thus let us move on to what positively the ontologists and metaphysicians say about our "knowledge" of the reality which eludes even the inquiries of science. Here the critical philosophies we have cited depart from Kant to explore via an "analogical metaphysics" the actuality from which science had abstracted signs.

The common methodological thread that guides these three ontologists out of the Kantian maze is the notion of "participation". We know reality through the senses and through science "from the outside", as an object over there; this is inescapably the perspective of science, and it results in the objectifying abstraction of science, in the "signs" of which Santayana spoke. But this external relation to the real process is not our only relation to it: that process manifests itself in us as well as in those objects. And further—and here is the point—this manifestation in us kindles, so to speak, our self-awareness: we are aware of our participation in being there, and we are aware of our awareness, our consciousness. In us being comes to self consciousness (Tillich, ST 168-9), prehensions change to apprehensions, consciousness and intellection (Whitehead), the rush of matter to the awareness of spirit (Santayana). As Tillich put it, "We know a tree from the outside, we do not know what it means to be a tree—but we do know what it means to be ourselves and to be human. Hence human being is the gateway to being." As we have seen, Whitehead proceeds to explore "participation", our self-awareness of our actuality in time, through an analysis of the non-sensory experience of causal efficacy: of being conformed to and united with the past, and being lured by the possibilities of the future. The result is a metaphysical discrimination of the structure of actuality which can provide the essential foundations for science, for culture and for an intelligent and confident praxis. Santayana also concentrates on the experience of existing, existing as a vulnerable, temporal and moral being in a surging world, and on the basis of that "animal faith", he can discriminate the structures of our real world and provide, not only a basis for the understanding of science, but also for all the needs of "spirit".[33] In these thinkers a modest metaphysical analysis discriminates an order in experience that corresponds to, is an analogue of, and so provides grounding for the more abstract, quantitative and necessitating order of science; it shows us how we can know that we know.

I will pursue this matter briefly with the help of Tillich, partly because his thought on this question is relatively undeveloped. We are asking why we can be assured that the order that we uncover in and through our inquiries is an order also characteristic of actuality, if our minds do, as they do, contribute that order to our knowing. Tillich's answer is that we participate from the inside in the same structure of being which inquiry examines from the outside. Thus however external, abstractive and "distant" scientific inquiry may be, and however lacking in direct grounding its (unconscious) assumptions of order and of continuity may be, we can have confidence in that inquiry. We can have confidence because we know that the order in our minds is the same as the order in being. And we know that because the order of our understanding, of our inquiring mind, is experienced as correlated with the order of actuality as the latter manifests itself directly in our participation in actuality in and through our own being. In our self-awareness of our being, we experience in ourselves the same order or logos in being which we find present in our minds through inquiry, a correlation of objective and subjective logos (ST 1, 168-9, 192).

We are, says Tillich, aware of our finitude "from the inside", aware of it as anxiety and as courage. This awareness appears in us in and through the forms of our finitude, through the categories: space, time, causality, and substance. We know these forms or categories, therefore, not only as the modes of our thinking (as in Kant) and so as the intellectual presuppositions of our science; even more we know them "existentially" and therefore directly as the forms of our own existence. In our awareness of our temporality ("of having to die"), of our being caused (of our vulnerability), and our being a cause (of our power), we possess an inner understanding of those external relations of temporality, of causality, and of effect which appear as the categories of actuality within us and yet as also the categories which order the phenomenal world of external and sensory experience.

As Whitehead had said about sensory experience and science alike, "the categories are derived elsewhere", as is the rational grounding of science in a universal order, and the basis of our certainty in it. This derivation comes through our inner participation in the same existence which externally we are investigating through science. Hence, our ontological or metaphysical analysis of our "participatory experience" (causal efficacy, animal faith, self-awareness of finitude) provides a point of unity between our subjectivity and the external world, between self and world, "subjective and objective logos", which science itself cannot provide. Knowledge is participation in the object known as well as distance from it, inner accord as well as external manipulation, a "knowing that we know" as well as an objective observing and checking of data. Without these inner participatory elements, known by self-awareness, elements that unite both subject knowing and actuality known, what we know is either an exclusive totality of objects that eliminates all subjects, or it is vulnerable to radical skepticism from the side of the triumphant subject.

* * *

Our argument has been that science is inconsistent and its self-understanding incredible if it seeks to understand itself merely in terms of itself, and as a consequence paints itself as a purely empiricist enterprise and its conclusions as a realistic portrayal of reality "out there". And we showed that this was precisely the way a number of current cosmologies presented science and the cosmology, the "world", science constructed.   An analysis of knowing, however, indicates that far from being a self-sufficient mode of knowing reality as it is, science is in significant part a construct of sensing observer and human knower. The possibilities of empirical inquiry, of intellectual understanding, and of theoretical judgment lie within the powers of mind or spirit; correspondingly the world disclosed by empirical study and described by science is a world constructed by the sense organs, the theoretical powers and the intellectual categories of human experience and thinking. It is a realm of human symbols analogous to and so relevant to reality as human signs of the latter; it is not a picture or mirror of that reality as it is.

This argument of critical philosophy posed, of course, the question: is reality then quite unknown? How do we understand the validity of science which we all recognize and affirm, and also the many activities of cultural life which are founded on a confidence that we know something, and something dependable, of what is going on? We have then tried to give examples of good arguments, based on epistemological and ontological or metaphysical analyses of experience which were enabled both to understand those basic aspects of experience which imply a valid cognitive ability and which give us a direct "acquaintance" with reality sufficient to undergird the inquiries of science.

If these arguments, and those that preceded them, are sound, then we have shown that an intelligent and self-consistent science points beyond itself to an ontological or metaphysical ground, to an analysis of actuality as inclusive of self and world, subjectivity and objectivity, purposes and causation. Such an analysis depends on extra-sensory and so extra-scientific experience: the self-awareness of our participation in actuality as existing, thinking and willing beings.   Such an analysis can provide a theoretical bridge between the significant activities of science and the cognizing subject of science, the existing, experiencing, willing and thinking scientist (who, otherwise, is quite omitted from the cosmological picture).   It can also provide the necessary theoretical point of unity between the cognitive disciplines and the other important aspects of human life now subordinated to if not excluded from the universe as it is pictured by scientific realism. The unity of the intellectual disciplines, and the unity of these disciplines with the actualities of life itself—not to mention the unity of human existence with nature—can only be achieved if an ontological base is provided which begins with the human as subject as well as with the "world" as object and thus can provide concepts that unite self, culture and world into an intelligible whole.

There is, however, a still further result of our line of argument. We have seen that scientific empiricism and scientific realism create a world within which there is even less room for religion—or any relevant objects of religious worship, experience and knowing—than there is for the science itself and for the humanistic activites of culture. Certainly the possibility of ontological analysis—a "knowing" of some sort beyond science—does not guarantee a universe in which religion is credible; Santayana shows this. But it does provide the possibility of such credibility. For, as both Whitehead and Tillich show, an ontological analysis of actuality in which self and world, subjectivity and objectivity represent participant polarities, presupposes that actuality (or "being") possesses, or can possess, the mystery, the richness and the "thick-ness" requisite for religion. If cognition is limited to the terms of scientific inquiry—as in scientific empiricism—then religion either in principle expires altogether or separates itself intellectually entirely from science. In the latter case, when religion (or "faith") seeks to interpret itself entirely in terms of itself, faith misunderstands itself as thoroughly as we have shown here science to misunderstand itself when it attempts to portray itself as self-sufficient. But if the reality that reveals itself to us and in us—to our senses, in and through our existence and our powers, in and through nature, in the sequences and events of history—if this reality is a mystery as well as an order, if it transcends our understanding as well as giving order and meaning to our existence, then a religious as well as an ontological analysis of it becomes possible. And religion as a response to reality as well as a human construction (as science is a response as well as a construction) becomes intelligible—and a philosophical theology is well under way.

In sum, I suggest that our cognitive life be conceived as composed of three interlocking but distinct hermeneutical inquiries: science, philosophy (ontology or metaphysics) and (philosophical) theology. These differ in the kinds of data or evidence in experience each appeals to; the areas of experience in which they work. They differ in the kind of intelligibility each seeks, the kinds of "explanation" each finds appropriate. They differ in the sorts of authority—or the interweaving of sorts of authority—to which each appeals. And finally they differ in the sorts of symbols each finds significant and useful. Briefly put, science seeks (on the basis of some 'pre-understanding') for the invariant structures of specific ontic processes, and it appeals to sensory, quantitative data both for its materials and for its forms of validation. Philosophy seeks from some chosen perspective for the universal structures of all that is, and it appeals to the entire width of experience; philosophy thus criticizes, formulates and reformulates the principles presupposed in science and in all the arts. Theology, on the basis of one perspective on existence, seeks for the meaning of the structures provided by the sciences and envisioned by philosophy; its fundamental symbols are drawn from its own religious tradition, but its explication of these symbols is in terms of the sciences and the philosophy of its time and place (i.e., in terms of the structure of existence as that is then understood).

These disciples are <u>hermeneutical</u> in the sense each searches in its own way for the <u>meaning</u> of the experiences in which it originates. They are distinct in that they search in significantly different ways and for different sorts or levels of meaning; and they are mutually interdependent and mutually corrective, as we have in part seen in the above. That is, as we have sought to show in this paper, science depends on philosophy for its most fundamental principles inclusive of self and of world—both of which are involved in cognition. Correspondingly it is clear that we recognize that any philosophical interpretation of the structure of existence and any theological interpretation of its meaning will be vastly dependent on what science knows that ontic structure to be. Further discussion of the mutual distinction and yet dependence of philosophy and theology—a subject thoroughly elaborated from a hundred perspectives in our own century—will have to wait for another time.[34]

Notes

1. The cosmologies include: John D. Barrow and Frank J. Tipler, *The Anthropic Cosmological Principle*, New York,, Oxford, 1986 (ACP): Richard Dawkins, *The Blind Watchmaker*, New York, W.W. Norton, 11986 (BW): Loren Eisley, *The Immense Journey*, New York, Vintage 1957 (<u>not</u> an example of our discussion); Heinz Pagels, *Perfect Symmetry*, New York, Bantam, 1986 (PS); Carl Sagan, *Cosmos*, New York, Ballantyne, 1985 (C): and Steven Weinberg, *The First Three Minutes* (FTM).

2. Cf. for discussions of these changes: Harold I. Brown, *Perception, Theory and Commitment*, Chicago, University of Chicago Press, 1979 (PCT); N. W. Hanson, *Patterns of Discovery*, 1958; Thomas S. Kuhn, *The Structure of Scientific Revolutions*, Chicago, University of Chicago Press, 1964; Michael Polanyi, *Personal Knowledge*, New York, Harper Torchbook, 1958; Steven Toulmin, *The Philosophy of Science*, New York, Harper Torchbook, 1953, and *Foresight and Understanding*, Harper Torchbook, 1961. For further philosophical discussion: Cf. Richard Bernstein, *Beyond Objectivism and*

178   Langdon Gilkey

Relativism, Philadelphia, University of Pennsylvania Press, 1983; Richard
Rorty, *Philosophy and the Mirror of Nature*, Princeton, Princeton University
Press, 1980, especially chapters VII and VIII; Bernard Lonergan, *Insight*,
London, Longmans, Green, 1964; and Mary Gerhart and Allan Russell,
Metaphoric Process, Fort Worth, Texas Christian Press, 1984. For a strong
defense of the objectivist position: Cf. Israel Scheffler, *Science and Subjectivity*, Indianapolis, Bobbs-Merrill, 1967; and Ernest Nagel, *The Structure of
Science*, New York Harcourt, Brace and World, 1961.
　　　3.　Cf. Alfred North Whitehead, *Science and the Modern World*, New
York, Macmillan, 1925 (SMW), pp. 72 f., 82 and also *Process and Reality*, page
11.
　　　4.　Cf. for example, Werner Heisenberg, *Physics and Beyond*, New
York, Harper Torchbook, 1971, especially chapters 3, 10 and 11.
　　　5.　Cf. R.G. Collingwood, *The Idea of Nature*, Oxford Clarendon Press,
1945, especially introduction; also, *An Essay on Metaphysics*, Oxford; A. N.
Whitehead, SMW, Chapters I, IV, V, IX XII; *Adventures of Ideas*, New York,
Macmillan and Company, 1933, pp. 150, 182-87 (AI), *Function of Reason*,
Princeton University Press, 1929, p. 57, *Process and Reality*, New York,
Macmillan, 1929, pp. 500-502 (PR), *Modes of Thought*, Cambridge, Cambridge University Press, 1928, pp. 145-6 (MT).
　　　6.　As Brown implies, there seemed to be no humans at work in this
understanding of science. First of all, either in shaping even constructing the
perceptions on which scientific facts are dependent, in organizing the schemes
of order within which they become facts, and envisioning the mystery of
existence in terms of certain underlying assumptions about the whole which
makes inquiry possible. And secondly, in following experienced "hunches"
about possible answers, acknowledging anomalies, recognizing events of
falsification and/or relative verification—and seeing through educated guesses
the fruitfulness of hypotheses. Cf.
PCT, chapters 1, 6, 7, 9, and especially Polanyi, op. cit.
　　　7.　Cf. E. A. Burtt, *The Metaphysical Foundations of Modern Science*,
London, Routledge and Kegan Paul, 1949.
　　　8.　Lonergan, op. cit., pp. 154, 157, 251-2, 424-5, 495-99, 500.
　　　9.　After his retirement the distinguished astronomer, Harlow Shapley,
lectured at many universities, including Vanderbilt, where I heard him, to
proclaim the "truth" which he had uncovered as an astronomer, namely that
science shows us "there is no God up there", but that on the other hand, science
can only exclaim to us—and here Shapley, wearing his white coat, raised his
arms in awe: "What a universe it is!" Scientists are not dogmatic within science,
and that is their glory; but many become unconsciously dogmatic about their
understanding of science, about its powers and its limits, and especially about
their (metaphysical or ontological) interpretations of its meaning. Interestingly
dogma here enters where philosophy and theology enter, that is precisely as
science leaves its own modes of certainty—where, in other words, as Toulmin

puts it, science shades into "myth" (Cf. Stephen Toulmin "Contemporary Scientific Mythology", in *Metaphysical Beliefs*, London, SCM Press, 1957, reprinted in the excellent book, *The Return to Cosmology*, Berkeley, University of California Press, 1982, Part I). This is ironic, for one major reason scientists become rightly irritated at religionists is the "dogmatic certainty" of the latter, where, say their critics, "they have no right to be so certain", their "beliefs" (i.e., metaphysical and/or theological propositions) not being provable as science understands proof. As we have shown, a goodly number of scientists fall into the same trap, and at the same place, and become uncharacteristically dogmatic, even apodictic ("Paley is simply wrong"; "the Cosmos is all there is") where they have no right to be, for this is not science, and where the religionist objects of their scorn had been dogmatic, namely in the area of "beliefs", views of the whole based on experience but not provable by empirical testing.

10. Whitehead agrees: "It is a contradiction in terms to assume that some explanatory fact can float into the actual world out of nonentity. Nonentity is nothingness. Every explanatory fact refers to the decision and to the efficacy of an actual thing." PR 73. Cf also Category of Explanation in XVIII, the "ontological principle", ibid. pp. 36-7, "actual entities are the only reasons. . ."

11. An ironic aspect of all this is that despite the evident "scientific" realism we have described, each of the authors cited takes pains to deny a realist stance, e.g., PS p. 134, and ACP p. 30. Dawkins recognizes openly the effects of our human senses, especially of the primacy of sight, on the "construction of our visible world"—and contrasts that constructed world with that of the bats, whose "world" is built on hearing. But he does not carry this radically critical or constructionist view beyond the levels of sense perception and on into the realms of intellectual understanding and reflective judgment, into the realm of science. If he had, he could not have been the "realist" he clearly was, CF. Dawkins, p. 34.

12. The prejudice against religion in these volumes is really fairly astounding. With regard to ideas which were held generally throughout culture in the past, by scientists, philosophers, literary persons as well as by clerics (for example, that species are permanent and so do not die out), it is the clerics who are blamed: ".. traditional Western religious traditions stoutly maintain the contrary (i.e., the contrary of the modern conception of the mortality of species), as for example the 1770 opinion of John Wesley. . ." (C 16) On this point of the ascription of the denial of the possibility of extinction not to religious tradition but to the traditional philosophical category of the "plenitude of being" Cf. ACP, p. 128. If Sagan had read John C. Greene's *The Death of Adam*, he would have seen Jefferson (hardly a cleric!) declaring "such is the economy of nature (sic) that no instance can be produced of her having permitted any one race of her animals to become extinct." John C. Greene, *The Death of Adam*, Ames, Iowa, Iowa State University Press, 1959, p. 88. Cf. also on this point Dawkins, 143, who speaks of the "smallmindedness" and

"conceit" of medieval Christians for thinking the human race was favored by God (BW 143).

13. In fact Pagels describes any non-reductionist ontology—be it established on metaphysical or on religious grounds—as representative of a "closed mind" as opposed to the openmindedness of the scientist, PS 167.

14. Whitehead argues throughout his works that the assumption of a continuing and omnipresent order throughout actuality is a necessary basis for science ("Thus yardsticks in Cambridge are good even in New Haven."), that this is the "hope of rationalism" and the "motive for the pursuit of all sciences alike", and that this hope is itself based on a "faith in reason"—a faith which establishes culture as a whole as well as metaphysics (PR 67). "This faith cannot be justified by any inductive generalization. It springs from direct inspection of the nature of things as disclosed in our own immediate present experience." (SMW 26) It is the task of the metaphysics of each age to elaborate the "world" established and upheld by this faith in reason and so to provide a rational basis for the sciences and for the culture which depend upon it.

Interestingly, another philosopher of science, Alexander Rosenberg, who has written what is to me a most intelligible and balanced survey of the philosophical issues in biological science, agrees that what Barrow and Tipler call "ontological reductionism" and "ontological determinism"—in fact, scientific realism—represents, unbeknownst to most biologists, an assumed metaphysics and not empirical science at all: "Provincialism (the view that biology can be reduced to physics) is a response to the epistemological embarrassment of the Positivists: It holds that where biological theory cannot be, in principle at least, connected to physical theory the biology should be negated as unscientific. But the grounds for this claim are sheer metaphysics: Nature is nothing but what physics tells us it is, so any account of nature, including animate nature, that is not reducible to physics must be wrong." Alexander Rosenberg, *The Structure of Biological Science*, Cambridge University Press, 1986, . 23, Cf. also pp. 72, 90.

15. Cf. the excellent summary of this in Brown, op cit., chapter 6, 7 and 8; also footnote 2 of this paper.

16. This is the major theme of Rorty's latest book, *Philosophy and the Mirror of Nature*, (Cf. Footnote 2 above), especially chapters 7 and 8. It is also the theme of Bernstein's *Beyond Subjectivism and Objectivism*, Parts I and II.

17. E. A. Burtt, op cit., Chapter III (Footnote 7 above).

18. Immanuel Kant, *The Critique of Pure Reason*, Part I; First Division, Book I and II, especially Chapter III; *Prolegomena to Any Future Metaphysics*, Second Part, #14-39, "How is the Science of Nature Possible?"

19. A goodly number of possible answers to this question come to mind: (1) Science has not seen itself as in any way dependent on philosophical foundations; accordingly its "realistic capabilities" are not challenged by philosophical criticism. (2) Neither philosophy of science nor the historical

traditions of epistemology and ontology relevant to science are considered significant for science and so neither is taught as an element within scientific graduate programs. (3) Philosophy itself has tended to eschew epistemological and ontological matters, preferring logical and language analysis. (4) The reigning philosophy of science has itself been empiricist and objectivist in character. (5) Sociologically, physical science is thoroughly "established" in modern technological culture, and thus intellectually its sovereignty and independence, its theoretical "aseity", is unassailed by most voices.

20. SMW 77-8. "Nature is a dull affair, soundless, scentless, colorless; merely the hurrying of material, endlessly, meaninglessly...No alternative system of organizing the pursuit of scientific truth has been suggested. It is not only reigning, but it is without a rival.

And yet—it is quite unbelievable. This conception of the universe is surely framed in terms of high abstractions, and the paradox only arises because we have mistaken an abstraction for concrete realities."

21. For Whitehead's view that the pervasive structures and so order of existence are not "data" of sense or therefore of empirical inquiry, Cf. *Process and Reality*, PR 6-7, AI 209, 232, MT 146-7; for the derivation of the "categories" of science from unconscious perceptions (causal efficacy), Cf. PR 180-1, 265-7, AI 232-7 and *Symbolism, Its Meaning and Effect*, New York, Macmillan, 1927, pp. 30-49; for the dependence of the rest of experience, of civilization, and of science on recognition or "knowledge" of these pervasive structures, Cf. AI 292.

22. PR 6-7, AI 209.

23. Cf. for the discussion of ontological and technical reason, Paul Tillich *Systematic Theology*, Chicago, University of Chicago Press, 1951, Volume I, pp. 71ff. and pp. 97ff.; Volume III, pp. 57ff.. Cf. also, "Science and Theology", in *Theology of Culture*, ed. R. C. Kimball, London, Oxford, 1959, pp. 127-32. For a fuller bibliography of Tillich's writings on science and technology, Cf. J. Mark Thomas, *Ethics and Technoculture*, Lanham MD, University Press of America, 1987.

24. Tillich's discussions of the ontological polarity of self and world, and its influence on the possibility of cognitive knowledge of world, are in ST, Volume I, Part I, Introduction and Basic Ontological Structure; Volume III, pp. 17-38, 57-65.

25. ST, Volume III, pp. 38-41.

26. ST, Volume I, pp. 168ff.

27. ST, Volume I, pp. 189ff.; on the experience of the "infinite ground of reason", Volume I, pp. 79ff., Volume III, pp. 87ff.

28. ST, Volume III, pp. 17-28, 313ff.

29. PR, 28, "...in the principles which actuality exemplifies all are on the same level". "The metaphysical first principles can never fail of exemplification. We can never catch the actual world taking a holiday from their sway", PR 7, PR 168. For Whitehead's defense of his method of interpreting

accordingto the principles by which our own experience of ourselves is interpreted, Cf.: "It is the accepted doctrine in physical science that a living body is to be interpreted according to what is known of other sections of the physical universe. This is a sound axiom: but it is double-edged. For it carries with it the converse deduction that other sections of the universe are to be interpreted in accordance with what we know of the human body." (ibid., 181-2) "The way in which one actual entity is qualified by other actual entities is the 'experience' of the actual world enjoyed by that actual entity, as subject. The subjectivist principle is that the whole universe consists of elements disclosed in the analysis of the experience of subjects." (PR, 252)

30. ST, Volume I, pp. 18ff.; PR 7-8, *Religion in the Making*, Cambridge, Mass., University Press, 1926, footnote on p. 84; and AI 187.

31. George Santayana, *Scepticism and Animal Faith*, New York, Scribners Sons, 1929, "Discourse is a language, not a mirror. The images in sense are parts of discourse, not parts of nature: they are the babble of our innocent organs under the stimulus of things; but these spontaneous images, like the sounds of the voice, may acquire the function of names..." 180.

32. Ibid., pp. 180, 178.

33. Ibid., chapters XV-XXI.

34. Previous efforts along this line, namely, attempts to discriminate the respective tasks of philosophy and theology and to show the positive and mutual dependence of these two on each other, are found in *Naming the Whirlwind, Religion and the Scientific Future*, especially Chapter 4, *Catholicism Confronts Modernity*, and *Reaping the Whirlwind*, Part I and Entre Act.

SOME COSMOLOGICAL PERSPECTIVES

Joseph Silk

Dept. of Astronomy
University of California
Berkeley, California

"The point of view of a sinner is that the church promises him hell in the future, but cosmology proves that there was a fiery hell in the past." Ya. B. Zel'dovich (1914-1987)

Why is the universe so large? Why is it so isotropic and relatively uniform? Why are the dominant structures galaxies and galaxy clusters? How did the complexities of structure arise on all scales? Modern cosmology has shed much light on these questions that even a decade ago might have been relegated to the domains of metaphysics or theology. Insight has been attained via the synergetic interaction between the fields of particle physics and astrophysics, the very early universe providing the ultimate frontier in both of these domains of scientific endeavour.

There is essentially universal acceptance among cosmologists of the Big Bang theory. Direct evidence enables us to be confident of the applicability of this theory over a period encompassing the expansion of the universe from an age of only one second to its present age of some fifteen billion years. By the very early universe I mean the first second of the Big Bang, and it is within this brief flash of cosmic fire that the seeds of large-scale structure were sown. The physics of the first second is inevitably speculative and controversial, since it rests on enormous extrapolations from our current knowledge. Nevertheless, progress has been made, and tentative answers can indeed be given to many questions about the origin of structure.

The Big Bang theory rests on three rather solid pillars. Each was a prediction that has been confirmed by many observations. The three predictions were that the universe is expanding, that some of the light elements were synthesized in the first minutes of the expansion, and that the cooled remnant of the primeval fireball radiation should be observable today.

Alexander Friedmann and Abbé Georges Lemaître each independently discovered the cosmological model that constitutes the standard big bang theory: homogeneous, isotropic, and consequently in a state of uniform expansion (or contraction) according to general relativity, provided that no cosmological constant (or vacuum energy density) was introduced. Lemaître argued that the galaxy redshifts known at that time could provide evidence for the linear expansion law he had derived. Only with Hubble's distance determinations was the expansion law confirmed: $v = H_o r$, where v is the recession velocity of a galaxy at a distance r and H_o is Hubble's constant. Modern determinations restrict Hubble's constant to 10 billion yr $\leq H_o \leq 20$ billion yr. The factor of 2 uncertainty is due to differences of opinion among astronomers about the use of local calibration techniques: the linear law itself is well confirmed. The fact that the above time-scale is in reasonable accord with two independent time-scales, derived from age-dating the oldest stars with stellar evolution models and age-dating uranium with fossil radioactivity, provides additional support for the finite age of the Big Bang theory: this coincidence cannot otherwise be simply understood.

The synthesis of light elements, in particular helium and deuterium, in the first minutes of the Big Bang also turns out to be a relatively unshakable prediction of the hot Big Bang theory. For example, helium is found to have a similar abundance in distant galaxies of varying chemical composition, a fact best understood if its origin is primordial. There is no plausible galactic origin for deuterium, and it is likely that the helium isotope of mass 3 and the lithium isotope of mass 7 are also produced in the Big Bang. Deuterium is only produced in sufficient abundance if the baryon (or ordinary matter) density is not too high, $\Omega_b \leq 0.1$, where Ω_b is the density of baryons relative to the critical density in a spatially flat universe. More generally, we describe the total density of matter, both baryonic and non-baryonic by Ω. If $\Omega < 1$, the spatial geometry of the universe is open and infinite, and the universe expands forever; if $\Omega > 1$, space is closed and finite, and the universe is destined to eventually recollapse in a Big Squeeze.

Finally, one consequence of the successful explanation of light element synthesis was the realization by Robert Dicke that there should be a detectable relic radiation field. Discovered in 1965 by Arno Penzias and Robert Wilson, the cosmic microwave background has since been found to have a blackbody spectrum with a temperature of 2.75K, with no significant spectral distortions at the ten percent level. Furthermore, the motion of the earth and sun relative to the frame defined by the cosmic background radiation has led to a detectable dipole anisotropy over 180° No other anisotropy has yet been measured on smaller angular scales, and I will discuss below the significance of the isotropy of the blackbody radiation.

All of this leads to a relatively secure model for the universe back to a temperature (which I shall measure in units of energy: 1 electron volt (eV) is equivalent to an electron temperature of 10,000°K) of 1 MeV or so, when the universe was one second old. However, before then, deviations from a Friedmann-Lemaître model cannot be excluded. The nature of elementary particles only begins to unfold once MeV energies are attained: such energies are necessary to begin to break up nuclei. Above 1 MeV, the weak nuclear interaction becomes important. A plasma at this energy prolifically emits neutrinos, and electrons and protons combine to form neutrons, both manifestations of the weak interaction. The strong nuclear interaction requires much higher energy to be revealed, namely an energy sufficient to break up a proton. Only in a plasma at a temperature of two hundred MeV or greater does one find a prolific number of quarks, the elementary particles which are the basic subnuclear units of matter that interact via the strong interaction. Elementary particle properties are currently studied in accelerator experiments that involve proton or electron collisions at energies up to some tens of GeV. The standard model, developed to understand weak and strong interactions, provides a well-tested framework for elementary particle physics up to the energies presently accessible in the largest terrestrial accelerators. This means that the cosmologist has considerable confidence in extrapolating the Big Bang theory to an energy of 100 GeV, or an epoch when the universe was only 10^{-10} second old.

The standard model is not expected to be applicable at higher energy: we are now in the realm of new, yet-to-be discovered physics. While the details of new particles that may exist are unknown, there is one fundamental argument that does enable one to extrapolate the theory to very much higher energy. This is the notion that ultimately the fundamental forces must become unified and indistinguishable. This is true for the electromagnetic and weak nuclear interactions, which merge together at about 100 GeV. This corresponds to the mass of a W or Z boson, particles which are the carriers of the weak interaction. Above this energy, these particles are massless, and one has perfect symmetry between weak and electromagnetic forces. As the energy or temperature of the universe drops below 100 GeV, the symmetry is spontaneously broken, and the weak interaction is distinct, and stronger than, electromagnetism, with the W and Z bosons only then acquiring their mass.

Electromagnetism is carried at these low energies by the relatively puny photon, which is massless and therefore effective only over a much larger range than the weak nuclear force. The range of a force is determined by the mass of the force carrier according to the uncertainty principle: a massive carrier particle has a correspondingly small range over which it is wave-like. An example of spontaneous symmetry braking is a ferromagnet: at high temperature, the iron atoms are randomly oriented, and there is no net magnetization, but as the temperature drops below a critical value, the iron molecules become aligned in a randomly chosen direction, and the phenomenon of magnetization has spontaneously appeared.

Extrapolations of this scheme of spontaneous symmetry braking to much higher energies suggest that at about 10^{15} GeV, the strong and weak nuclear interactions become unified, along with the electromagnetic interactions. Finally, at the ultimate energy scale of 10^{19} GeV, the Planck scale, we expect the gravitational force to become unified with the other fundamental forces. The Planck scale represents the energy at which quantum and gravitational effects are comparable. For example, the Compton wavelength that quantum theory assigns to a particle is enormously greater than the Schwarzschild radius of the particle, the size it would have if compressed to form a black hole. However, as the energy of an elementary particle increases, its Compton wavelength gets smaller, and the Planck scale denotes the energy at which the two are comparable. Such elementary particles, which would simultaneously be black holes if classical general relativity were to provide an accurate description of their behaviour, would weigh 10^{19} proton masses. The instant when this energy was attained was only 10^{-43} second after the Big Bang. This truly demarcates the beginning of classical cosmology.

To proceed earlier requires the development of quantum cosmology, the marriage between gravity and quantum physics. We can only speculate about this initial phase of creation, but there are theories under study that promise to provide a description of creation itself. One approach argues that the beginning was in a state of quantum chaos that had existed for eternity, but in which a chance fluctuation triggered the spontaneous growth of our universe out of one isolated bubble that grew to dominate its surroundings. Another approach invokes bizarre objects called superstrings that account for a unified description of the fundamental forces and for the origin of space-time itself. These theories are in too preliminary a stage of development at present to have much to say on the evolution of the universe at later times, although one hopes that, in principal, all of the ensuing evolution will eventually be explained.

What has emerged, however, from studies of the spontaneous breaking of the symmetry of the grand unification phase above 10^{15} GeV when the strong, weak and electromagnetic forces are unified has had a considerable impact on cosmology. The phase transition as the universe cools below 10^{15} GeV can result in a considerable injection of energy into the universe. This energy is analogous to latent heat, made available as the universe undergoes a phase transition from a hotter to a colder phase. The first phase is the symmetric state of grand unification, but the latter resembles our observed universe in which the strong nuclear force greatly exceeds in strength the other fundamental forces. Despite the continuing expansion of the universe, the injection of energy means that the energy density of the universe remains, for a brief period, nearly constant. During this phase, the universe expands at an exponential rate: that is to say, the separation between particles increases exponentially rapidly. This has a dramatic effect on the causal structure of the universe: one finds that light can now travel throughout the vast regions of the universe, whereas immediately before or after this phase, light travel was limited to the distance traversed during the time it had taken the universe to expand at its ordinarily sedate rate to that epoch. Imagine running on a continuously expanding racetrack: the best athlete will never complete a lap. But if the expansion temporarily halts, he will be able to complete any number of laps (if he has the necessary endurance). Take the racetrack to represent the energy density in the universe and the athlete to be a quantum of light, and you have an analogue of inflation.

The distance light can travel (or the light horizon) is found to increase exponentially rapidly during this phase of nearly constant energy density, and we consequently call this the phase of inflation. Inflation explains the puzzle of why the universe is so isotropic: regions so far apart that they do not appear to be in causal contact in the recent past would once have been causally connected during the inflationary phase. Inflation is soon over: the universe makes the transition to the observed phase of broken symmetry, and the usual expansion described by the Big Bang theory continues, to take us from an epoch of 10^{-35} second up to the present epoch.

Inflation accounts for another outstanding puzzle. While on large scales the universe is highly homogeneous, it cannot have been perfectly homogeneous, otherwise we would not be here. The seed fluctuations which gave rise to galaxies originated as quantum fluctuations at the beginning of time, that is to say at 10^{-43} second after the Big Bang. These fluctuations were amplified by inflation up to the macroscopic scales of galaxies and even galaxy clusters. Inflationary cosmology actually predicts the size distribution of the fluctuations. It also predicts that the universe is full of dark matter in the form of exotic weakly interacting particles. The success of primordial nucleosynthesis requires the density of ordinary matter, namely baryons, the matter out of which stars are made, to constitute only about one-tenth of the critical value required to result in a closed universe. Inflation, however, results in the density being at precisely the critical value: any significant deviation from the critical density would result in the universe having spatially curved space-sections, and inflation generically erases any curvature. Thus ninety percent of the density must be non-baryonic, in the form of weakly interacting dark matter, if the inflationary scenario is adopted.

There are other arguments that support the hypothesis of a dark matter-dominated universe. For example, if the universe contained exclusively baryonic matter and hence was open, with the expansion energy dominating the gravitational potential energy, then as one extrapolates backwards in time, the deviation between the actual universe and one at the critical density, with an exact balance between gravitational potential and kinetic energy, becomes smaller and smaller. In fact, at the Planck epoch, the two types of energy must have only differed by about 1 part in 10^{60}. This fine-tuning seems abhorrent to some cosmologists, who prefer to argue that the universe always was at precisely the critical density.

Another issue is the remarkable isotropy of the cosmic microwave background radiation. Apart from a dipole term due to our motion, no anisotropies have been measured to better than 0.01 percent. Galaxies form by the process of growth via gravitational instability of infinitesimal fluctuations that are the relics of inflation. These fluctuations leave an imprint in the cosmic microwave background, which provides us with a window on the early universe. If the universe were open and hence expansion-dominated in the recent past, then over the past several expansion times, gravity played a negligible role in enhancing the growth of the fluctuations that gave rise to galaxies. Thus galaxies must have formed rather earlier in an open universe than in a closed universe. This has the consequence that the primordial fluctuations from which galaxies formed must have had larger amplitude in an open universe, since there was less time for their growth. In a dark matter-dominated universe, fluctuation growth occurs continuously up until the present epoch, so that galaxies formed relatively late, and the primordial fluctuations have minimal amplitude. This means that a dark matter-dominated universe can more easily be reconciled with the extreme smoothness of the microwave background.

There are two generic varieties of dark matter, which may be called hot and cold. For simplicity, we assume the universe to be dominated by one or the other, although there is no reason why both could not be present in comparable amounts. Cold dark matter refers to any massive particle (mass >> 1 MeV) candidate, whose mass guarantees that, when the universe first becomes matter-dominated at a temperature of about 10 eV, the cold dark matter is, literally, cold: the particles have negligible random velocities. The inflation-generated spectrum guarantees that the largest amplitude fluctuations are present on small scales, containing less than 10^9 solar masses or so, and consequently the cold dark matter accretes first on these scales. Fluctuations increase in density, condense out of the expanding universe as their own self-gravity plays an ever increasing role, and eventually collapse to form dwarf galaxies. Subsequently, larger and larger fluctuations condense out, with galaxy cluster mass scales just going non-linear at the present epoch. This bottom-up scenario for structure formation tells us that dwarf galaxies formed at an epoch some 10^9 years or so after the Big Bang, and large galaxies began to form several billion years later. Galaxy formation is a recent phenomenon in a cold dark matter-dominated universe. In terms of redshift, which denotes the factor by which the universe has expanded, galaxy formation should have been a common occurrence at $z \sim 1$.

By contrast, hot dark matter denotes a particle such as the neutrino with a mass of about 30 eV. These particles have considerable velocity dispersion at the epoch of matter domination, their random velocities being an appreciable fraction of the speed of light. Fluctuations cannot grow under these circumstances; indeed, the smaller scale fluctuations that would otherwise form galaxies are completely disrupted. However on much larger scales, corresponding to those of galaxy clusters, there is not enough time for disruption to occur. Consequently, the first bound structures to develop have the masses of galaxy clusters, ~ 10^{15} solar masses, and these subsequently collapse and fragment into galaxies. The generic collapse of these coherent massive structures tends to result in transient formation of a sheet or a pancake, which then fragments into galactic-scale or even smaller clumps. This top-down scenario for structure formation results in a very different distribution of matter on large scales from the bottom-up scenario. The universe is found to be very clumpy. If the observed luminous galaxies are reasonable tracers of the underlying matter distribution, then one can probably eliminate a hot dark matter scenario on the grounds of excessive large-scale clumpiness.

This brings up another uncertainty, however: we have no guarantee that light is a fair tracer of mass. If there is a substantial bias, or antibias, in forming galaxies, one could end up with very different conclusions. An antibias, with galaxies avoiding the dense regions, would help the top-down scenario, although it is likely that gas infall to the densest clumps would still make them observable via gas heating and ensuing x-ray emission. The cold dark matter scenario is not without its problems: it requires a bias, in that galaxies must be more non-uniformly distributed than the underlying matter. In this matter, one can reconcile the high density of dark matter required to close the universe with the much lower density inferred from dynamical measurements of galaxy clusters and superclusters, which appear to favour an open universe. A more smoothly distributed dark matter component would not be easily detectable via these dynamical measurements on scales greater than 10 megaparsecs or so.

A final issue that merits attention concerns the scales of the large structures in the universe. Why are galaxies typically 10^{11} solar masses? And why do the great galaxy clusters contain on the order of 10^{15} solar masses? Let us tackle the large-scale issue first. The universe has a natural scale, imprinted on any primordial fluctuation spectrum, that corresponds to the largest structures that have been able to grow continuously during the epoch of matter-domination. Very large-scale fluctuations commence their growth later than small-scale fluctuations, since fluctuations must be causal, that is smaller than the horizon or light travel distance since the beginning of the universe, in order for gravitational accretion and growth to be effective. Thus the structures which have grown most range in size up to the horizon at the epoch when the universe first became matter-dominated. Larger structures experience less "growing time." Remarkably this scale translates to a scale today of about 12 Mpc, and a sphere of this diameter encompasses about 10^{15} solar masses. Great clusters should therefore be a very prominent feature in the universe, if the spectrum of fluctuations is adjusted so that these scales are undergoing non-linear collapse at present. Coincidentally, this latter condition also guarantees that the great clusters have the observed size as well as the observed mass: their explanation is a great success of the cold dark matter theory.

The physics of clustering is straightforward because only gravity is involved. Galaxy formation, however, is a much more complex process. The physics of star formation is not fully understood today, and extrapolation of star formation theory to the early universe is extremely uncertain. There is one key process that surely played an important role, however, namely gaseous dissipation. Very high densities must be attained in order to form stars, and gaseous dissipation via radiative cooling provides a natural means of achieving high density in an inhomogeneously collapsing gas cloud. A simple comparison of the time scales for the competing processes of gaseous dissipation and gravitational collapse is instructive. A galactic mass cloud which dissipates rapidly will efficiently form stars: it may collapse to a sheet, and break up into stellar fragments. Much of the free-fall collapse energy will be retained in bulk motions of the fragments: certainly such a system will not have time to spin up as it contracts before the stars have formed. Once the stars have formed, the gaseous dissipation stops: stars interact only gravitationally. The end product is likely to be a slowly rotating spheroid of stars. We would identify this with an elliptical galaxy. On the other hand, in a cloud in which the dissipation rate was very slow, the collapse would be impeded, and the gas would slowly contract, flatten, and spin up, continuously fragmenting and forming stars in a disk. The end-product might well be a disk or spiral galaxy.

The interplay between the two time-scales, for collapse and for dissipation, is evidently a critical factor in determining the type of galaxy that forms. The condition for the two time-scales to be comparable is in fact precisely equivalent to requiring the cloud to have a mass of 10^{11} solar masses. A larger cloud cools inefficiently. If the cooling is too inefficient, one simply will not form enough stars to result in a luminous mass of $\sim 10^{11}$ solar masses because the self-regulation of collapse and dissipation allows the most efficient mode of star formation.

Understanding the characteristic scales of the dominant structures in the universe represents a major breakthrough in cosmology. An equally dramatic advance has been our insight into the origin of the seed fluctuations from which all structure evolved, a consequence of the inflationary theory that has enabled us to probe ever closer to the instant of creation itself. Experimental proofs of these theories are still needed, to place them on a secure basis. Perhaps this will come with the discovery of dark matter, the dominant constituent of the universe, or with observations of protogalaxies and exploration of the elusive breeding ground of forming galaxies in the remote past.

Modern cosmology provides a novel twist to the Copernican revolution. Not only is our sun one star among a billion trillion, not only is our Milky Way one galaxy among billions, but the very matter of which man and our solar system is made is inconsequential besides the dominant form of matter in the universe.

The universe began from a state of unimaginable heat and extreme density. Yet it was in a state of perfect symmetry among the fundamental forces of nature. These forces control every motion, and every cell of our bodies. As the temperature fell, the symmetry was broken. Order gradually developed as first ordinary matter and later structure "froze" out. Eventually aggregation processes led to stars and galaxies and to complex molecules in the oceans of primordial planets. Studies of non-linear dynamical systems tell us that it is impossible to predict their future evolution after a long time has elapsed. And so it is with the early universe: our cosmology cannot guarantee that the primordial soup of organic molecules that was present on our planet some 4.5 billion years ago results in the evolution of life. The scientific viewpoint seeks a scientific explanation for the complexities of nature.

There is another viewpoint of course. Existence of a watch implies that there was a watchmaker: the teleologists urge us to take the logical next step, that existence of a flower implies that a Cosmic Flowermaker must once have plied his craft. From the flower, it is simple to inquire about the origin of a sentient being, and presto, we have proven the existence of a diversity. There is, of course, a flaw in this logical progression, and I wish that all budding Grand Designers would take due note. We know how to make a watch, hence we correctly infer the existence of a watchmaker. Our cleverest botanists do not know how to create a daisy, still father are we from constructing a chimpanzee. Hence we can conclude nothing about their designers: we lack the information necessary to make any inference.

A reductionist approach fails utterly to account for a solitary daisy. The laws of physics, applied to the individual molecules, could succeed only with negligible probability. Some additional ingredient is needed. Is this necessarily where the theologians enter?

The scientific approach may proceed along a more rational route. Unpredictability is a vital element of many non-linear systems. Push the simple pendulum just so far, and it no longer exhibits its predictable swing. The turbulent patterns, whether of cream stirred in coffee or of cumulus cloud formations, are infinitely more complex than their basic elements (coffee, cream, or water vapour). The theory of the behavior of simple dynamical systems provide us with an understanding of how nonlinearity can trigger seemingly chaotic patterns. It is when one goes from physical to biological systems that an intriguing question arises. Is biological complexity mechanistic in origin, or do we need to go beyond the laws of physics and chemistry to account for the diversity of a living system? Perhaps the nonlinearities that arise when a complex broth of primordial amino acids is suitably processed will induce sufficiently non-random mutations and syntheses to lead to otherwise highly improbably primitive life forms.

The real challenge is yet to come. Is a sentient being no more nor less than a highly complex non-linear dynamical system? Certainly, the implausibility arguments of Crick, Hoyle, *et al.* which purport to demonstrate the need for an extraterrestrial origin of life are no longer viable. They must be abandoned in the face of chaotic behavior and the ensuing unpredictability of dynamical systems. Whether consciousness, which is an extreme form of organization, can arise in this manner cannot be answered, if we do not know the capacity of matter for self-organization.

Some cosmologists take the view expressed by the strong anthropic principle: the universe is such that man's existence is inevitable. In any other universe, conditions would not be congenial for our existence. However this argument is flawed: it does not distinguish beasts from butterflies. Nor does it tell us why the universe is the way it is. Inflationary cosmology has taken us part of the way to within 10^{-43} second of the beginning, quantum cosmology will take us back even further, to the very instant of creation itself.

Modern cosmology has explained many properties of the structure of the universe. Understanding galaxy clusters, the formation of galaxies, of stars, of planets, all are now well within our grasp. Whether the same physical principles will take us even further, to explore the origins of life, remains to be seen.

Some Issues in Quantum and Statistical Physics

James V. Maher

Department of Physics and Astronomy
University of Pittsburgh
Pittsburgh, PA

It is with some trepidation that I have agreed to present a paper at a conference with such an ambitious title. It is my very strong conviction that the rules of the game we call science make it in principle impossible for science ever to address the questions of greatest importance to theology. This conviction I share with the vast majority of my scientific colleagues, some of whom are religious and some of whom are not. Physicists do bandy about such words as "cosmology" and "philosophy", but they mean very different things by these words than do most theologians. When I use the word cosmology below, I mean no more than the implications of our current knowledge of physical law for the way we think about the very long ago and the very far future of our physical world, with absolutely no prejudice as to whether or not the physical laws governing this world were purposefully contrived. Similarly when I say that something is of philosophical interest, I mean that it is of interest to philosophy of science in its quest to examine the content of current formulations of physical law.

This paper, then, will address only issues of physics. It will concern itself with the state of our knowledge about the quantum mechanical measurement problem and some issues in nonequilibrium statistical physics. These are subjects of very active current research along with being of philosophical interest. Since they have traditionally been considered to be very distinct fields, I will discuss each as a separate entity, pointing out the most interesting self-contained issues as they arise, and only at the end will it be clear why one might regard the two as having a close connection.

Before discussing the quantum mechanical measurement problem, let us sketch a layman's- level outline of quantum mechanics. Quantum mechanics was developed during the first three decades of this century to describe the behavior of atoms and small molecules. Large objects like golf balls and automobiles obey the laws of classical mechanics whose central rules, Newton's laws, allow one to predict the behavior of an object through all future time if one knows all forces which will be applied to the object and if one knows, at any one time, the exact position and momentum of the object. In the nineteenth century many physicists believed that Newton's laws could in principle be used to determine the entire future course of the universe without ambiguity and that the only stumbling block was the lack of a large enough computer. However, as experiments probed deeper and deeper into the submicroscopic world, more and more anomalous effects arose, forcing the development of the new mechanics which we call quantum mechanics. We will not discuss all the anomalous effects but will concentrate on a few examples which will allow us to illustrate two features peculiar to quantum mechanics, the wave-particle duality and the role of probability in microscopic physics (by microscopic I mean systems with spatial scales of at most a few atomic diameters, far smaller than could be seen with an optical microscope).

The photoelectric effect provides a striking example of the peculiarities of quantum effects. Most people are aware that the light meters used by photographers contain a cell which produces an electric current proportional to the intensity of the light which strikes the cell. Careful experiments performed in the late nineteenth century showed that the current produced in such a cell resulted from electrons (negatively charged particles of very low mass) which were ejected from the surface of a metal plate when light struck the plate. The peculiar feature of the phenomenon was that the incoming light appeared to act like a large number of particles of energy, one particle being needed to eject one electron. Since light was known to show wave properties as it travelled through space, it was very difficult to see how it could act like a particle upon arriving at the metal surface. This wave-particle duality has since been seen in every microscopic object; whether we originally thought of it as a particle (e.g., an electron, a proton, a neutron etc.) or as a wave-like light, each object can be shown to travel like a wave until it interacts with another object at which point it acts like a particle. To appreciate the difficulties with this behavior, one need only remember that a particle is a well-defined object with a definite spatial extent and position and velocity while a wave is intrinsically a diffuse object which can perfectly well propagate in many directions at once. Thus when we think of a water wave, we do not think of something like a billiard ball but rather of energy passing through the water by alternately raising and lowering the level of the water over a broad range of spatial positions. If someone asked you to locate a water wave on a picture of the ocean, you would tend to draw many long narrow boxes around the crests of the wave pattern and your boxes would eventually cover a large part of the picture. If you were also asked to identify the position of a fish in the picture, you would draw one box around a very well-defined object. With these ideas in mind you can imagine the surprise of the early quantum physicists when they realized that the light coming into a light meter, even though it acts like a wave as it travels through space and even though its wave shape is spread out over hundreds of millions of electrons on the surface of the metal, somehow chooses one electron with which to interact. The macroscopic analog would be a water wave which comes crashing in over a hundred yard long stretch of beach, making no noise and failing to shake the beach even a slight bit under your feet, but instead selecting one single grain of sand and sending it into orbit around the earth. Even though this peculiar behavior never appears on the beach (at least to those who haven't been drinking), it happens all the time in the microscopic world.

Quantum physicists then had to find some way to come to grips with the dual nature of small bits of matter. After many experiments the picture that emerged involved probability. The wave form that propagates through space when an object moves is a probability amplitude; its square when evaluated at a definite position and a definite time will tell you the probability that the object was at that position at that time. If you observe that the object interacts with another object, you observe a particle-like interaction (for example, in the photoelectric effect described above we give the small burst of light which gives all its energy to one electron the name photon to emphasize its particle-like interaction and its similarity to electrons, protons and all other microscopic objects in obeying the rules of quantum mechanics). If, after observing an interaction, the physicist wants to predict the future behavior of the system, he/she must treat all the objects coming out of the interaction as probability waves and let them propagate through the surrounding matter much as a sound wave can propagate through all the rooms of a house. Each time the probability wave passes another object there is some probability that it will interact and some probability that it will pass by without interaction. (The exact sizes of these probabilities depend on the kinds of objects which are encountering each other and on their energies, but the complexification of probability amplitudes is common to all microscopic phenomena.) After some time has elapsed there are in general many paths which any one object may have taken and many interactions which may have occurred along each of those paths. What then has really happened? Quantum mechanics says that the only way to find out is to make an observation and that many repetitions of the same experiments, each ended with an observation, will result in all the allowed outcomes, each outcome appearing with a frequency proportional to its probability. A definite result of a measurement can be predicted a priori only under relatively rare circumstances in which the experimenter has designed so many constraints that only one outcome is possible.

Many good scientists, including Einstein, have intensely disliked the implications of the probability interpretation of quantum phenomena. They have tended to put their faith in "hidden variable" theories, theories which assume that a probabilist interpretation is needed only because we have not found a way to observe all the physically important variables needed for a complete description of the situation. For fifty years the discussion has gone slowly but steadily against the hidden variable theories. Within the last few years they have been dealt a crushing blow, as Aspect has performed a very convincing experiment realizing a test for quantum mechanics originally proposed by Einstein, Podolski and Rosen. A slightly simplified version of this experiment can be imagined in the following way: two particles are to emanate from a common source, each particle having the same spin (think of spin as something like the earth's rotation about the axis which passes through the north and south poles; imagine an arrow pointing through the particle with arrow head up for rotation in the same sense as the earth's and down for rotation in the other sense.) The spins of these two particles must add to zero; i.e., if one particle has spin up, then the other must have spin down. On the other hand, the probability of any one particle being up is just 50% if we know nothing about the other particle. One can wait until the two particles are quite far apart before measuring either of them. Quantum mechanics says that as soon as one particle's spin is measured, the spin of the other is determined even though either particle's spin is truly random before the first measurement. All local hidden variable theories give a quantitatively different prediction than does quantum mechanics, and Aspect's experiment is in unequivocal agreement with quantum mechanics. (The adjective local above obviously leaves the hidden variable team with a way out, but one which most of them would prefer not to take. Nonlocal hidden variable theories are even more peculiar than quantum mechanics, and are especially distasteful to those who dislike the philosophical implications of quantum mechanics.)

So let us assume that the probabilistic interpretation of quantum mechanics is correct. Does the theory have any remaining problems? The answer is a resounding "yes". The outstanding remaining problem is the "measurement problem". We could discuss the measurement problem in several ways but all would come down to the following problem: at what point can we say that an event has definitely and irreversibly happened? Let me illustrate this question with an example rather than try to be rigorous. First imagine that we want to follow our photon as it strikes the surface of a metal in a photoelectric effect experiment. The photon propagates like a wave, gently washing over many electrons as it impinges on the surface. As each electron is encountered, the wave form is slightly changed, just as the pilings of a long fishing pier will slightly alter ocean waves as they pass under the pier. The wave form becomes more and more complicated as it is altered by more and more electrons, but it still acts like a wave and continues to propagate. Then abruptly the photon interacts violently with one electron, giving the electron all its energy and ceasing to exist. The electron then proceeds to propagate, like a wave, through the sea of brother electrons until it exits the metal and enters our detector. Until the electron encounters our detector, nothing has happened which could not be run backwards. The calculation quantum mechanics makes would be a sum of wave forms for all possible places that a photon could either give or not give all or part of its energy to an electron. One could arrange for the electron to run through another apparatus and interact in such a way as to produce a new photon whose final direction is the same as that of the original photon, leaving nothing observably different. According to standard quantum theory, it is only when the observer gets involved, using his detector to make the death of the photon part of recorded history, that the story becomes irreversible.

This gives rise to the fascinating question, "What constitutes a detector?" Clearly detectors are made of material which obeys the same physical laws as does the rest of nature. How then can this very successful theory make such a clean, unambiguous distinction between the observer and the observed? (It has been obvious for a long time that social scientists have this problem in a very serious way, but physical scientists had thought themselves rather immune.)

Schrodinger, one of the developers of quantum mechanics but very reluctant to accept its probabilistic results, focussed attention on this measurement problem with a reductio ad absurdum, the "half-dead cat". He described a thought experiment in which a cat is inserted in a closed apparatus and subjected to an experiment in which he will be shot by a pistol within the apparatus if a certain electron has its spin up and not shot if the spin is down. Until the box is opened and the cat examined, the mathematics of quantum mechanics might be invoked to say that the cat is propagating through time as a wave with probability amplitudes, some of which involve being dead, others of which involve being alive, and all of which can in principle be reversed until we actually open the box and look at the cat. No one really wants to accept this. The only question is how to make the cat's survival or death a part of irreversible history as soon as the electron either does or does not trigger the pistol without saying that the cat doesn't have to obey the same underlying physical laws as does the electron.

One very common approach is to point out that, while all objects must obey quantum mechanics, the probabilistic peculiarities of quantum mechanics become smaller and smaller as the object becomes larger. Thus a detector must be large enough that very large fluctuations from its most probable behavior become of vanishing likelihood. This argument by and large works for a working physicist since available detectors are always large enough and insensitive enough that they cannot show erratic behavior due to their own quantum mechanical fluctuations and the reversal of their results is very unlikely. But the argument cannot remove the problem that, in principle, a detector is a quantum system and all its history could conceivably be reversed. Philosophically minded physicists have taken a variety of approaches to this difficulty. In particular, some argue that the human mind does indeed stand somehow outside of nature and that an event becomes part of history only when some human mind grasps it.

As a working scientist, I have always found this approach unpalatable. I truly believe that when I leave my apparatus running through the night with detectors generating signals which drive the pen on a chart recorder, the trace left by the pen becomes part of history whether I come into the lab to view it again or not. If my prejudice is right, what are my alternatives? Some have been forced so far as to posit the existence of extra worlds; these say that each time two microscopic objects encounter each other and create new possibilities, new worlds come into being in sufficient numbers that, averaged over all these worlds, the quantum probability distribution will be obeyed, but in any one world the result is immediately a definite part of the history of that world. Then the result of my measurement becomes an accident of which of these worlds I happen to end up in. I'll assume we can reject this theory also. It's hard to express how many worlds would have to exist to satisfy this theory and each such world would be splitting an enormous number of times each second. Such a theory cannot be disproven, but it is certainly very cumbersome, full of unobservable effects (something that scientific theories are supposed to avoid) and more problem ridden than the standard theory it is supposed to replace.

(Elsewhere in this conference, I assume some paper will raise the issue of cosmologies which assume that we are in one of an enormous number of universes, not to avoid the measurement problem but to explain the extremely low probability that our world could be an accident in an otherwise chaotic and unplanned universe. The proponents of that cosmology point out quite reasonably that, in a chaotic environment, it is only in the extremely small number of universes where consciousness could accidentally evolve that people would be philosophizing in the first place; they go on to argue that, since numerical estimates seem to indicate that the evolution of consciousness is extremely improbable and since these philosophers regard a universe with a purpose to be unpalatable, then the entire result of our "big bang" must be one of an enormous number of universes. Neither this nor the analogous argument constructed to eliminate the measurement problem in quantum mechanics is logically inconsistent, but each is an example of the sort of thinking that originally Occam's razor and later the notion of scientific simplicity were invented to dispose of, and each can usefully serve to demonstrate the fact that scientists and philosophers also have pet presuppositions which they will struggle to protect. None of these remarks apply to inflationary universe theories, which may also come up in this conference. Inflationary universe theories do involve the possibility of there being a large number of other, undetectable universes, but they make definite and testable predictions about our own universe and will stand or fall according to the success of those predictions.)

If one thus rejects all the above approaches, how does one solve the measurement problem? I'll temporarily take the obvious dodge of saying it's an open question. There is is one intriguing and promising conjecture which I will discuss later. But before this conjecture can be introduced, we must discuss the otherwise quite disparate but very important modern field of nonequilibrium statistical physics. As we did with quantum mechanics, we'll start with a layman's-level sketch of the features of the well-established parts of statistical mechanics which are needed to appreciate the motivation for and implications of the current research work to be discussed.

Statistical mechanics seeks to relate the observable properties of macroscopic pieces of matter to the properties of the atoms and molecules of which the material is constructed. Since any visible sample of material contains an enormous number of atoms, it would be hopelessly out of the ability of even the best modern computer to actually calculate the details of the expected behavior of each atom. (Even if an adequate computer existed, the human mind could not digest all the detail!) Instead one tries to construct interesting average properties and then relate these to feasible measurements. For example, what we all call temperature is closely related to the average kinetic energy of a molecule. Also, the specific heat of a material can in principle be calculated as the rate of change of the energy of the average molecule with temperature. One can construct more and more exotic observables, but all involve statistical averages of molecular behavior over an assumed distribution of molecular energies and under an assumed set of external constraints.

This enterprise has been spectacularly successful for the special case of what are called equilibrium states. An equilibrium state is an unrealizable idealization which can be sufficiently well approximated in careful laboratory experiments to demonstrate the great success of statistical mechanics. In an equilibrium state one assumes 1) that a system (some well-defined set of objects) is very well isolated from the rest of the universe and so cannot exchange energy, momentum, particles or any other observable quantity with the external world, and 2) that the system has been isolated for a long enough time that its macroscopic properties are no longer changing and the system has "forgotten" everything peculiar to its life before it reached equilibrium. This does not mean that there is nothing dynamic about the equilibrium system; the constituent atoms are in violent motion, colliding with each other regularly and trading properties like energy and momentum in the collisions, but there are so many collisions per second that particles of any one energy and momentum are on the average replaced as fast as they are depleted. Under the assumption that observable properties of large systems can be calculated for these equilibrium states by averaging over the expected distributions of atomic energies and momenta, statistical mechanics has succeeded in calculating an impressive variety of properties of relatively simple systems (e.g., dilute gases and paramagnets).

The most exotic property of large systems which statistical mechanics appears to have explained is the tendency to maximize entropy. We all know from experience that systems will tend to drift in only one direction in time. If we walked into a room and found all the oxygen and nitrogen molecules in the room to be concentrated in a cubic inch near one corner of the ceiling, we would be very loath to say that we were observing an accidental fluctuation. Even though such a fluctuation is perfectly possible, it is so unlikely that one can confidently discard fluctuation as an explanation and look for another mechanism. The most likely explanation is that just before we observed the room it had been evacuated and all its gas put in a one cubic inch container near the corner of the ceiling and that the container burst just as we entered the room. This explanation is the more likely because we know that gas will expand out of a container spontaneously but will not spontaneously go back in. ·Thermodynamics, the predecessor of statistical mechanics, explained this and many other irreversible processes by inventing entropy as a mathematically defined measure of the disorder of a system and then enunciating the famous second law of thermodynamics which says that, when you relax a constraint on an equilibrium system (for example, when you break the gas container we just discussed), the system will maximize its entropy(disorder) in the process of finding its way to its new, less constrained equilibrium. Entropy remained a rather abstruse quantity throughout the nineteenth century until, just before the beginning of the present century Gibbs and Boltzmann independently identified statistical mechanical entropy with the number of possible ways to arrange the appropriate number of atoms to satisfy all the relevant constraints. In the case of the example of the gas in the room, this means that there are many more ways to arrange the molecules using the full volume of the room than there are by insisting that the room stay empty except for one cubic inch, so when the container breaks the gas doesn't come to equilibrium again until the molecules have taken advantage of the newly provided possibilities. Afterward, so few of the available possibilities involve having all the gas within the original cubic inch that the probability of finding the gas all within that volume is vanishingly small.

Despite the fact that the second law of thermodynamics clearly indicates a direction that systems will evolve in time, it does not necessarily conflict with the characteristic reversibility of quantum mechanics. The number of possibilities open to a given macroscopic system is so great that the time required for a given configuration of its atoms to reappear exactly the same in all detail is enormous, larger than the currrent age of the universe. However, it can perfectly well be argued that, for a system at equilibrium, the mathematics says the exact configuration will eventually recur.

The real difficulty with statistical physics, and the focus of much current research, arises from our almost total failure to develop successful theories for the behavior of systems which are not at equilibrium. There are equations which we believe to be appropriate for wide classes of problems, but these equations are nonlinear differential equations, and there is at present no general theory of nonlinear differential equations. To make this discussion more concrete, let me point out that we have a perfectly plausible nonlinear differential equation, called the Navier-Stokes equation, which we can relate to statistical mechanics and which we think should be useful to predict the weather. It is only within the last few years that we have had sufficiently large computers that weather prediction inspires any trust at all, and we all know that the weather reporters are totally incapable of supplying any fine details about exact location and timing of significant weather events.

Since we lack the ability to extract detailed predictions from the nonlinear equations which should govern nonequilibrium statistical physics, we cannot say for sure that we have a firm understanding of the physical principles which underlie the phenomena of this field. Some physicists argue that all is in principle understood and that we lack only a computer large enough to prove us right. Others argue, for reasons which would drag us too far afield to discuss here, that there are lots of reasons to expect new physics to emerge as we find ways to deepen our knowledge. Current fundamental research on the subject divides into two general categories, work on the simplest of nonlinear systems and work on what physicists call "chaos". Despite the fact that I find the recent work on the simplest nonlinear systems to be extremely interesting (in fact, all of my current experiments would fit in this category), I will say very little about it and will concentrate my remarks on chaos research because that area has the more obvious connection to the cosmological questions which I have been asked to survey. For the experiments on simple systems, let it suffice to say that: 1) recent advances in pure mathematics have allowed some progress in predicting some (but maybe not all!) solutions to the relevant equations; 2) large scale computer calculations can now at least hope to provide numerical solutions; and 3) well controlled experiments are currently feasible. All this allows one to hope that soon we will understand the great symmetry and very recognizable patterns we see in snowflakes and metallurgical dendrites despite the well-known fact that such objects come in an enormous variety of shapes.

Chaos research concerns itself with disorderly physical systems. For instance, consider a turbulent fluid like the atmosphere during a very violent storm. Even though the Navier-Stokes equation is deterministic (i.e., it is expected to give a definite time evolution to the system for any definite starting condition), the behavior of the system is so sensitive to very small changes in the starting conditions that it is impossible to do either of the following: 1) make sufficiently accurate observations to allow accurate predictions of the system's future, even if an infinitely accurate computer were available, or 2) achieve high enough numerical accuracy on any existing or conceivable computer to calculate the system's behavior very far into the future no matter how accurate the specification of the starting conditions. In fact, and this is the issue of greatest interest for this paper, one can show that for some physically realizable nonequilibrium classical systems there are operating points which are so unstable that, even though the relevant classical equation is technically deterministic at the operating point, no neighborhood of the operating point is small enough to avoid containing rival operating points which would yield violently different futures for the system. This mathematical result puts extreme pressure on determinism; no set of initial conditions can be specified to arbitrary accuracy. Even if the specification of positions of the constituents of the system were made much smaller than the size of an atom (in which case the classical equations would no longer be valid and quantum mechanical indeterminism would apply), the equation would still provide for a rich variety of futures depending on which of the points in the neighborhood was chosen as the operating point.

This problem raises many interesting possibilities. For instance, it has been suggested that living systems, which are known to be very far from thermodynamic equilibrium, may be isolated from equilibriuim thermodynamic systems by the need to cross a veritable mine field of chaotic singular points. If this is true, then, even though living systems would in principle obey the laws of physics, the only way to learn about those laws might be to pursue biology as a separate science. This is obviously what we're currently doing anyway, but some people assume that in principle a large enough computer could use the statistical mechanical laws to calculate the properties of biological systems and that the existence of biology as a separate science is a matter of convenience forced by our current limitations.

Even though there are many more issues of great interest which we could discuss, let us summarize the issues crucial for our cosmology discussion and then return to that discussion. Despite the impressive successes of equilibrium statistical mechanics and thermodynamics, we have not achieved such successes in treating nonequilibrium systems. Our best current knowledge indicates that such systems can frequently be put into such chaotic states that their futures are in fact (and in some sense in principle) random. One feature which is, however, well established is that if one doesn't keep supplying the disturbance which kept the system away from equilibrium (for example, energy in the form of food for a living being or in a mechanical form for a hurricane), the system will eventually return toward equilibrium. And while the details of the return toward equilibrium are too hard for us to predict, we do expect our entropic principle to tell us which way time will run; that is, there will be none of the reversibility of processes which one encounters in quantum mechanics.

For the final part of this discussion, let us consider quantum mechanics and nonequilibrium statistical physics together. Some physicists prefer to think that unmodified quantum mechanics must govern the entire behavior of the universe. For them, entropy is a local phenomenon wherein we are fooled (by the enormous number of possibilities toward which our systems can evolve) into thinking that the second law of thermodynamics contains extra content over and above that of quantum mechanics. Some of them would argue that 1) if we think of the universe as one big quantum mechanical system we could dispense with thermodynamics entirely (at least for philosophical discussions) and 2) if the universe turns out to be closed, then when it eventually collapses, this large quantum system may run backward, possibly with such perfect time reversibility that people could find themselves living their lives again backwards. At present there is nothing demonstrably wrong with this viewpoint, but it does hinge on applying an unmodified quantum mechanics to a very large system. I.e., it ignores the measurement problem.

Another large group of physicists take a position counter to the one just described. These argue that the statistical physics, and in particular nonequilibrium statistical physics, probably does contain extra physics not implicitly contained in quantum mechanics. In this case, some physical mechanism puts in irreversibility for processes containing more matter than is contained in a typical quantum system but less matter than is contained in a typical detector. There is no general agreement on how to put in the extra physics needed to marry the small scale to the large scale. Some relativists would like the extra physics to come from gravity, which does provide a significant nonlinear modification to the fundamental quantum mechanical equations at a plausible length scale. The very speculative Nobel Prize winning chemist, Ilya Prigogine, argues in the fascinating book listed in the bibliography that isolated quantum states are an approximation and that the real world is intrinsically irreversible. He says that the proper resolution to the measurement problem is to realize that the intrinsic irreversibility embodied in nonequilibrium statistical physics must eventually overwhelm the quantum isolation approximation as the size of the quantum system becomes larger. He, like the relativists, invokes a cross-over to irreversible behavior at the same length scale needed for the measurement problem.

I find the ideas discussed above fascinating and stimulating, and I hope I have succeeded in communicating some of that fascination in this paper. But let me conclude as I began with a plea not to intermingle science with religion. It is true that scientific results can comment on some issues which some denominations consider to be of theological importance; for instance, there is overwhelming scientific evidence that the world is much older than the age derived from a literal reading of scripture. This does leave the literalist theologian in an awkward position of having to argue that the world was created a few thousand years ago in such a way that it is decorated with rocks and fossils which pass all scientific tests needed to construct a very plausible twenty-billion-year-long pre-history. However, for the issues of real importance to theologians, questions like whether or not there is a God who personally and lovingly selected the physical laws of our world, science cannot comment in any meaningful way and the Church will only burn its fingers by tying its metaphysical structures too closely to the science of any one generation. Let me add that, even though I have no particular expertise in the biological sciences, I am confident that the same caveat applies to those sciences: no biological theory can in principle comment on the ultimate questions addressed by theologians, and theologians will only embarrass themselves if they tie their arguments too closely to contemporary biological theory.

Bibliography

The books listed here are written for a nontechnical audience. These are secondary but very readable sources, and the proper scientic references can be found in them.

Rae, Alastair. *Quantum Physics: Illusion or Reality?* (Cambridge University Press, Cambridge, 1986)
Prigogine, Ilya and Stengers, Isabelle. *Order Out of Chaos* (Bantam, New York, 1984)

Evolutionary Biology and the Study of Human Nature[1]

Philip T. Spieth

Department of Genetics
University of California at Berkeley
Berkeley, CA

Introduction

What, one might ask, is a paper on evolutionary biology doing in the midst of a symposium on cosmology and theology? Biology deals with the nature and history of living organisms on the planet Earth. It can hardly have much, if anything, to say about the origin and structure of the universe. Nor can it be expected to contribute much to knowledge of God other than in the same sense that studying the collected works of Picasso can provide hints of knowledge about Picasso the man. Nevertheless, evolutionary biology is a fitting and proper topic in any discussion of science and religion. Whereas cosmology deals with objects of the incomprehensibly vast scale of astronomy and the equally incomprehensible infinitesimal scale of sub-atomic physics, biology deals with phenomena on the scale of ordinary human experience. Whereas cosmology deals with the most distant origins of the universe, evolutionary biology brings the story home to the origins of the human species. If we take anthropocentric views of cosmology and theology, both topics converge upon questions of understanding the place of humans in the natural world and their relationship to God. These issues are of fundamental concern to all people, even if they never consciously formulate the questions. Throughout history people have turned to religion or to science or to both to find answers to these questions. Biology, in general, and evolutionary biology, in particular, provide definite, albeit partial, answers. As a result evolutionary biology perhaps more than any other branch of science, lies on the leading edge of the interface between science and religion. Certainly it is the area of science that has seen the highest level of open conflict and hostility between science and religion in recent times.

Defining the purpose and meaning of human existence is the exclusive task of religion. Traditionally, the ancillary tasks of explaining human origins and describing human nature were also considered to lie entirely upon religion's turf. That tradition was irrevocably shattered by Darwin's publication of *The Origin of Species* in 1859. Much has been written upon the significance of Darwin's work. William Irvine (1955, p. 83) summed up its impact upon the relationship between science and religion with the statement:

Darwin's great investigation was not only central to scientific
thought in many fields. It placed him directly athwart almost every
great issue in philosophy, ethics, and religion. The old questions of
necessity and free will, mechanism and spontaneity, matter and
spirit, realism and nominalism, relativism and the absolute were
faced all over again and argued in new light because of *The Origin
of Species.*

There may be a touch of hyperbole in this quote: Irvine was, after all, an
enthusiastic biographer writing on the eve of the Darwinian centennial.
Nevertheless, there is no denying that when biology began to provide results
that bear upon the issues of human origins and human nature it was, not
surprisingly, regarded in many quarters as an intruder, and its results were
greeted with hostility and rejection. The resistance that evolutionary biology
has met with is common knowledge. Consider, for example, the observation
that four General Assemblies of the Presbyterian Church in America denied the
validity of biological evolution; not until 110 years after the publication of *The
Origin of Species* were the results of evolutionary biology deemed acceptable
to the Church![2] Very much in evidence even today is an active and energetic
creationist movement with wide grass root appeal and dedicated, for all
practical purposes, to the proposition that the entire field of evolutionary
biology is philosophically misguided and erroneous in its central conclusions.[3]

At least two distinct themes can be discerned behind the historical
resistance to evolutionary biology.   First, early Darwinism, especially in
Victorian England, was not infrequently associated with an avowedly agnostic
metaphysical world view. Thomas Henry Huxley was not only "Darwin's
bulldog," championing the claims of evolutionary biology, he was also a
leading spokesman and popularizer of a movement that Frank Turner has called
"scientific naturalism." Turner (Chapter 2) gives a good account of scientific
naturalism, which, with some over-simplification, is succinctly described by
Turner's quotation from Beatrice Webb as "an implicit faith that by the
methods of physical science, and by these methods alone, could be solved all
the problems arising out of the relation of man to man and of man towards the
universe."[4]

The birth of evolutionary biology undoubtedly provided impetus to the
development of scientific naturalism. It is also probably true that many
supporters of evolutionary biology (both past and, to a lesser extent, present)
found scientific naturalism appealing as a personal religious philosophy.
Nevertheless, the scientific baby, evolutionary biology, should not be confused
with the dirty metaphysical bath water of scientific naturalism in which the
young baby was washed. It is a serious mistake to equate scientific naturalism
either with science in general or with evolutionary biology in particular. In the

last century evolutionary biology has matured into a broad, secure body of scientific knowledge, while, during the same period, scientific naturalism's naive faith in innate progress and the ability of technology to solve all problems of human existence has been found inadequate by philosophers, theologians, many scientists and much of the general public. Unfortunately, the early association of scientific naturalism with evolutionary biology left a legacy that still persists in the popular mind. Attempts to discredit evolutionary biology through allegations of "evolutionism", secular humanism, or atheism all reflect a continuing failure to distinguish true science from the metaphysics of scientific naturalism.

A second factor in the resistance to evolutionary biology is not so much a matter of evolutionary biology per se as it is a problem of theological doctrines concerning Biblical inspiration and authority. The facts of modern biology make untenable any literal, or semi-literal, interpretation of Genesis that demands a totally separate creation for humans. Perceived conflicts with Biblical authority are probably at the root of most of the resistance to evolutionary biology. The explicit objection of the General Assemblies of the Presbyterian Church in the United States prior to 1969 was that Scripture is opposed to the theory of evolution.[5]

That the real issue is Biblical interpretation rather than science is reflected by the apparent correlation among Christian denominations between a group's resistance to evolutionary biology and the emphasis that the group puts upon the role of Scripture in matters of faith and practice.[6] For example, in the Anglican communion, with its three-fold rule of Scripture, tradition, and reason, the conflict between evolutionary biology and Christian theology was resolved rather quickly. In a 1930 letter William Temple, then Archbishop of York, wrote.

"When my Father [Frederick Temple, Archbishop of Canterbury] announced and defended his acceptance of evolution in his Brough Lectures in 1884 it provoked no serious amount of criticism....The particular battle over evolution was already won by 1884."[7]

The slower acceptance by Reformed churches is consistent with what Hasselink (1983) calls their "high view of Scripture." The staunchest opposition comes from creationists committed to a strong doctrinal hypothesis of Biblical literalism. Eileen Barker (1987) strikes a familiar cord with her observation that: "For the creationist, to believe in evolution is to reject God's Word. To concede an error anywhere would be to allow for errors everywhere...To deny that God created the world and all-that-therein-is in the manner described by Genesis is to deny Him His role as Creator."

The resistance to evolutionary biology engendered by problems with scientific naturalism and by problems with Biblical interpretation is real. In both cases, however, the problems are metaphysical and theological problems. Neither case has anything to do with the empirical evidence or the scientific issues with which evolutionary biologists are actually concerned. If theologians and other non-biologists are to appreciate the contributions of evolutionary biology, the first task is to resolve the philosophical issues that cloud proper understanding of biology's role in describing human nature. Doing so is not the task of this paper; however, I suggest that the key to the problem lies in failure to appreciate the complexity of human nature and the need for pluralistic approaches to the study of it. Both scientific naturalism and Biblical literalism presuppose monistic epistemologies. Huxley believed that there is but one kind of knowledge and that it is scientific knowledge. For Biblical literalists the Bible, in all that it says, takes precedence over all sources of knowledge. Human nature is too complex to be unveiled by a monistic epistemology. Attempting to do so leads to a modified scientific naturalism or, alternatively, forces one into some form of Biblical literalism in order to hold fast to the great truths of religion. Until we recognize the different roles played by science and religion and establish the epistemological domains of each we can expect to achieve only partial and conflicting understanding of human nature. In the words of the biologist John Maynard Smith (1984) "We need both myths and scientific theories, but we must be as clear as we can about which is which."[8]

Major Issues in Evolutionary Biology

If we are to be clear about the implications of evolutionary biology for understanding human nature, we need a clear understanding of contemporary knowledge of biological evolution. When the President of the United States says about biological evolution that "it is a scientific theory only and it has in recent years been challenged in the world of science and is not yet believed in the scientific community to be as infallible as it once was believed."[9] he is reflecting the general public's widespread ignorance and confusion about the historical developments, content, and current status of evolutionary biology. In this section I shall attempt to disentangle some misconceptions about the major issues of evolutionary biology. In the next section I shall give a synopsis of the historical developments in evolutionary theory since Darwin.

Evolutionary biology is a multifarious enterprise. The phrase "biological evolution" is used in a number of different contexts. Distinction of three fundamentally different components of contemporary biological understanding of evolution is central to keeping the issues in perspective and for disentangling much of the misunderstanding that accompanies debates about evolution. For want of better names, these three contexts can be titled.

1. The Principle of Biological Evolution.
2. Theories of Evolutionary Processes.
3. Historical Scenarios of Evolutionary Change.

Each of these three categories makes a separate contribution to the overall fabric of evolutionary biology.

1. The Principle of Biological Evolution. In broad terms, the "principle of biological evolution" is a statement about the phylogenetic relatedness of species and about modification of characters through time. At its irreducible core it is recognition that genealogical connections exist among all living organisms on earth. The elementary step in a genealogy is the biological relationship of parent and offspring. A genealogy is commonly represented by a family tree, which is nothing more than a branching network of varying degrees of relationship built upon repeated linkages of parents with offspring. The principle of biological evolution states that the history of organic life is the history of single family tree of immense scale and complexity. The principle of biological evolution is, therefore, an assertion that living organisms have a specific property: universal genealogical relatedness. Establishing the truth of this assertion is an empirical matter. When biologists insist that evolution is a fact they are simply saying that there is convincing evidence that the world does indeed have the property that the principle of biological evolution asserts.

The fact of genealogical relatedness has an immediate corollary when it is coupled with the observations that (1) a vast diversity of organisms, differing greatly in form and function, inhabit the earth and that (2) the current array of species differs greatly from the constellations of species that existed in previous times. Clearly, species have changed through time. The principle of biological evolution, therefore, has two components; genealogical relatedness and transmutation of species.

Modern biology is clear on the fact of evolution. The genealogical relatedness of organisms is attested to by an enormous body of data drawn from diverse, independent lines of evidence—comparative anatomy, paleontology, comparative physiology, biosystematics, comparative ethology, embryology, genetics and molecular biology. The multiplicity, diversity, and independence of the lines of evidence cannot be emphasized too much. The copious evidence that Darwin assembled constitutes a miniscule fraction of the data that now exist. In every area of biology are found tell-tale signs of genealogical relatedness. To say that everything in biology attests to the principle of evolution is, at worst, a mild exaggeration. A century and a quarter after the publication of *The Origin of Species*, biologists can say with confidence that universal genealogical relatedness is a conclusion of science that is as firmly established as the revolution of the earth about the sun. Anyone can, of course, deny this conclusion. To do so, however, is possible only by denying the collective professional judgment of a large segment of the scientific community. (This statement does not refer to facile assertions from a few overly enthusiastic popularizers of evolution or to biased opinions of some hypothetical group of atheistic biologists. It refers to the studied concensus of hundreds of conscientious biologists who are intimately familiar with the organisms, the phenomena, and the data that constitute the evidence upon which the principle of evolution is supported.)

2. Theories of Evolutionary Processes. Recognition of the fact of biological evolution is one thing. Explanation of the processes by which the events occurred is another. Darwin recognized this distinction, and his greatness lies in the fact that his work encompassed both elements. Not only did he build a strong case for establishing the fact of evolution, he also conceived the theory of natural selection as the mechanism responsible for giving direction to the transformation of species. The idea of evolution was not new with Darwin. Earlier writers such as Buffon, Erasmus Darwin, Lamarck, and Robert Chambers, whose popular *Vestiges of the Natural History of Creation* was published in 1844, recognized the possibilities of transmutation and relatedness of species. Without a mechanism that could account for the origin of adaptations, however, their ideas failed to arouse strong interest from the scientific community. The exquisite adaptations of organisms to their various roles in the economy of nature were obvious to naturalists and were the basis for the prevalent "argument for design," which interpreted the apparent design in nature as direct evidence of God's active role as designer. By providing a mechanism to account for adaptive change, Darwin's theory of natural selection has the joint distinction of being the primary factor responsible for convincing the scientific community of the fact of evolution and, at the same time, being the primary cause for the negative reaction by the religious community who saw in the theory of natural selection a denial of God's role as the designer of creation.

The difference between the theory of natural selection and recognition of the evolutionary relatedness of organisms is made apparent by the distinct histories of the two concepts over the century following publication of *The Origin of Species*. General acceptance by the scientific community of the principle of evolution came relatively quickly, and once established, acceptance continued to grow as more and more independent lines of evidence attesting to its reality were provided by ever expanding biological research. The theory of natural selection, on the other hand, experienced far less congenial treatment. Although the theory of natural selection has proved to be extremely seaworthy, it has sailed on rough seas and at times was thought to be on the verge of floundering. A major theme in the history of evolutionary biology over the last 125 years is debate over the role of natural selection as a mechanism of evolutionary change.

A synopsis of this history will be given later. The key point for now is that biologists are now increasingly aware that evolutionary processes are pluralistic. Darwin's theory of natural selection, Sewall Wright's shifting-balance theory, Kimura's neutral allele theory, Gould's punctuated equilibria, and a variety of models of speciation are all examples of theories concerning the mechanisms of evolutionary change. All of these theories, which are properly regarded as complementary rather than all-or-none mutually exclusive alternatives, are concerned with mode and tempo of evolutionary change. The principle of genealogical relatedness is common to all. Contemporary debates are over the relative importance and relevance of these different theories as explanations of the evolutionary processes that have actually occurred. When geologists discovered plate tectonics, they did not cease to regard erosion as a mechanism of geologic change. So too, few, if any, biologists doubt the central role of natural selection in the events of biological evolution, but they will argue heatedly over whether the role of natural selection, relative to other mechanisms, should be awarded a mere plurality, a simple majority, a landslide victory in the American sense, or the unanimous victory of a totalitarian election.

3. Historical Scenarios of Evolutionary Change. A third component of evolutionary biology is the component concerned with reconstructions of specific genealogies and elucidation of specific changes that led to transformation of specific traits and characters found in individual species. This component, which is the broadest and most diverse of the three, is the area of evolutionary biology most directly of concern to taxonomists, systematists, and morphologists, who deal with establishing natural relationships among different kinds of organisms and their structures. Not surprisingly, it is also the area that laypersons most often have in mind when they think of evolution. People like stories, especially detective stories, and detective stories are what this category is all about. Like cosmology, geology, and forensic science, evolutionary biology is a science of history. Unlike experimental sciences in which data are generated by experiments designed to test some process of nature, the data of the sciences of history are the preserved results of past processes that are hidden in the current universe. Whereas the potential data of experimental sciences are limited only by the abilities of investigators to devise critical experiments, the data base of historical sciences is limited to the finite evidence that history has left. In both cases, however the conclusions and theories of the field are always open to the possibility of revision (or even falsification) in the light of new empirical evidence.

The problem of reconstructing specific scenarios is distinct both from the principle of evolution and from theories about the processes of evolutionary change. Genealogical patterns of branching can be studied independently of whatever processes were responsible for their creation. In fact, a group of taxonomists known as cladists, whose goal is construction of a system of classification that is based exclusively upon genealogical relationships, have developed a productive methodology that rigorously excludes any consideration of process. Because of the latter, cladists have been cited by critics of evolutionary biology as having made the very concept of evolution questionable. The criticism is ironic. To accuse cladism, which is rooted on the principle of evolution, of casting doubt upon the existence of evolution demonstrates a colossal failure to distinguish the principle of evolution from processes of evolutionary change.[10]

Reconstruction of specific scenarios utilizes the same kinds of evidence that forms the basis for the principle of evolution. The principle of evolution, however, rests upon widespread evidence of genealogical relatedness throughout all the living kingdoms. Historical scenarios, on the other hand, require clues that reveal the nitty-gritty details of particular branching points in an individual genealogical tree. The reconstruction of specific scenarios is the area in which individual pieces are most subject to debate and revision as new information comes to light. Some scenarios have been worked out in considerable detail with support from substantial amounts of evidence. Others, for which data are sparse, are highly speculative. Little general importance, however, rides on the rise or fall of any one scenario. The principle of evolution does not hinge upon the accuracy with which any one scenario is known.

Consider, for example, the case of the species *Homo sapiens*. The conclusion that humans and chimps are close cousins is supported beyond any reasonable doubt by a variety of independent lines of evidence from sources as disparate as biochemistry, anatomy, behavior, paleontology and archeology. The increasingly refined evidence from the fossil record is only one part. Popular attention has been given to debates about whether the recently discovered fossil specimen named "Lucy" proves to have belonged to a directly ancestoral group or to a group that is more equivalent to a great-great-aunt. There is an implication in the popular view that if Lucy is not a direct ancestor then the relatedness of humans and chimps is still in doubt. The inference is clearly mistaken—aunts and nieces, too, are relatives. The debates may raise valid questions about details in the genealogy but not about the existence of a common genealogy.[11]

An analogy will perhaps better illustrate the relationship between the principle of evolution and reconstruction of the history of human evolution. Think of doing a large picture puzzle without benefit of a picture on the box to tell us what the puzzle is to look like. Suppose, for purposes of illustration, that we are at a stage in which we have the edge pieces in place and about 50 percent of the interior completed. We see sky and clouds forming across the top; a water fall is becoming apparent in the lower left and mountains across the middle of the right half; in the lower right corner only a few pieces of a reed filled meadow have been assembled. From what we have done there is as yet no connection between the mountains and the sky, but we have, however, fitted together a few pieces, showing mountain tops against the sky, which we have yet to fit into the picture as a whole. At this stage it is unquestionable that mountains and sky are both major parts of the picture and that they must come together at some point and our partially assembled pieces will be included. That is akin to recognition of genealogical relatedness between humans and chimps. Determination of precisely where our partially assembled pieces will fit into the picture is akin to reconstruction of the specific scenario of human evolution.[12]

A Synoptic History of Evolutionary Theory Since Darwin

Cladists may eschew discussion of process in favor of their methodology for doing taxonomy. Most evolutionary biologists, however, are fundamentally interested in processes of evolutionary change as well as in reconstructing specific genealogies. Even if our goal is restricted to an understanding of human evolution, consideration of evolutionary processes is an important element in whatever understanding we might achieve. Darwin's view of evolution has proved to have been surprisingly accurate in its main features (in spite of his gross ignorance of some important details such as the mechanism of inheritance); nevertheless, there have been major developments in evolutionary theory since his time. A synopsis of the history of evolutionary theory will help clarify our current understanding of the processes of evolutionary change. The treatment presented here will necessarily be cursory.[13] To do a full job is a task worthy of an entire career![14]

Biological evolution has three component processes: phyletic evolution, diversification, and extinction. Phyletic evolution refers to changes in the genetic composition and characteristics of individual lineages through time. Typically (but not exclusively) it involves the cumulative development of adaptations. Diversification, formally known as speciation, entails the splitting of lineages, with different parts of an individual lineage diverging along different paths of phyletic evolution. Extinction is the disappearance of a lineage through failure to reproduce itself from generation to generation. Darwin saw the natural selection of individuals within variable populations as being the mechanism that provides direction to phyletic evolution. He saw the diversification of species as being the result of situations in which a part of a species finds itself in changed conditions under which natural selection takes it on a new and different path of phyletic evolution.

The cornerstone upon which Darwin founded his theory of natural selection is the existence of inheritable variations among individuals within a species. From biogeography and natural history Darwin was aware of the widespread existence of minor differences among individuals as an empirical fact, but he lacked any theory to account for the production of variation. Likewise, he recognized the fact of heredity but was encumbered with the theory of blending inheritance (which proved, nearly half a century later, to be grossly incorrect) that was inadequate, on theoretical grounds, to support the variation required by the theory of natural selection. Under blending inheritance, occasional rare variants with distinct effects (known as "sports" in Darwin's time) would have their effects quickly diluted by sexual reproduction. Darwin, therefore, viewed minor variations as the stuff upon which natural selection acts, and he emphasized gradual and continuous change as the primary mode of phyletic evolution, with natural selection as a process (not a force) analogous to the geological process of erosion.

Ignorance of the nature and origin of variation and the mechanisms of inheritance plagued evolutionary biology until the 1920's. In the latter part of the 19th century these difficulties led to Darwin's theory of evolution by natural selection falling into disfavor within large segments of the scientific community, which, nevertheless, had come by that time to recognize the validity of the principle of evolution. A large number of theories were proposed to explain transmutation of species. Two major anti-Darwinian themes were prevalent in the popular theories and debates. First, the inheritance of acquired characters -- variously attributed to use and disuse, or to direct induction by environmental conditions (Geoffroyism), or to innate tendencies within the individual towards perfection (Orthogenesis) -- was widely held to be the primary mechanism responsible for producing new adaptations. It remained the dominant alternative to natural selection as the direction giving mechanism of evolution in the minds of many biologists until well into the 20th century. Second, Darwin's emphasis upon gradual, continuous change was criticized by many naturalists who felt that discontinuous variations, termed "saltations" by Huxley, were the typical raw material from which new species were created. For example, Darwin's cousin Francis Galton, creator of the statistical concept of regression on the mean, was, in general, a strong supporter of Darwin, yet he argued against gradualism by drawing an analogy between supposedly discontinuous jumps of evolution and the pushing of a roughly hewn stone from resting upon one facet into a new resting position upon an adjacent facet. Even Huxley chastised Darwin for burdening himself unnecessarily with the view that *Natura non facit saltum.*

The tide first turned against the notion of inheritance of acquired characters with the work of the German embryologist August Weismann who observed that (in animals, at least) the cell lineage that leads to an individual's germ cells (eggs or sperm) from which the next generation is formed is independent from the cell lineages that differentiate into the structures of the body (soma). Weismann could see no possibility for a mechanism that would translate changes acquired by somatic structures into changes in the hereditary material in the germ cells. He is reputed to have argued that inheritance of an acquired character would be as if one were to send a telegram to China and it arrived translated into Chinese.[15]

The advent of modern genetics came with the rediscovery of Mendel's laws at the turn of the century. The initial reaction precipitated a stormy and bitter debate that lasted for almost two decades. Mendel's success was due to his use of variants that have discrete effects—green versus yellow seeds, red versus white flowers, etc.—which enabled him to recognize the particulate nature of the genetic material. Recessive variants (i.e. those whose effects cannot be seen in the traits of offspring of crosses between two pure bred lines) do not blend with the alternative (dominant) variants in such crosses. Instead, the recessive variants maintain their integrity, even though their effects are hidden in the immediate offspring, and can reappear in their original form in predictable proportions in later generations. This was a new insight of major significance: the genetic variation required for the theory of natural selection is not destroyed by sexual reproduction: the difficulties imposed by the theory of blending inheritance are irrelevant.

Early Mendelian geneticists, led by William Bateson in England, focused their attention exclusively upon variants with discrete effects and eschewed any work with traits, such as body shape or size, that show a continuous spectrum of variations in populations of organisms. The latter were regarded by the Mendelians as mere random fluctuations about the norm, having neither genetic basis nor evolutionary significance. The Mendelians held to a view of evolution proceeding through discontinuous jumps. They viewed the role of natural selection as being that of maintaining the norm for a species, and they generally favored the theory, proposed by Hugo de Vries in 1900, of evolution through mutation as the basis for the creation of new species.[16]

On the other side of the debate was a group known as the biometricians. Led by Karl Pearson they subscribed to Darwin's views of continuous variation and gradual evolution through natural selection. They gathered voluminous data on continuous variations and developed statistical methods for analyzing the degree to which offspring resemble their parents. For the biometricians evolutionary change was primarily a statistical problem;   they dismissed

Mendelian genetics and the discrete variants with which the Mendelians worked as irrelevant to natural populations. In short, the biometricians were onto the important kind of variation but had no genetics, whereas the Mendelians had begun to get genetics straight but could not yet deal with continuous variation.

Such was the state of affairs half a century after publication of *The Origin of Species*. In the following decade things began to change dramatically. Modern genetics had been born and proceeded to grow on its own. Speculative theories of inheritance were replaced by hard facts and sound understanding. It was inevitable that sooner or later the results of genetics would be incorporated into evolutionary biology. Within the Mendelian camp, discovery of traits that are conditioned by multiple, independent, Mendelian factors and breeding experiments that showed the effectiveness of selection for producing permanent change in a character led many geneticists such as William Castle and Thomas Hunt Morgan, who initially had been openly hostile to Darwinism, to recognize Mendelian inheritance and Darwinian selection as complementary elements of the evolutionary process. In 1918, Ronald A. Fisher, who came out of the biometricians' school, published a theoretical mathematical model with which he showed that the correlations between relatives studied by the biometricians could be derived from Mendelian genetics. (Pearson dismissed the paper without reading it because it dealt with Mendelism! The Royal Society declined to publish the paper.)

Fisher's introduction of mathematical theory into evolutionary biology marks the birth of theoretical population genetics, which ultimately clinched the synthesis of Mendelism, Darwinism, and biometry and ushered in a new era in the history of evolutionary biology. The development of theoretical population genetics is synonymous with the work of R. A. Fisher, Sewall Wright, and J. B. S. Haldane. Landmark publications, published relatively early in their respective careers, were Fisher's *The Genetical Theory of Natural Selection* in 1930, Wright's 62-page paper on "Evolution in Mendelian Populations" in the journal *Genetics* in 1931, and Haldane's *The Causes of Evolution* in 1932. If there were a Nobel Prize in evolutionary biology, each of these men would surely have received it. Between the three of them they constructed -- often in mutual antagonism over some fine point -- a remarkable body of quantitative theory that combined Mendelian genetics, natural selection, population structure, mating systems, and stochastic effects due to population size to describe the genetical basis of evolutionary change. Among other achievements, their work provided a firm theoretical foundation for the theory of natural selection and secured its permanent place within evolutionary biology.[17]

The synthesis of Mendelism and Darwinism achieved by the theoretical population geneticists was the first stage in a larger synthesis that came to fruition in the 1940's and is commonly referred to as "neo-Darwinism" or "The New Synthesis". Theoretical population genetics grew out of laboratory and agricultural genetics and deals almost exclusively with fundamental processes of phyletic evolution. Its incorporation into the larger fabric of evolutionary biology as a whole was accomplished by an equally remarkable body of field work and qualitative theory produced by a group of biologists with diverse interests in natural populations and natural history. The history of the synthesis and its impact upon modern biology are documented in the essays in Mayr and Provine (1980). Three key figures (all of Nobel Prize caliber) stand out among an illustrious crowd: geneticist Theodosus Dobzhansky, ornithologist and biosystematist Ernst Mayr, and paleontologist George Gaylord Simpson.[18] Their seminal works from which the synthesis grew were Dobzhansky's *Genetics and the Origin of Species* (1937), Mayr's *Systematics and the Origin of Species* (1942), and Simpson's *Tempo and Mode in Evolution* (1944).

In broadest terms, the new synthesis created a single coherent view of evolution in which patterns of variation at all levels of biological organization are seen to be consistent with processes of change centered upon Mendelian genetics and Darwinian selection. Alternative explanations such as Lamarkianism, orthogenesis, and de Vries's mutation theory were put to rest. The synthesis -- especially in the works of Dobzhansky and Mayr on the processes of speciation -- completed the revolution Darwin had begun in thinking about biological species. In Mayr's words, typological thinking had been replaced by populational thinking. Prior to Darwin, species were viewed as fixed, unbridgable types within which individual variations were regarded as aberrant deviations from the Platonic essence of the type. In contrast, the biological species concept of the new synthesis recognizes species as populations of variable individuals for which the variations, rather than the type, are the reality of fundamental importance.[19]

The accomplishments of the new synthesis can be viewed in several perspectives. In a narrow sense, the new synthesis embodies a specific model of evolutionary change. The major components of this "neo-Darwinian" model are (1) adaptive change through the natural selection of genetic variations produced by mutation and recombination, (2) allopatric speciation (i.e. speciation in which geographical separation is a necessary prerequisite), and (3) gradual divergence of reproductively isolated populations through successive adaptive changes of small magnitude. In a more general sense the new synthesis established a broad theoretical framework upon which specific biological processes at levels as diverse as genetics, ecology, biosystematics, and paleontology can be fitted into a unified view of evolutionary change. In the explosion of scientific activity that has characterized the past 30 years since

Sputnik, the framework established by the new synthesis has been fleshed out by empirical and theoretical work in all areas of evolutionary biology. Field studies, involving all kinds of organisms, have generated a wealth of information on genetic, cytological, morphological, physiological, and behavioral variability within and among species. Theoretical models have been constructed for a wide variety of specific biological processes to provide mathematical analyses of their expected effects on evolutionary change and speciation.

The most significant new development is the spectacular growth of molecular biology which has brought about new understanding of the underlying molecular mechanisms of inheritance and development. It has also made possible the detection of genetic variation at the molecular level. Early studies of molecular variation revealed two important facts: enormous amounts of small molecular differences exist among individuals of the same species, and many of these molecular variations show patterns of evolutionary changes that appear to have occurred at approximately constant rates. These observations opened a new window for viewing genealogical relationships. The degree to which small chemical differences are found in the structure of particular proteins occurring in different organisms correlates highly with the degree to which the organisms are related.[20] In principle, the molecular data could have been inconsistent with the patterns of genealogical relationships deduced from other lines of evidence such as the fossil record or studies of morphological homologies. Instead, the molecular data have confirmed the previously deduced patterns and provide some of the clearest testimonies to the genealogical relatedness of all organisms.

On the whole, post-synthesis developments have given contemporary evolutionary biology a broad empirical foundation and a robust theoretical structure. This does not mean, however, that our understanding of biological evolution is essentially complete and that all that remains is to fit in a few stray pieces. On the one hand, the principle of genealogical relatedness is supported beyond any reasonable doubt by empirical evidence; historical scenarios for more and more groups have become increasingly refined; and the neo-Darwinian model of the new synthesis is well established as a relevant component in many, if not most, scenarios. On the other hand, there still remain parts of the puzzle that need filling in and fitting together. The heterogeneity of the processes of biological evolution is only beginning to be properly appreciated. Integration of stochastical and historical components of evolutionary change with the neo-Darwinian model of adaptive evolution is only partially complete. Theoretical understanding of the conditions and processes of speciation currently lags behind the large body of empirical data that has been accumulated. Many biologists who are concerned with large scale patterns of evolution beyond the level of species feel that the neo-Darwinian model, while not incorrect, is insufficient to account for large scale macro-evolutionary trends observed by paleontologists and biogeographers and needs to be expanded.[21] In all of these areas, evolutionary biologists are actively searching for an even more comprehensive theory of evolutionary processes.

Evolution and Human Nature

The preceding sections have been devoted to providing an historical perspective for the major features of contemporary evolutionary biology. Theology has been conspicuously absent. The discussion has been of science as science, and, as the historian Basil Willey (1961, p. 15) observed, science—to the discomfort of its religious critics—"must be provisionally atheistic or cease to be itself." Before concluding, however, I wish to return to the study of human nature as a topic on which both theology and evolutionary biology bring needed insights. In his essay on science and religion John Maynard Smith (1984) illustrated the interplay of science and religion in our thinking about the human condition with the following vignette:

> If, before going into battle, a man sharpens his spear and undergoes ritual purification (or, for that matter, cleans his rifle and goes to mass), he may regard the two procedures as equally efficacious. Indeed, they may well be so, one in preparation of the spear and the other of himself. If we regard the former as more practical, we do so only because we understand metallurgy better than psychology.

Christian theology recognizes that in a real and important sense humans have been created in the image of God. Biology explicates the evolutionary heritage of the human condition. At first sight, the perspectives of biology and theology would seem to be directed at distinct and, as yet, unreconciled facets of human nature. There are, however, places where the respective domains of science and theology are in sufficiently close proximity that efforts directed toward achieving something approaching a joint synthesis are worthy of serious consideration. Two particular areas of biology come to mind. The first, for which I have no expertise and can only suggest as a candidate for further consideration, is biological psychology and the evolution of the human mind. The second is sociobiology.

Sociobiology can be described as the systematic study of the biological basis of all forms of social behavior from an evolutionary perspective.[22] Many biologists are strongly opposed to any suggestion of genetic determinism in human behavior. From the start sociobiology has been a subject of controversy among biologists and has been unduly popularized by its supporters and politicized by its critics. Sociobiology is a young field with ambitious goals. Its constructions of evolutionary scenarios for behavioral traits are still in immature stages in which they are supported more by mere plausibility than by a preponderance of evidence.[23] Nevertheless, when stripped of its populari- zation, sociobiology marks the beginning of a serious scientific endeavor to combine ethology with evolutionary biology. As it matures, it can be expected to provide increasingly refined elucidation of the biological roots of human nature.

In principle sociobiology is concerned solely with facts about the biological roots of social behavior and not at all with any value judgments about those facts. In practice, however, whenever evolutionary biology is applied to human behavior, attention inevitably focuses upon ethics and the evolution of moral behavior. This is not a problem new to sociobiology. Attempts to derive philosophical ethical systems from the theories of evolutionary biology are as old as evolutionary biology. Herbert Spencer was famous among the scientific naturalists of the Victorian era; at the time of the new synthesis, biologists C. H. Waddington and Julian Huxley both proposed theories of evolutionary ethics; Richards (1986) provides a contemporary example. Invariably, such attempts have been fatally criticized for committing the "naturalistic fallacy" of attempting to derive imperative conclusions from indicative premises: values from facts; ought from is. See, for example, the views of Henry Sidgwick in Turner (1974, Chapter 3), Dobzhansky's (1973) criticism of Waddington and Huxley and Voorzanger's (1987) critique of Richards. Ayala (1987) succinctly summarizes the futility of evolutionary ethics: "The evalu- ation of moral codes or human actions must take into account biological knowledge. But for deciding which moral codes should be accepted, biology alone is palpably insufficient."

The point is well taken. Introduction of ethics and values -- not to mention concepts of morality and sin -- into the study of human nature is beyond the competence of biology. The task calls for theology, and not just natural theology. Natural theology alone can only give us evolutionary ethics under a different name and with a different vocabulary. Insights from revealed theology are essential. For the Christian theologian, therefore, the major problem is one of integrating scientific knowledge with Biblical interpretation. The problem is not trivial. Two quotations from earlier Christians may help guide the way.

In the 1830's British evangelicals belonging to the famous Clapham sect wrote: "If sound science appears to contradict the Bible, we may be sure that it is our interpretation of the Bible that is at fault."[24] On the other side of the same coin is William Temple's admonition in a 1930 letter to an English bishop: "You say 'The story of Adam and Eve is, of course, incompatible with modern knowledge, and the serious theologian sets it aside.' I should have said that the serious theologian never sets anything aside without asking what (if anything) of spiritual value has been faultily expressed here and taking care to give it better expression."(25)

Achieving a worthwhile synthesis of revealed theology and sociobiology will not be a simple task. If sociobiology is to mature it necessarily will have to do so in the "provisionally atheistic" mode of true science. The onus will be upon theologians to develop a Biblical exegesis that will neither ignore nor overemphasize the biological facts of human behavior while remaining true to Biblical revelation of human nature. The task is eminently worthy of the challenge. Only by bringing together the insights of both biology and theology can we begin truly to know ourselves.

NOTES

1.   Presented to the "Consultation on the Church and Contemporary Cosmology: of the Presbyterian Church of the U.S.A. on 11 December 1987 in Burlingame, CA.

2.   See the General Assembly's 1982 paper on "The Dialogue Between Theology and Science."

3.   The activity of the Creation Research Society is familiar to both theologians and biologists. For a brief history of the movement see Numbers (1987). Good responses from the scientific community to the "science" of creation science are provided by Godfrey (1983). Futuyama (1983), and Kitcher (1983).

4.   Beatrice Webb, *My Apprenticeship* (London: Longmans, Green & Co., 1926), p. 83. Quoted in Turner (1974, p. 12).

5.   "Dialogue", p. 13.

6.   See, for example, the polls cited by Numbers (1987) for a clear demonstration of the correlation between denominational affiliation and rejection of biological evolution.

7.   Quoted in Iremonger (1984, p. 491).

8.   Throughout this delightful and highly recommended essay, Maynard Smith uses the word myth in a way that is more or less equivalent to religion or to theology.

9.   Associated Press, "Reagan's Pitch to Fundamentalists," *San Francisco Chronicle*, September 26, 1980. Quoted by Ingraham (1982).

10.   See Gould (1987) for a brief, clear discussion of this mistaken criticism of the cladists.

11.   For recent, moderately detailed, but readable, discussions of human evolution see Brace (1983) and Isaac (1983).

12.   To push the analogy further, suppose that the meadow in the lower right

corner turns out to have a pond in the middle and that our assembled pieces of mountain tops and sky actually fit into the puzzle as reflections in the pond. That would be akin to a major scientific revision. But note that, even with such a major revision, our current knowledge that mountain tops and sky are part of the puzzle's picture would still be correct.

13.   The historical statements in the following narrative draw heavily upon the treatments found in Mayr (1980) and Provine (1971). Provine (1986, Chapter 7) contains additional material relevant to this discussion. These books give extensive and quite readable treatments of the major issues. Maynard Smith (1982, pp. 1-6) also gives a short synopsis of the recent history of evolution.

14.   The historian William Provine is, in fact, presently in the middle of what promises to be an illustrious career devoted primarily to the history of evolutionary biology in the 20th century.

15.   Recounted by Maynard Smith (1982, p. 2)

16.   De Vries supported his mutation theory with his experimental work with the plant *Oenothera*. It is one of the odd quirks in the history of science that *Oenothera* has a highly unusual genetic system. Two decades later, de Vries's "mutants" were shown to be the result of this atypical genetic system and not mutants at all in the normal sense.

17.   A degree of historical perspective is afforded by realization that these major developments in evolutionary biology occurred several years after the famous Scopes trial.

18.   Other notable contributors to the synthesis include botanist G. Ledyard Stebbins, German systematist Bernhard Rensch, and, in England, zoologist Julian Huxley (grandson of T. H. and brother of Aldous) and ecological geneticist E. B. Ford.

19.   See Mayr (1978) for a simple, lucid discussion of the significance of populational thinking.

20.   For example, cytochrome C is a protein involved in cellular respiration and is found in almost every kind of organism. The cytochrome C found in, say, horses is quite similar in molecular structure to that found in turtles, slightly less similar to that in fish, still less similar to that in insects, and very much less similar to that in bacteria.

21.   See Gould (1982) for a fairly detailed assessment of the modern synthesis from the perspective of a macro-evolutionist.

22.   Introductions to sociobiology by sociobiologists can be found in Wilson (1975) and Barash (1981). For an outsider's discussion of sociobiology, see Kitcher (1985).

23.   See Gould and Lewontin (1979) for a critique of the dangers inherent in jumping too rapidly to adaptational explanations for particular traits.

24.   *Christian Observer*, 1832, p. 437. Quoted in Neill (1960, p. 240).

25.   Iremonger (1948, p. 491).

LITERATURE CITED

Ayala, F. J. 1987. The biological roots of morality. *Biology and Philosophy* 2: 235-252.

Barash, D. P. 1981 *Behavior and Sociobiology* Elsevier North Holland. New York.

Barker, E. 1987. Does it matter how we got here? Dangers perceived in literalism and evolutionism. *Zygon* 22: 213-226.

Brace, C. L. 1983. Humans in time and space, pp. 245-282. In L. R. Godfrey (ed), *Scientists Confront Creationism*. W.W. Norton & Co., New York, London.

"The Dialogue Between Theology and Science." Presbyterian Church in the U.S. Atlanta, GA 1982.

Dobzhansky, T. 1973. Ethics and values in biological and cultural evolution. *Zygon* 8: 261-281.

Futuyama, D. J. 1983. *Science on Trial*. Pantheon Books. New York.

Godfrey, L. R. 1983. *Scientists Confront Creationism*. W. W. Norton & Co. New York.

Gould, S. J. 1982. Darwinism and the Expansion of Evolutionary Theory. *Science* 216: 380-387.

Gould, S. J. 1987. Darwinism defined: The difference between fact and theory. *Discover* (January) : 64-70.

Gould, S. J., and R. C. Lewontin. 1979. The spandrels of San Marco and the Panglossian paradigm: a critique of the adaptionist programme. *Procedings of the Royal Society of London.* B 205: 581-598.

Hesselink, I. J. 1983. *On Being Reformed*. Servant Books. Ann Arbor.

Ingraham, R. L. 1982. Evolution in context. *San Jose Studies* 8(3): 4-20.

Iremonger, F. A. 1948. *William Temple, Archbishop of Canterbury, His Life and Letters*, Oxford Univ. Press. London.

Irvine, W. 1955. *Apes, Angles, & Victorians*, McGraw-Hill. New York

Isaac, G. L. 1983. Aspects of human evolution, pp. 509-544. In D.S. Bendall (ed.), *Evolution from Molecules to Men*. Cambridge Univ. Press, Cambridge.

Kitcher, P. 1982. *Abusing Science: The Case Against Creationism*. MIT Press. Cambridge.

Kitcher, P. 1985. *Vaulting Ambition*. MIT Press. Cambridge.

Maynard Smith, J. 1982. *Evolution Today*. W. H. Freeman and Co. San Francisco.

Maynard Smith, J. 1984. Science and myth. *Natural History* 93(11): 10-24.

Mayr, E. 1978. Evolution. *Scientific American* 239(3): 46-55

Mayr, E. 1980. Prologue: Some thoughts on the history of the evolutionary synthesis, pp. 1-50. In E. Mayr and W.B. Provine (eds), *The Evolutionary Synthesis*. Harvard Univ. Press. Cambridge.

Mayr, E., and W. B. Provine. 1980. *The Evolutionary Synthesis: Perspectives on the Unification of Biology.* Harvard Univ. Press. Cambridge.

Neill, S. 1960. *Anglicanism.* Penguin Books Inc. Baltimore.

Numbers, R. L. 1987. The Creationists. *Zygon* 22: 133-164.

Provine, W. B. 1971. *The Origins of Theoretical Population Genetics.* Univ. of Chicago Press. Chicago.

Provine, W. B. 1986. *Sewall Wright and Evolutionary Biology.* Univ. of Chicago Press. Chicago.

Turner, F. M. 1974. *Between Science and Religion.* Yale Univ. Press. New Haven.

Voorzanger, B. 1987. No norms and no nature -- The moral relevance of evolutionary biology. *Biology and Philosophy* 2: 253-270.

Willey, B. 1961. Darwin's place in the history of thought, pp. 1-16. In M. Banton (ed), *Darwinism and the Study of Society.* Quadrangle Books. Chicago.

Wilson, E. O. 1975. *Sociobiology: The New Synthesis.* Belknap Press. Cambridge.

The New Biotechnology:
Its Promises and Challenges

Stephen Phillips

Dept. of Microbiology, Biochemistry and Molecular Biology
University of Pittsburgh School of Medicine
Pittsburgh, PA

Biotechnology is not new. The human species has been doing biotechnology for thousands of years. Baking, fermentation and food preservation are surely as old as humankind. Our highly successful agricultural system has been built around the selection of plant and animal species which provide specific products or services. A few obvious examples are the dairy cow, the Labrador retriever, high yield wheat, the baking potato and high yield short stemmed rice. These have all been produced by that realm of biotechnology called applied genetics.

What is the cause of the resurgent interest in biotechnology? I believe much of it is based on our newly acquired ability to directly manipulate the hereditary substance and to return it to living cells. These techniques are frequently referred to as genetic engineering and were developed by scientists pursuing fundamental knowledge about the structure and function of genes and chromosomes.

So, what does genetic engineering actually enable one to do? Before I answer this question, let's review what is meant by the unit of heredity called the gene. Genes are composed of a chemical substance known as deoxyribonucleic acid or DNA. They are very large as molecules go and are composed of a long linear array of four building blocks called base pairs. Each gene contains a unique sequence of these building blocks. Furthermore, genes range from less than 1000 to more than 80,000 base pairs long.

Genes confer characteristics on cells or individuals that are inherited by their progeny. Genes do this by directing cells to produce another class of molecules called proteins. It is the proteins that are responsible for much of the structure of living cells and which catalyze the metabolic reactions that sustain life. The number of genes in each cell varies from one organism to another. It may be as few as several thousand in a typical microbe, perhaps ten to fifteen thousand in bakers yeast, and hundreds of thousands in a human cell. Some viruses contain less than ten genes.

The first thing the new genetic technology has enabled us to do is to obtain single genes from cells and to handle them as pure chemical compounds in the test tube. We can determine the precise structure of a gene. This has enabled us to learn a great deal about the molecular language cells use to store and retrieve genetic information. Furthermore, not a month goes by in medicine without the announcement of the precise molecular defect that causes one of the numerous genetic diseases of humanity. For example, we know that some genetic diseases such as alpha-thalassemia, a serious blood disorder which is responsible for more deaths of young people world-wide than sickle cell anemia, are caused by the complete loss of an essential gene whereas others such as familial hypercholesterolimia (elevated blood fat that causes increased risk of cardiovascular disease) may be caused by a gene that contains a single incorrect building block.

Second, the availability of pure preparations of genes along with knowledge of their structure has led to the development of new chemical techniques for the synthesis of DNA in the test tube and for the modification of these genes. Third, we have an increasingly adept technology for inserting purified genes back into the chromosomal apparatus of living cells. These genes become a permanent part of cells and will be transmitted to their progeny. In some instances scientists have been able to engineer a gene so that it will direct a cell to synthesize a protein it has never produced before. It is the capability to obtain a pure gene, to determine and modify its structure and to insert it back into a different type of cell that is at the heart of much of the current activity in the growing field of biotechnology.

Examples of Where the New Applied Genetic Technology Will Make an Increasingly Large Impact on our Society

A. The production of rare and valuable human proteins: The incidence of diabetes has shown a steady increase for many years. The source of insulin has been a by-product of the beef and hog slaughterhouse industry and therefore is partly subject to the economic forces which control the demand for meat. Although the insulin supply has not been a serious problem in the past, it may become so in the future. In addition, some diabetics are allergic to the animal insulins. Eli Lilly and Co. is producing Humalin; a human insulin produced by a modified human insulin gene engineered into the chromosome of a bacterial cell. Humalin is produced by classical bacterial fermentation techniques which are completely at the disposal of the company's biotechnologists. Bacterial cells have been engineered to produce many other valuable human proteins. These include several of the human interferons. human growth hormone and human tissue plasminogen activator (for the treatment of heart attacks). The next several years will witness the production of many other rare human proteins such as neuroactive peptides and arteriole growth factors.

Foot and mouth disease is a major viral disease of domestic animals around the world. Vaccine production which requires the growth of the virus in animal cells is quite difficult and very expensive because of the need to avoid the spread of the virus from the production facility. Outbreaks of the disease in central Africa are known to have been caused by leaks from such facilities. The gene for the virus coat has recently been engineered into harmless bacterial cells. This gene directs the bacterial cell to synthesize large quantities of the virus coat which is harmless but may be used to confer immunity to the foot and mouth virus. A similar approach is currently being attempted at the National Institute of Health with the virus that causes acquired immune deficiency syndrome (AIDS).

Many other advances are on the horizon. For example, insertion of genes for cellulolytic enzymes and for heavy metal binding proteins into bacteria are being considered as a way to improve the effectiveness of our biomass waste management programs. Genetic engineering techniques are also being considered to improve the economics of the production of important organic chemicals such as methanol and ethanol. Furthermore, improved microbial production of methane and hydrogen are new areas of R & D work.

B.   The direct modification of the genetic apparatus of plants and animals: Genetic modification of plants and animals has been carried out in the past by the passive selection of variants with the desired characteristics. Experiments to demonstrate the feasibility of directly modifying domestic plants or animals are just beginning. The best and most publicized example of this work was published several years ago by Drs. Palmiter and Brinster. A pure preparation of the human growth hormone gene was injected into fertilized mouse eggs. Some of the eggs receiving this treatment incorporated the gene into their chromosomal apparatus and the resulting mice grew to approximately twice the size of normal adults. Applied science laboratories all over the world are examining the generality of these findings with a view towards the more efficient production of animal products. Similar efforts are also being directed towards the improvement of crop plants to increase their nutritional value, and to increase their resistance to disease, drought, salt water and frost. Investigations are also underway of the complex genetics of nitrogen fixation with a view towards extending this capability to a larger variety of plants.

C.   New approaches to the identification and treatment of genetic diseases: It is estimated that 25% of all admissions to the large pediatric hospitals in this country are caused by heritable disorders. The medical profession has been unable to offer a cure for any of these diseases. And for many of these disorders, physicians are only marginally able to assist family members in learning whether they carry a silent genetic defect which may appear as a serious medical problem in their offspring.

The availability of a number of human genes and a detailed knowledge of their structure has led to the development of highly sensitive techniques for the direct detection of genetic defects. In an increasing number of cases, a defective gene may be detected prior to the appearance of illness. Because very, very tiny amounts of tissue are required for the test, prenatal diagnosis can be routinely carried out in the second trimester of pregnancy. And new experimental procedures promise to push this time back to the eighth week. I anticipate that within the next ten years this diagnostic service will become available at most large medical centers.

Attempts are currently being planned to use gene therapy to treat several of our lethal genetic diseases such as forms of heredity immune deficiency and thalassemia. The availability of pure preparations of normal genes and techniques that are modestly successful in transferring DNA into several types of human cells has prompted this interest. However, major technical problems remain to be overcome. Not the least of these includes being unable to insert a gene into the chromosomal apparatus of a cell in such a way as to assure that it functions properly and does not damage the cell's own genes. Because of the risks inherent in our ignorance, use of this procedure on human sperm or ova is premature at best. Thus, gene therapy currently only promises symptomatic cure. An afflicted individual who has had successful therapy will no longer suffer from disease symptoms. But the descendants of this individual will remain at risk for the disease because his or her reproductive cells will contain the defective gene.

Clearly, biotechnology will continue to have a profound effect on humanity. Economic forces and the promises of new products and improved human health will continue to drive accelerating research and development activities.

Have These New Scientific Discoveries and Technical Developments in Genetics Faced Us with New Social and Ethical Questions?

One may be tempted to respond to this question with a resounding yes because it appears that the normal barriers which limit the movement of genes between different kinds of living cells have been broken! Transferring genes willy-nilly from one cell type to another with no respect for "natural processes" raises the prospect of the accidental "Andromeda Strain" or of a new scientific imperialism which will tempt us to remake the living world according to our own images of what it should be. It may be the realization of our deepest fears that no mystery remains and that each of us is no more than a collection of chemical reactions marching to the beat of a mechanistic time-keeper. Perhaps it is our intrinsic fear of the unknown and distrust of our capacity as a species to wisely use our newly found powers that feeds this position. However, even though the caution that this view engenders is appropriate, I believe that several of its underlying premises should be questioned. The first is that interspecies movement of DNA does not occur in nature. And the second is a philosophical/ religious perspective which places our position in the grand scheme of things at risk for being found out because of too much knowledge. In addition I believe it is difficult to emerge from this view with a useful personal strategy for going forward.

An alternate view is to consider that these new developments in biotechnology force us to consider important old issues in a new and perhaps more urgent setting. Examples of specific issues would include:

1.   **Public policy:** Many of the new genetic engineering techniques were developed using public monies. Thus, we must be wise in the distribution of the benefits derived from these techniques vis-a-vis private development, patient rights and regulation for the public good.

2.   **Misuse of new powerful bioactive agents:** Human growth hormone is currently available to athletes on the black market. Is this the anabolic steroid problem all over again? Sports medicine is replete with stories of ambitious fathers asking not whether this material should be used, but how much should be given to their sons to assure a competitive advantage on the field or court. Some physicians believe growth hormone should be a controlled substance.

3.   **The morality of therapeutic abortion:** This is not a question imposed on society by the new genetic technology. Families carrying defective genes causing diseases such as Hunter's Syndrome (a debilitating and fatal molecular storage disease) have faced this issue for a number of years. However, fetal genotyping using the new techniques will dramatically increase the occasions when therapeutic abortion may be considered because of the diminished trauma to the woman undergoing a first trimester abortion and because of the large number of genetic diseases the medical profession will be able to detect. Further-more, definitive detection of fetuses carrying one normal copy of

a gene and one defective copy will become a frequent occurrence. Thus, requests to abort asymptomatic carriers is certain to increase on the grounds that this will be an effective way of of sparing future generations the risk of genetic disease by eliminating a defective gene from a family line.

How should we approach these issues individually and as a society? I believe there are no easy answers. However, we must not ignore the challenge. We must recognize that anticipation and preparation are far better than reaction and recovery. We must focus our energies on supporting educational institutions which will provide our young people with an optimal learning experience and social institutions which will promote serious dialogue between persons whose perspectives are founded in our rich histories of religious, philosophical, and scientific thought. And we must strive to promote the broad dissemination of knowledge through dialogue between the expert and the layperson, the experienced and the inexperienced and the privileged and the underprivileged.

The Inter-Impingement of Theology and Science

Harold P. Nebelsick

Professor of Doctrinal Theology
Louisville Presbyterian Theological Seminary
Louisville, Kentucky

The following paper is an introduction to an ongoing research program with respect to the Judeo-Christian theology/natural science integration that seems to be apropos to the relationship of the church and the scientific-technological age in which we live. In the scientific sense we are in the midst of an experiment to test whether or not the categories of theological thought and natural scientific thought are in any way compatible. We are asking whether ways will reveal themselves in which, while remaining true to its theology as based upon scripture, the church's thought may be articulated in relationship to the scientific-technological milieu of our time.

I should like to report the progress of the experiment under three headings. First, I should like to recount the earliest stages of the modern dialogue betwen theology and natural science. Second, I should like to point out some of the epistemological procedures of quantum physics that may be applicable to theological thinking. Third, I should like to show how some of the espistemological procedures used in natural science may have applicability to our talk about God.

An important insight of modern science is that science has a history. The report of any experiment must include a history of the experiment. So, too, the experiment in which we are here engaged, that of examining the possible relationships between theology and cosmology, is based on the history of former experiments in the dialogue between theology and natural science.

· It is an ongoing experiment that I entered while on a fifteen-month sabbatical study leave in Göttingen in 1975-76. As far as I know the record, the modern experiment of the dialogue between theological science and natural science was first conceived in the year 1938. In referring to this experiment, I want to stress the role of the ideas more than of the identities of those involved. However, because it is unscientific to abstract the role of persons in any experiment from the results obtained, knowledge of the persons is also important.

Günter Howe was a teacher of mathematics in Hamburg when he became convinced that the time was ripe to relate the thought of theology with that of natural science, especially physics. By his own admission, Howe was re-converted from being a nominal member of the church to an active Christian with a renewed understanding of the Christian faith, by a lecture delivered by Karl Barth in 1932. In the lecture Barth pointed out that the Protestant Church of Germany had lost its effectiveness because it had abandoned its proper biblically-oriented theological base.

As Howe began to read Barth's theology, he found that Barth's thought was especially relevant to the world as informed by quantum physics because it was "scientific" in two senses. First in proper regard for its "object," Barth understood God in biblical terms and had reasserted God's unqualified "otherness" from his creation, a creation that in his providence he held in contingent relationship to himself. According to Howe, Barth thus avoided the traps of any *deus sive natura* conceptuality that identifies God with nature and inevitably leads to some kind of natural theology with its Aristotelian logic of *operari sequitur esse*, (function follows essence). In such theology the knowledge of God is extrapolated from nature and what God does follows deductively from his being. In addition, and in compatibility with the Theory of Complementarity in quantum physics, Barth had overcome the usual dichotomy between the being of God and the characteristics of God under the theme of "The Actuality of God." From here, and I quote Howe:

> "Barth . . . moved to very new theological conceptualities that until now hardly have been appreciated and which, in part, show a surprising relationship with questions formulated by modern mathematics and physics."[1]

Modern natural science, especially physics, had overcome the Cartesian dichotomy of subject and object, *res cogitans*—the thinking thing, and *res extensa*—the object of thought. Barth's theology, surprisingly enough without reference to developments in modern science, had made the same kind of adjustment.[2] Barth states that theology, like any other science, is "a human concern with a definite object." It has "a definite and self-consistent path of knowledge." It "must give an account of this path to itself and to all others who are capable of concern for this object and the treading of the path."[3]

Especially surprising to those who have failed to read Barth beyond his dialectical period when he portrayed God as the rather distant "completely other," is that later Barth stresses that God, while remaining transcendent from the world, God engages himself with the world. "The God of the Gospel is the God who mercifully dedicates himself to the life of all men—including their theologies." Theology is a *theologia viatorum* (theology of the wayfarer). It follows the living God "in those unfolding historical events in which he is God."[4]

The dichotomy between subject and object, that had been characteristic of the dominant trend in western thought since Descartes, resulted in splitting consciousness from material, on the one hand and nature from God, on the other. Descartes' understanding, articulated in *The Meditations*, isolated the subject, the mind that observes, from the object, that which is observed. The scheme became endemic to the science on the basis of which the Newtonian world-view came into being.

Nature was thought to be "out there," quite separate and independent of the mind that conceived it. The concepts of mind were correct insofar as what it thought reflected the object, that which was thought about. For Newton the world was a "billiard ball world." The balls were subject to inertia and were inter-related by gravity understood as action at a distance. The objects of the world, were located in infinitely extended and empty space. All was conditioned by infinite time and caught in the nexus of cause and effect. In the scheme God was understood in deistic terms. He was the "clockmaker" who had created the world, wound it up with an eternally energized spring and let it go. As the spring unwound in an eternal unwinding, the world ran according to its design and first impulse.

For the sake of accuracy, it should be pointed out that for Newton himself, when God rested on the Sabbath after creating the world, he did not retire completely. He had made the wonderful works of creation, the sun, moon and planets, and had placed the planets in their orbits around the sun at proper intervals. He sustained that order by his divine providence. In addition, because the orbit of the planets Jupiter and Saturn intersected, God maintained the cosmic order by playing the heavenly mechanic, at least on occasion. From time to time (Newton was unable to calculate the periodicities of the intervals) it was necessary for God to intervene and realign the orbits of the two planets in order to prevent a collision of cosmic propostions.

Pierre Laplace was soon to remove the mystery, however. Working on the basis of the mathematics of Joseph LaGrange, Laplace was able to demonstrate that the orbits of Jupiter and Saturn were self-correcting in a periodicity of 929+ years. For all intents and purposes, as far as the physical world was concerned, God was redundant. As the German theologian David Friedrich Strauss was to put it, science had shown that "God was homeless and unemployed."

The explanation of science had to do with more than science, of course.

Indeed, we are here at this consultation to consider the possible relationships between theology and cosmology. Kantian metaphysics, that like the philosophy of Descartes split subject from object, was worked out on the basis of Newtonian physics. It formed the basic epistemology for much of Enlightenment thought, including a large portion of Protestant theology from the time of Schleirmacher onward. Kant had taught both mathematics and cosmology at Konigsberg before turning to philosophy. His philosophical thought arose in direct response to David Hume's having called Newtonian causality and, hence, natural science as conceived at the time was called into question. Hume, true to the empiricist logic on the basis of which seventeenth-century science was done, saw that causality could not be verified empirically. He claimed that it was merely a "convention without proof."

In his *Prolegomena to Any Future Metaphysics*, Kant admitted quite frankly that it was Hume's scepticism that first interrupted his dogmatic slumber and gave his investigation into philosophy a new direction.[5] Accordingly, Kant formulated his critical metaphysic in order to justify knowledge "on the secure path of science."[6] The move was from John Locke's concept of mind as a *tabula rasa* (a clean slate), upon which the images of the things of reality impressed themselves through sense impression to an understanding that made space, time, and causality the *a priori* categories of intuition. For Kant, rather than mind conforming to reality, mind forced the appearance of reality to conform to it. In ordering the way reality appeared in the process of apprehension, space, time, and causality were constitutive of the perception of reality that the mind understood. Phenomena, the forms in which reality shows itself to us, were subject to mind rather than vice versa.

Kant's Copernican revolution, regarding the way we know the world, moved the focus of knowledge from that which was thought about, the object (Descartes' *res extensa*), to the subject (Descartes' *res cogitans*). In Descartes' scheme, God was integral to the process. Descartes called upon God to match concept with reality so that thought correlated with that which was thought about. Kant, however, left that job of God to the concepts of understanding themselves. Thus, "the understanding does not draw its laws (*a posteriori*) from nature but prescribes them (*a priori*) and its prescriptions determine the way nature shows itself to us."[7] Since the principles that make experience possible are identical with the universal laws of nature, then the intricate way that mind was enabled to conceive nature is the way nature is.[8] There is thus an "isomorphic" relationship between thought and reality as we are enabled to know it by the activity of mind.

Rather than speaking of Kant's epistemological concepts as constituting a "Copernican revolution," it would be more accurate to think of them in terms of a return to Ptolemy. Copernicus, following the third century B.C. Aristarchus of Samos, and perhaps the influences of Hermetic neo-Pythagorean philosophy as well, put the sun in the middle of the world. Kant, on the other hand, followed the Aristotelian-Ptolemaic world view in his epistemology by insisting that we, like the earth in Ptolemy's scheme, stand at the center of reality. For Kant, God, along with freedom and immortality, is relegated or elevated (as the case may be) to an assumption that is necessary for the moral life. Since in Kant's understanding God was not subject to space, time and causality, Kant had the integrity not to identify him either with the phenomena of reality or with the world's processes. He recognized that, under the categories of thought as he conceived them, God, like the noumena, *das Ding an sich* (the thing in itself) could not be known.[9] This, of course, is the background for Schleiermacher's conviction that God cannot be apprehended by thought but "ascertained" by *das Gefuhl* (feeling). One may be able to feel God's presence and realize that one is or should be absolutely dependent upon him, but conceptuality, as such, is inappropriate to the case.

The Newtonian-Laplacian world-view that formed the continuing back-drop of Kantian epistemology reigned but a few decades before evidence arose that began to question its total hegemony over science. In the fourth decade of the nineteenth century, Hans Christian Oersted's experiments with electro-magnetism, Michael Faraday's discovery of the electro-magnetic field and James Clerk Maxwell's field equations began to challenge the Newtonian-Laplacian deterministic world view from within science itself. The discovery of the electromagnetic field made evident that the world was no longer composed simply of bodies in empty space that attracted one another at a distance. Electro-magnetic particles that made up the field attracted one another only if they were of opposite charge. They repelled one another if of like charge. Maxwell's equations, that gave mathematical notation to Faraday's discoveries, were to become the basis for Hendrik Lorentz's transformations at the end of the nineteenth century. Through Lorentz, they became the foundation of Einstein's Special Theory of Relativity at the beginning of our own century. Nature itself had begun to speak in somewhat different terms than the conceptualities of Newtonian physics, magnificent as these were and are.

Physics in our time is dominated largely by the concepts of quantum physics. Quantum physics began with Max Planck's analysis of black body radiation (1900) and Einstein's interpretation of the photoelectric effect (1905). Both showed that electro-magnetic energy consisted of distinct units and these Einstein named "quanta." The two principles of quantum physics that were especially relevant to those who were responsible for beginning the modern discussions between theology and science were to follow within approximately twenty years. In 1926, Werner Heisenberg announced the Principle of Uncertainty. A year later, Heisenberg's teacher, Niels Bohr, propounded the Theory of Complementarity (1927).

Because of the new view of reality that those theories engendered, Günter Howe, and Carl Friedrich von Weizsäcker, Professor of Physics at Göttingen, were convinced in 1938 that the time was at hand for conversations between physicists and theologians. It was something more than portentious that in January of that year Otto Hahn and Fritz Strassmann realized that, in having produced barium in the process of bombarding uranium with neutrons, they had split the atom in their laboratory in Berlin. The Second World War was soon to ensue.

It ended, as we all know, with the catastrophes of the explosions of the uranium bomb over Hiroshima and the plutonium bomb over Nagasaki, evidence indeed that Francis Bacon was right at the beginning of the seventeenth century revolution in science when he said, "Science is power." The explosions were also evidence that humankind's most brilliant achievements in science and technology can be utilized for destruction. At a consultation such as this we should remember that none of our activities, even those of pure science, are "value free." The same science and technology that can be used for good, can be used in the cause of evil.

I say that after more than a little consideration. I myself had just returned to my unit from a hospital on the island of Ikonawa, having been wounded and having become sick with dysentery when the bombs were dropped on Japan. The battle on Okinawa had come to an end. We and the Japanese together with shelling and counter-shelling, bombardment and counter-bombardment had levelled the cities and buildings of the island. About the only place left to take refuge were in the many caves that penetrated the hilly terrain. We were in the process of planning the invasion of the mainland of Japan. On Okinawa, my unit took over a hundred percent casualties as based on the battalion count. Replacements, of which I, having just turned 20, was one, made up for the wounded and the dead. According to all estimates at the time, the casualty count in the planned invasion of the main island of Japan would have been at least as heavy as it was on Okinawa to say nothing of the civilian Japanese that would have been killed and wounded in the invasion and the ensuing battle. Was I enabled to survive and have the opportunity to speak to you today because of the evil of the bomb, science and technology gone wrong?

After the war, Günter Howe was more convinced than ever that it was necessary for the physicists and the theologians to speak to one another. In the first instance as indicated, Howe was spurred toward the conversations by the theology of Karl Barth. He understood Barth's thought as having relieved theology of the fallacy of conflating God and nature that he saw as characterizing much of nineteenth-century Neo-Protestant theology. The identification of the ways of God with those of this world produced a *Kulturchristentum* (a culture Christianity) that blurred distinctions between the Christian Faith and the German Culture, and allowed the majority of the members of the German church to accept the Hitler regime without undue protest.

The war had propelled the world into the new atomic age, an age that was and is dangerous indeed. Howe was convinced that the strength and courage of the minority *Bekennende Kirche* (The Confessing Church) that, like himself, had been inspired by the theology of Karl Barth and had resisted the powers of Hitler during the war, could be called upon to re-think theology so that it would be equipped to speak to the post-war world. It was a world, to paraphrase Einstein, that had changed in every way except in the way that we think about it.

As those of you who are familiar with the story know, the Göttinger Gespräche, the conversations between theologians and physicists took place on an annual basis in Göttingen for thirteen consecutive years, from 1949-1961. A second phase took place at the nuclear experimental complex in Karlsruhe between younger members of the group from about 1963 to 1968 (I do not have the exact dates). In spite of the fact that the impetus for the conversations had been given by the theology of Karl Barth, despite the fact that Howe pleaded with Barth on more than one occasion to join in the discussions, Barth never came. One letter of Howe to Barth is particularly pertinent. He wrote:

> The theologians have had 25 years to occupy themselves with your thoughts. If that had taken place with only a little more intensity then the situation in the church would look different from what it is. Then there would be at least one theology which would be able adequately to portray what you have said about the subject of time and could carry on a conversation with Heisenberg in your name.... The physicists have earned the right that you should have a little time for them.[10]

Rather than Barth, it was left to Friedrich Gogarten, with whose somewhat existentialistically-oriented theology Howe deeply disagreed, to be the main theological voice in the conversations. Gogarten, as is generally known, had become *persona non grata* to Barth. The two were fellow travelers in the early twenties in the struggle against nineteenth-century Neo-Protestant liberalism as epitomized by Adolf von Harnack. In 1923, they had joined forces in founding the theological journal *Zwischen den Zeiten* (*Between the Times*), to express their views. In the early days of the Nazi movement, however, Gogarten had joined the Nazi-sympathetic *Deutsche Christen Bewegung* (The German-Christian Movement). Barth was never able to forgive him.

Barth had begun his teaching career in Göttingen in 1922. Gogarten joined the faculty in 1935, the same year Barth was expelled from Germany. On one occasion after the war, when Barth returned to Göttingen to deliver a lecture, Gogarten was present. After the lecture as Barth came down from the podium, their eyes met but Barth detected a look so sheepish that he thought it best not to speak to his former friend. The two never spoke to one another again.

The Göttingen conversations between theologians and physicists, along with a number of philosophers were not highly successful. Although people of the stature of Werner Heisenberg, Carl Friedrich von Weizsäcker, Pascual Jordan, Georg Picht, Eberhard Scheibe, Otto Weber, Ernst Wolf, Walter Zimmerli, Friedrich Gogarten and others were regularly in attendance, the theologians seemed willing to accept the physicists' point of view only insofar as it fitted within their theological conceptions. The physicists, on the other hand, seemed willing to enter the church only insofar as they could take their physics with them. Nevertheless, the physicist Pascual Jordan could say in one of the conversations, "Physics that once said *Nein* to God had taken its *Nein* back again." The lawyer Ulrich Scheuner said with reference to nuclear fission. "We will be enabled to solve the problems posed for us by nuclear fission only when we confront the implications of God in all their profundity."[11] Howe, a natural scientist himself was perhaps even more profound when he stated:

> God reveals himself in that he objectifies himself in a piece of the world's reality. Theology, therefore, has no other choice but to explicate this piece of historical-social (and also physical) reality with the materials of thought that are available at the time and thus to make them a part of the Church's proclamation and doctrinal system.[12]

This would seem to indicate that the wall that had once separated science, thought about the world, and theology, thought about God, had been breached, not much, but a little. In these days, together, we are attempting to move back and forth through the breach.

After the war, Carl Friedrich von Weizsäcker moved from his Chair of Physics at Göttingen to a Chair of Philosophy at the University of Hamburg and from there to the *Max Planck Institut fur Lebensbedingungen in der wissen-schaftlich-technischen Zeitalter*, (The Requirements for Life in the Scientific-Technological Age). He retired from his last position about three years ago. When recounting the early Göttingen conversations, Weizsäcker pointed out that their initial purpose was epistemological in nature. The question was, "How is knowledge possible and how is our way of knowledge that is relevant to faith relevant to knowledge of our world and vice versa?"[13]

The first aspect of the Göttingen conversations that I should like to emphasize as having continuing relevance for any discussion between theology and natural science refers to epistemology. True to the epistemology of science that method must be adapted to its peculiar object, the Göttingen group decided from the outset that analogies between theology and natural science are relational in nature rather than ontological. They are relational because the same mind that does theology is also structured to do natural science. Theological science, like natural science, is a human endeavor. The categories of the two sciences are not ontologically related because their objects are discrete from one another. God, who is the "object" of theology, is transcendent from the world that he sustains in separate but contingent relationships with himself. To say it again, according to the mind of the Göttingen group, with which mind I tend to agree, the way we know both God and the world are related to one another. However, in that God and the world represent ontologically non-related "levels of reality," ontological relationships in this case are ruled out.

The second aspect of the Göttingen discussion that I would like to emphasize as having continuing relevance to our conversation in these days concerns the question of the relation of subject to object. Quantum physics, at least in the Copenhagen understanding of it that was accepted by the Göttingen group, shows that there is a quality of non-objectifiability involved in the knowing process.

In this regard, it is very important to respect the way the term "objective" is used in reference to scientific knowledge. In one sense one may talk about "objectivity" insofar as it is inter-subjective. Insofar as different people, i.e., different subjects following identical procedures in the experimental process, get recognizably identical results, science may be characterized as "objective." In this sense all accepted theory in science leads to "objective knowledge." Theories in fact are judged as valid or invalid on the basis of whether or not such inter-subjective agreement can be verified.

By contrast to classical Cartesian-Newtonian understanding, wherein any particular of nature is what it is in itself outside of any relationship whatever to the person (the subject) who observes it, takes cognizance of it and describes it, quantum physics includes the observer within the matrix of that which is being observed. A phenomenon is described in relationship to the way in which it has appeared to someone in a particular process of observation. The way nature appears under experimental conditions is inter-related with the way the experiment is set up. As a result any "description" of the "object" discerned in a particular experiment demands a description of the process by which the discernment was made. While it would be quite incorrect to say that the observing process produces the phenomenon, it would be equally wrong to speak of a particular phenomenon except as it was actually observed.[14]

If we transfer this aspect of epistemology to theology, we may say <u>for the moment</u> that the data of revelation is based on an inter-relationship of some person with God. Likewise, we can say that when the "revelational experience" is reiterated and/or recorded, the data of that experience must be accounted for in terms of the particulars of experience in which the data came into being.

A third possible parallel between the Copenhagen interpretation of quantum theory and theology is the recognition that our everyday language and logic is quite inadequate for the conception of that which we may attempt to understand. As Heisenberg has pointed out, quantum phenomena must be measured and described in terms of classical physics even though it is recognized that the terms of classical physics themselves are quite inadequate for the phenomena referred to.[15] The problem at this point, a problem that physics would seem to share with theology, is that our space-time conceptions are inadequate to the realities that we seek to know and talk about. Our language and logic may be the best we have, and that best must be respected, but we must admit that, as in quantum physics so in theology, a one-to-one relationship between statement and reality is not possible. An "isomorphic" relationship between concept and reality in which language is a proper match for the reality is quite beyond the faculties we have been given to apprehend or to refer to reality in any of its aspects.

That does not mean, however, that we may overstress Kantian subjectivity, wherein mind orders reality, and name any <u>particular</u> of reality as we desire simply because we somehow disagree with the way that particular has been referred to up to now. This is especially true if the terminological change is caused not by new evidence regarding the particular in question, but because it is thought that the manipulation of the referential apparatus will effect a modification of the reality of the referent itself or of our apprehension of it.

Here Weizsäcker's warning to the effect that our epistemology has more to do with the way we look at reality than the reality we look at, has relevance.[16] If John Wheeler's "Final Anthropic Principle" reflects valid insight into the nature of things, however, we may have to qualify Weizsäcker's stand with regard to our knowledge of the reality of <u>this world</u>. The principle would seem to attest to the "fact" that, although we do not create *ex nihilo*, we certainly modify creation by the way we attend to it and handle it. Tony Rothmann may have gone a little far when he entitled his article popularizing the anthropic principle, "A 'What You See is What You Beget' Theory," but we can hardly avoid taking cognizance of our active role in the modification of nature, that follows from the way we see it, interpret it, and attend to it.[17]

To put it quite simply, the Anthropic Principle, as most of you know, indicates that we are of the stuff of the stars. There is, therefore, a fundamental identity between star structure and our structure. We, the contemplative parts of nature, were made possible by the structure of nature from the beginning and the cosmos would not be complete without us and our observation of it. When we look at nature we look at that of which we are a part and that which is a part of us. Our observations and understanding of nature as well as our intervention in it is a part of nature's continuing dynamic existence.

It is at this point that the theory-laden aspect of all factuality and the reality-constrained aspect of all theory, that science in general and quantum physics in particular illustrate for us, come into play. It is true that all facts are theory-laden, hence what we know will to some extent depend on how we are prepared to know. It is definitely not true, however, that any theory will do. Theories used to explain reality must fall within the realm of possibility. Testing by the experimental process, as Heisenberg has pointed out, demands a correlation between the experimental apparatus and the matter being tested.

Experiment produces results when an irreversible transition from the possible to the factual takes place in the experimental process. The possible becomes the factual when a particular aspect of "the object" being measured takes on an interaction (*Wechselwirking*) with the measuring device that has been constructed according to a certain theory. That aspect of the "system under test," i.e., wave or particle in elementary particle experiments, is selected by the experimental apparatus if, and only if the experimental apparatus has been programmed in a way that is harmonious with at least one aspect of the "object" being measured.[18] Only if there is an affinity between the testing apparatus (that is inevitably set up according to some theory or other) and that which is being tested will the transition from the possible to the factual occur. This means that factuality rests upon possibility and possibility rests on the degree of the relationship of the theory of an object and the object itself.

Bohr's Theory of Complementarity is especially subject to misuse in this regard. It is easy indeed to use it to explain the necessity of "entities" one or both of which may simply be an illusion produced by false procedures. Only those aspects of reality are allowable under the theory that, although contradictory to one another, cannot be eliminated by the most rigorous of testing procedures. As that is true of natural science so, too, it is true of theological science. Theology, rightly understood, is also a science. It has a terminology, a body of knowledge, a method of interpretation, an authenticating community and a particular "object." In theology that "object" is God, who by nature always remains "subject." In relationship to him the whole of theology is qualified.

Bohr's use of the Theory of Complementarity to explain the relationship between the direct application of a concept and the analysis of its meaning is related to the way understanding takes place in both natural science and in theological science. The whole enterprise rests upon trust in tacit and therefore non-articulated concepts which form the foundation of the sciences in question. It is on the basis of these non-articulated concepts that knowledge can come about. They are fundamental to any meaningful conversation within or between the two sciences.

To return to Bohr, if for example one uses concepts of a systematically-constructed science, mathematics for instance, one has the option to define the concepts or to use them as undefined. Since the definition of a concept can only be done by reference to other undefined concepts and so on *ad infinitum*, eventually one is forced willy-nilly to use concepts that are undefined. To Bohr's mind and also the mind of Michael Polanyi by the way, meaning is only possible by utilizing concepts, the meaning of which is thought to be under-stood but which are not analyzed.[19]

The complementarity between the analyzation of concepts and their application means that, in understanding, our use of concepts is complementary to the fact that we do not analyze the concepts we use. We may well opt to define certain concepts. We do so, however, only when we no longer are assured that they are adequate to reveal the reality to which they point. We may use concepts or analyze them but we cannot do both. When we focus on the one, the other recedes into the background of consciousness. Our concepts always point beyond themselves to that which they do not and can not explain.[20] All final concepts are taken for granted. They are matters of faith.

I mentioned earlier that Howe was attracted to Barth's theology, because Barth had worked out such apparently contradictory characteristics of God's love and God's justice in a complementary way. Bohr's comparison of the particle-wave differentiation in quantum physics to the difference between that which is discrete and that which is continuous is a case in point. If we put this in spatial terms, it becomes obvious that one can chose only <u>between the two</u>, i.e., we may choose either discreteness or continuity. There is no third option. At the same time, while in any particular instance, one must select the one over the other, the one not selected is not obviated.

Weizsäcker illustrates the matter by referring to the pattern shown by hits on a photographic plate made by a stream of elementary particles: electrons, protons, photons, particles, etc. The pattern follows the probability distribution, as determined by the laws of the wave field, and as conditioned by the interference of the waves involved. Hence, both waves and particles must be considered parts of the process that causes the patterns even though the "wave picture" and "particle picture" are incompatible. In theology, in addition to the complementarities of love and justice that I have already mentioned, it may be legitimate to understand the seemingly contradictory concepts of gospel and law, election and freedom, grace and obedience, transcendence and immanence, etc., as complementary aspects of realities of faith.

The final point in this investigation in which we have designated some possible parallels between natural scientific thought and theological thought as based upon scripture is to ask: "How now do we speak of God in a quantum qualified world?" First, in that, according to biblical understanding, God is known in a faith relationship in which he is the subject (he reveals himself to us so that we may know him) our speaking of God depends upon his having given us the mind to apprehend him. Apprehension is a matter of faith seeking understanding (Anselm's *fides quaerens intellectum*). Second, although God may well adopt our concepts to reveal himself, concepts with reference to God are neither perfectly adequate nor perfectly clear. We trust that they are sufficient to transfer meaning to ourselves and to others whose apprehending apparatus is similar to ours and whose experience of God parallels ours. They are never perfectly adequate, however. They are, therefore, always subject to reform in the light of new evidence of that particular to which the concepts are intended to refer. Third, although God is in no sense to be categorized among objects, he is known analogously to the way knowledge is acquired about anything else that comes to us in experience.

Experience *per se* is not a category of knowledge, however. Rather, our experience is conditioned by our experiencing apparatus, i.e., mind that itself is informed by doctrine. Doctrine theory-loads mind and qualifies the impressions of God that the mind may be enabled to receive. In the "knowing process" there is an inter-subjective relationship between God and the believer that may eventuate in factuality if indeed the mind is doctrinally-loaded, consciously or unconsciously, in a way that corresponds to God in his revelation. This factuality, in turn, may be tested for its validity in relationship to the factuality gained by other believers who have experienced God in his revelation. Testing in theology therefore, like testing in science, is an inter-subjective process.

The believers who are qualified to perform the inter-subjective test, are members of a community of faith just because they confess to know God in recognizably similar ways. These ways of knowledge are productive of the factuality that correlates with the record of faith, the scriptures, the creeds, and the teaching that the group of believers in question hold in common and to which they confess. It is on the basis of that common confession that they are authenticated as members of the authenticating community.

A particular experience may be judged as authentic when, in the mind of the believing community, the experience appears to represent an interaction between the believer and God that resonates with what the community believes. Factuality occurs when the paradigms that are supplied by the milieu of the community and the milieu of the world in which the community lives resonates both with God who is the "obsubject" (object who remains subject) of faith and the teachings on the basis of which the community has articulated its faith up to now. If the factuality that has resulted in the experience with God appears to be new, but is so persuasive in its own right that it is accepted by the community as valid in spite of its "novelty," then the faith of the present and that of the past as well as the anticipation of the future will be qualified in accordance with that new factuality.[21]

In any report of the experience of God, God and those who experience him, like that which is measured and the measuring device in quantum physics, cannot be separated from one another. An accounting of the person involved and a description of the interaction that ensued between God and the one to whom God revealed himself in the experience is a necessary part of the report. Withal God remains subject, however. Statements about God, like faith itself, are useful in witnessing to God insofar as God himself chooses to use them as witness. Although he is the "object" of which we speak, he remains the "subject" not only of revelational experiences, but of effective speech about revelation as well. Communication about God, like experience of God, is a gift of grace.

NOTES

1.   Günter Howe, *Mensch und Physik*, Berlin, 1963, s. 56.
2.   Cf, Harold Nebelsick, "Karl Barth's Understanding of Science," *Theology Beyond Christendom*, John Thompson, ed., Allison Park, 1986.
3.   Karl Barth, *Church Dogmatics*, Edinburgh, Second Edition, 1975, I/1, 7 f.
4.   Karl Barth, *Evangelical Theology: An Introduction*, New York, 1963, pp. 6 ff. Italics added.
5.   Cf. Harold Nebelsick, *Theology and Science in Mutual Modification*, New York, 1981, pp. 63 ff.
6.   Immanuel Kant, *The Critique of Pure Reason*, Great Books of the Western World, Chicago, 1952, Vol. 42, p. 6.
7.   Immanuel Kant, *Prolegomena to Any Future Metaphysics*, London, 1889, p. 79.
8.   Ibid., p. 78.
9.   Nebelsick, *Theology and Science*, pp. 68 f.
10.   Günter Howe, Letter dated October 13, 1948 in *Die Christenheit im Atomzeitalter*, Stuttgart, 1970, s. 343.
11.   Günter Howe, *Gott und die Technik*, Hamburg, 1971, s. 23.

13.   C. F. von Weizsäcker, "Das Gesprach zwischen Glaube und Nasturwissenschaft in Historischem Aspect," Bossey bei Celigny, 1958, s. 19 ff

14.   Ibid.

15.   Cf. Werner Heisenberg, *Physik und Philosophie*, Gessamelte Werke, Munchen, 1984, s. 41f.

16.   Weizsäcker, loc. cit.

17.   Tony Rothmann, "A 'What you See is What You Beget' Theory," *Discover*, May 1987, pp. 90 ff.

18.   Heisenberg, *Physik und Philosophie*, s. 38 f.

19.   Cf. Michael Polanyi, *The Tacit Dimension*, Garden City, 1966.

20.   Weizsäcker, loc. cit.

21.   Cf. Thomas S. Kuhn, *The Structure of Scientific Revolutions*, Chicago, 1962.

Theological Implications of Physics and Cosmology

Robert John Russell

Associate Professor of Theology and Science
The Graduate Theological Union
Berkeley, CA

I. INTRODUCTION

Our conference represents a unique opportunity for the church to take contemporary science with radical seriousness. We are called to rethink and reaffirm our tradition in the context of revolutionary discoveries about the universe, the evolution of life and the nature and destiny of humankind. We cannot ignore science if we are to have any significant voice regarding today's staggering ethical challenges in technology, ecology and human need. We cannot ignore science if we are to make intelligible and compelling once again the story of a man and a cross and the eternal life that continues to be offered through that gift to an age in which miracles seem impossible, metaphysics seems meaningless, religion seems irrational, and science offers the sure path to knowledge. The task of theology is, at an event like ours, to serve the church in faithfully thinking through, without hesitation, everything which we affirm in the Sacraments, in liturgy, in Word, in prayer, and in deed. The promise is that our understanding of God's infinite mercy and work in the universe will be enriched a hundredfold, and our joy reborn on the wings of a cosmic vision and setting unparalleled in former times.

Of course, before attacking our task — the conceptual relation between theology and science — we should make a methodological decision, though we should not stop there as many do. I would not defend a natural theology, yet I must include nature in theology. But in doing such theology, is my method and motive kerygmatic or apologetic? Even this distinction, like other methodological issues, is difficult to make consistently. The Gospel cannot be preached if it is insulated from the language, questions and discoveries of our age. Yet if our explication becomes overly shaped by the conceptions and limitations of culture the challenge it brings is compromised. So are we to start with theology as somehow given, whether primarily by Scripture, Creed, or experience, and then work out a theological interpretation of science or an ethical response to technology? Or are we to start with culture and look for its implicit theological dimensions found in boundary experiences, metaphysical assumptions, matters of ultimate concern, or life choices?

Clearly these are perennial methodological problems. For my part I propose that, taking a cue from recent philosophy of science, our approach combine a hypothetical-deductive method with paradigm analysis.[1] Though we start with the Word of God we must somehow learn to think ecumenically rather than denominationally, to understand the truths of various traditions within Jewish, Christian and Islamic monotheism, to listen to other world religions in inter-religious dialogue — indeed to recognize the disclosures of God through any source including science — and then to form our own vision guided by God's Word, to grow where we are planted in this age and culture. I believe that the common role played by metaphor in both theological and scientific language, and a common approach of critical realism to the theories in science and theories (i.e., doctrines) in theology, are helpful to our work. Most importantly, I believe we must radically test and reformulate our theology in the open marketplace of scientific culture if dialogue is to proceed. (Though science too must be open to critique, such as from the sociology of knowledge, our task is to tend to our part of the bargain.) Let us listen and learn before we speak, and when speaking what we must, let us use the language to which we listen and from which we have learned.

Finally, I think it helpful to keep in mind that the term "theology and science" is really, and has always been (though it has not always been understood as) a generic designation for a variety of research agendas which, I believe, are slowly becoming disentangled. Ignoring the modes of conflict on the one hand, such as "creation science" or reductionistic scientific material-ism, or of divorce on the other, primarily the "two worlds" approach frequently advocated by theologians, scientists and their respective professional societies, one should distinguish among the following types of constructive projects: (1) epistemological and methodological parallels ("bridges") between theology and science, permitting concepts and claims to be related between the two fields; (2) theological research in light of science; (3) scientific research in light of theology; (4) synthetic work integrating theology and science. Most writers in "theology and science" are primarily interested in type (1) or (2); a few theologians and an even fewer number of scientists are aware of the creative possibilities of type (3); while type (4) is sparsely populated by scholars (though writers for the "general public" usually claim this as their prized goal!).

My present paper falls into type (2). In general, though, I am interested in all four types, and the possibility of type (3), i.e., of carrying on scientific research while keeping self-consciously aware of its implicit metaphysical and theological dimensions, and their potentially fruitful (indispensable?) role in science, is becoming increasingly attractive to me.

II. THEOLOGICAL QUESTIONS IN SCIENTIFIC PERSPECTIVE; BRIEF OVERVIEW

With these preliminary comments I would like to suggest several areas in which contemporary physics and cosmology bear upon Christian theology. Some of the details have been worked out in other papers; others are still in the research stage. The purpose of this section is to give a brief overview of where the work is headed. Hence, though a thorough list would be inordinately long, the following suggests some of the research topics warranted by a careful interaction between contemporary theology and science:

— How does the cosmic perspective of contemporary cosmology change our theological understanding of humanity: our nature and destiny in the universe? How will the discoveries of physics, cosmology, thermodynamics, and evolutionary biology and genetics affect our talk about humanity as created in God's image, about purpose, design, order, intelligibility, and meaning in the physical world?

— How does the origin of the universe in physical cosmology relate to the doctrine of creation, *ex nihilo*? How do the changing scientific and philosophical conceptions of space and time affect the doctrine of the Incarnation? How do we deal with the 'scandal of particularity' in a cosmological perspective? What is the cosmic significance to 'sin and salvation'?

— How does the pluralism of truth claims in the theory of relativity relate to cultural absolutism / relativism / nihilism?

— How do we interpret the divine attributes of infinity in light of the infinities in cosmology and quantum physics?

— Does field theory, as Maxwell and Einstein developed it, provide us with useful language for the doctrine of the Holy Spirit?

— How does divine purpose and will relate to chance and law in nature? In particular does the irreducibly statistical character of data on the microscopic level lead to a new physical ontology and, in turn, to a reformulation of our language about God's transcendence and immanence?

— Could the geometic interpretation of conservation laws (as in general relativity) suggest a deeper relation between creation, divine governance and providence?

— How do we conceive of the creation "of" time, rather than "in" time? What light does cosmology shed on our understanding of God's relation to time and eternity? How does the physical arrow of time, with all its ambiguities (viz. its role in astrophysics and classical and non-linear non-equilibrium thermodynamics, but certainly not in relativity or quantum theory), relate to subjective time, passage, and duration, and to the relation between God, temporality and history?

— In some grand unified theories, the 'origin' of the universe is viewed as a fluctuation in a quantum field of which the vacuum is the quiescent state; in other quantum cosmological scenarios there is no prior vacuum. How does the problem of the quantum vacuum in physical cosmology shed light on the concept of non-being and cosmic origination in doctrine of creation?

— Does the challenge to critical realism stemming from cosmology and quantum physics undermine a rationalist theological program, with its emphasis on God as knowable, nature as intelligibility, and the scientific character of theology?

— What is the meaning of (proleptic) eschatology in light of the far future (of at least one hundred billion years) portrayed by physical cosmology?

— Does the challenge implicit in relativity and quantum physics to modern epistemology (in both its Newtonian/Cartesian, Kantian and the Hegelian forms) signal the need for a theological break with the modern period? How does science relate to a post-modern theology?

Clearly this list only scratches the surface of the problem of "theology and science." In this paper I have chosen two questions drawn from the preceding list for a more detailed, but still summary, discussion. For more details see Robert John Russell, "Creation, Cosmology and Contingency" in *Cosmos and Creation* edited by Ted Peters.

III. DOCTRINE OF CREATION AND CONTEMPORARY COSMOLOGY[2]

The history of the doctrine of creation is a subject for extensive discussion in its own right. Suffice it to say, here, that in the Early Church, the meaning of divine creation was articulated in terms of two important models: *creatio ex nihilo* (creation out of nothing) and *creatio continua* (continuous creation). The former tends to language about contingency (specifically finitude) and purpose, the latter about novelty, hope and the future. Much of the original intent of these two models survives in contemporary Protestant and Roman Catholic literature, though with notable exceptions (such as in process theology, where *creatio ex nihilo* is dismissed). Moreover, a careful treatment of the doctrine of creation will lead to the Trinity, with particular emphasis on Christology and in turn to the doctrine of the Holy Spirit, theological anthropology, theodicy, etc.. Nevertheless many works in theology and science begin (and tend to end) with the doctrine of creation.

In this essay I will focus on one principal theme in creation theology: contingency, and ask how it relates to the contemporary cosmology (see Addendum A).

A. "t=0." Physical cosmology would at first sight seem to lend itself quite naturally to discussions about finitude and hence contingency. Before pursuing this, however, a digression seems in order. Most discussions of creation and cosmos pivot around a simple version of the claim that the universe is finite, namely that it began a finite time in the past, at "t=0." I.e., the meaning of finitude is usually given in terms of time, so that the logic seems to move from *ex nihilo* to contingency to finitude to creation of the universe "at the beginning."

Of course this raises a profound theological question in turn" how does the work of God the creator relate to time? In his *Confessions*, Augustine gave us a profound insight into this question when he argued that God did not create the universe in time, but rather that God created time as well as the world. With the rise of Copernican and Newtonian science, however, theological and scientific ideas about cosmological origins began to conflict. Even as the Enlightenment shift to historical inquiry challenged Biblical history and Enlightenment science challenged miracles, the absolute space and absolute time of Newtonian cosmology, though initially giving grounds for God's relation to the world (in terms of the divine sensorium) led through Kant to the abandonment of the physical interpretation of creation theology. Protestant theology since Kant has in general worked within the sphere of subjectivity or human history leaving nature to ("objective") science. What then of contingency, finitude, t=0?

In the theories of special and general relativity of Albert Einstein (1905, 1915), space and time are once again given a physical interpretation. Einstein's theory overcame Kant's claim that space and time are *a priori* synthetic; instead they merge into a four-dimensional continuum whose metric (distance) properties are determined by the cosmological distribution of mass and, in turn, determine the motion of the mass of the universe. Combined with the astronomical data by Edwin Hubble and others (1929), the recession of galaxies and hence the expansion of the universe was discovered: arguably the most profound discovery of contemporary science. Today this Big Bang theory has overcome all competitors (principally Fred Hoyle's steady state cosmology), although it raises profound questions of its own: What does it mean to think of a universe of finite age, some 10-15 billion years old? (This and other questions have led some scientists to construct alternative scenarios for the initial instants of the universe: the inflationary cosmologies.)

Some have argued for a strong tie — at last — between the doctrine of creation (as *ex nihilo*) and t=0. However we should be cautious: both theological and scientific theories are subject to change (and are changing...), and a strict identification can lead opponents to separate science from religion by appealing to alternative languages, domains of data, methods, etc. Anything that looks like natural theology, etc., tends others to drive a wedge between theologians and scientists before any fruitful dialog has really even begun.

Accordingly I suggest that we work at a higher level of abstraction, and that we work hypothetico-deductively between theological and scientific theories about creation and cosmos. Finitude in cosmology includes spatial finitude as well as temporal finitude about the future as well as the past of the universe. Moreover, finitude implies the question of infinity and these lead back to concepts both of contingency and necessity, the relative and the absolute. Hence our first task is to understand how finitude and infinity operate in physical cosmology.

B. Contingency as finitude: Is the universe finite? The idea of the origin of the universe at t=0 is only one aspect of the more general concept of finitude. In addition to its age we can ask if the universe is finite or infinite in size and whether it will go on forever or someday end.

Of course, we can only answer questions like these within one or another model of the universe. No data is sufficient to force us into univocal answers to its age, size, or future. Within the two options afforded by the standard Big Bang models, most scientists presently believe that the data indicates that the universe is marginally open, and believe that it is infinite in size and will expand forever, though many still hope it will turn out to be closed (finite in size and future) for theoretical reasons. This conclusion is based on estimates of the average density of clusters, estimates of dark matter, assuming that certain elementary particles, such as neutrinos, are massless, and other factors. If this is the case the universe is already infinite in size and will expand forever. If neutrinos are in fact massive, the universe would probably be closed. Clearly the issue is far from settled!

Yet from a spacetime perspective, the 'size' or 'finitude' of the universe becomes an even more intriguing and elusive concept since from a 4-dimensional perspective, space and time are really more like directions on a four-dimensional 'object.' From this perspective we can ask whether spacetime stretches in all 'directions' to infinity, or whether it has 'edges' along some directions or folds back smoothly onto itself like a sphere along others. Since the closed universe is spatially finite and since it has a finite past and a finite future, as a spacetime model it can be classified as homogeneous or strictly finite. Its spatial sections are smooth spheres, finite in size with no edges, but reaching back into the finite past or forward into the finite future we come to a singularity whose structure, at least in some mathematical representations, is like an edge. Hence its finitude is bought at a price: the essential singularity that poses the greatest crisis physics has ever faced, according to John Archibald Wheeler.

Strange as this may be, the open model raises an even more intriguing paradox about infinity. In this model the universe is spatially infinite and its future is infinite; yet like the closed model its past age is finite! Therefore as a spacetime model it is heterogeneous or mixed, displaying both finite and infinite characteristics!

Actually theoretical cosmology includes still other possible combinations of finitude and infinity if we modify Einstein's equations of general relativity to include the so-called "cosmological constant" lambda. This constant was originally introduced by Einstein because his initial calculations showed that even the simplest models of the universe were time dependent: expanding or contracting, features which he considered unacceptable. Later after the red-shift of distant galaxies was discovered, indicating that the universe actually was expanding, Einstein retracted the cosmological constant Recently, however, a number of theorists have argued for its re-inclusion because of technical problems with the very early universe.

If we include a non-zero value for the cosmological constant, seven theoretical models are permitted by general relativity, and they may be classified according to the kind of infinities they assign to the past, future, and size of the universe, as summarized in Table 1.

Here Type I (closed) and V (open) are the standard Big Bang models (with lambda equal to zero). Types II (the closed "hesitation universe"), III (a closed contracting universe, the time reversal of type II), and IV (the closed "turnaround universe" and, for a critical value of lambda, Einstein's original static model are extensions of the open model for non-zero lambda. Except for type I, all of these models are heterogeneous. Interestingly, though one can have a homogeneously finite model, no homogeneously infinite model, such as

Fred Hoyle's steady state model (represented here as type VIII) is possible in standard general relativity!

Table 1

TYPE	TIME		SPACE	LAMBDA	TOPOLOGY/ NAME
	Past	Future			
I	finite	finite	finite	0	closed (standard)
II	finite	INFINITE	finite	+	closed ("hesitation")
III	INFINITE	finite	finite	+	closed
IV	INFINITE	INFINITE	finite	+	closed ("turnaround")
V	finite	INFINITE	INFINITE	0, +	open (standard)
VI	INFINITE	finite	INFINITE	0, +	open
VII	finite	finite	INFINITE	-	open
VIII	INFINITE	INFINITE	INFINITE	----	open ("steady state")

Table 1. Eight types of cosmological models classified by their temporal and spatial infinities. Types I-VII are consistent with Einstein's general relativity (if we include a non-zero cosmological constant, lambda, in some cases; notably case IV, where Einstein first introduced it to give a static model universe). Type VIII, and a special case of Type V, represent the kind of homogeneous infinity found in Fred Hoyle's steady state cosmology.

The pedigree of these models is clear: they arose out of a dominant paradigm in twentieth-century physics. Their value for us lies in that they offer a set of mathematically self-consistent representations of finitude and infinity within the framework of a dominant scientific paradigm. Of course the radical differences they suggest about the kind of universe we live in could lead one to abandon the attempt to draw any theological conclusions from cosmology. Moreover, since most of these models have been rejected on empirical grounds (although not entirely, since the possibility of lambda being non-zero has once again emerged in cosmology), one could object that they are irrelevant to theology today.

However what is significant for our purposes is not the present empirical status of any particular model, since that will inevitably change. Instead the advantage of inspecting a set of recent, historical models lies in the lessons to be gained when we approach the much more complex question of working at our own present frontier. Here too there are several competing models, but in this case we do not have tomorrow's hindsight to help weed out weak candidates among our current competitors. Moreover the most relevant factor for theology may not, indeed should not, be linked to a precise characteristic of the model that prevails but on something more general that characterizes all those models in competition at one time. In my view, then, while we ought not expect a direct relation between t=0, temporal finitude, or any other individual feature in cosmology and theology, a concept such as contingency, operating at a more abstract level within science, can provide a common framework for relating creation theology and scientific cosmology. I believe such elements as contingency and necessity or finitude and infinity in Einsteinian models share something in consonance even as we move into the future and discover new cosmologies beyond our present horizon.

In this spirit I propose a working hypothesis, that the particular form of contingency in a given cosmological model both interprets and limits the theological claim that creation is contingent, and that elements of necessity which also occur in these models through the concept of infinity introduce an additional much-needed element of dissonance between scientific cosmology and creation theology.

We can test this hypothesis by a specific question: if finitude is a form of contingency how do the various types of cosmologies interpret the temporal and physical meaning of finitude and what sorts of trade-offs with infinity occur in these models?

Let's start with the notion of a finite past as the hypothetical correlate of the theological affirmation of finitude in creation, and see how far we should press this correlation. In a recent article, Ernan McMullin argued that although we can <u>not</u> claim that the Big Bang model supports the Christian doctrine of creation, "...what one <u>could</u> readily say, however, is that if the universe began in time through the act of a Creator, from our vantage point it would look something like the Big Bang that cosmologists are now talking about."[3] This is a very helpful move, neither tying a theological commitment directly to a scientific result (as in deistic and fundamentalist thought) nor severing their ties entirely (as in neo-orthodoxy, existentialist and liberal Protestant theology).

However, looking more closely at our cosmological models we find that there are <u>not one but four</u> different models which depict the <u>past as finite</u>: I, II, V, and VII. <u>As far as a finite past is concerned, these models are equivalent</u>: they would all "look something like the Big Bang that cosmologists are now talking about", to use McMullin's phrase. Yet the kind of <u>future</u> they depict includes both varieties: finite (I and VII) and infinite (II and V). Similarly their <u>spatial size</u> includes both varieties: finite (I, II) and infinite (V, VII). (They also vary in terms of the cosmological constant, lambda; in fact this is what accounts for their diversity.) Clearly then if we focus on a finite past, we cannot claim that scientific models describing a finite past will also necessarily describe a fully finite universe, since an infinite and an infinite size is compatible with a finite past in these models!

Figure 1.
Combinations of finite and infinite in Einsteinian cosmological models.

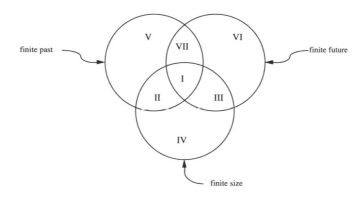

Figure 1. The circles in this graph represent the properties of finite past, finite future, and finite spatial size, respectively. Models lie in the areas which represent their finite properties. Hence Type I, being homogeneously finite, lies in the intersection of all three circles. Types II, III and VII are finite in two aspects; for example, Type VII is finite in both past and future and hence lies in the area common to both upper circles but excluded from the lower circle. Types V, VI and IV are finite in only one aspect.

Alternatively we might start with the requirement of a finite size as the correlate of theological finitude and hence contingency. Now we find a different set of appropriate models: I, II, III, and IV. Moreover in this case we couldn't be guaranteed of the finitude of time since some of these models involve temporal infinity (II, finite future; IV, finite past and future). Figure 1 summarizes these results.

C. Conclusions. What this analysis suggests is that we if we equate contingency with finitude, and thence to a finite past, we must acknowledge that the scientific models in consonance with this move also admit that the universe can be infinite in its future or size or both. Contemporary cosmology both interprets and limits our discussion of contingency as finitude. It admits either temporal or spatial interpretations of finitude but it limits them by showing that we cannot necessarily claim both temporal and spatial finitude. Of course there is a fully finite model, type I. However, if we identify our 'contingency as finitude' argument with type I uniquely, we run the perennial risk of tying theology to a particular physical model — the very outcome we were trying to avoid by abstracting to the level of contingency.

Hence if we want to avoid a direct linkage between a specific cosmology (such as type I) and a particular interpretation of theological terms we must allow for a degree of dissonance as well as consonance between theological and scientific claims. (e.g., that the universe is in some respects infinite as well as finite). So we must extend McMullin's suggestion and define consonance more carefully in terms of the following three alternatives:

    i)   consonance in terms of the past but dissonance regarding
          the future and size of the universe;
    ii)   consonance in terms of the future but dissonance over the
          past and size;
    iii) consonance in terms of the size but dissonance over the
          past and future.

One might be tempted to raise this sort of trade-off to a tentative epistemological principle: When comparing theological and scientific models of more abstract concepts, there will always be some agreement between some features of the theological and scientific models, but one cannot expect simultaneous agreement between all such features. The contradictions (dissonances) as well as agreements (consonances) are beneficial: without contradiction one would be open to reductionism or idolatry; of course without agreement one would be back in the very problem of fully compartmentalized language games and non-intersecting spheres of rationality that we set out to overcome. The method then is to find the appropriate balance between abstraction and concrete language so that, as we carefully tune our instruments, they ring with consonance and dissonance.

IV. QUANTUM PHYSICS,
THEOLOGICAL EPISTEMOLOGY AND
THE PROBLEM OF GOD'S ACTION IN THE WORLD.[4]

Quantum physics, as developed from 1900 to the late 1920's, has become a source of deep change within science. It is now an irreducible part of fundamental physics. In combination with special relativity, it is essential to the whole range of research at the frontiers of physics today, from high energy physics to superconductivity to astrophysics and cosmology. Yet quantum physics is still the subject of a variety of competing interpretations, making its theological appropriation difficult. Our task will first be to summarize these interpretations and then suggest how two of the most influential might be relevant to the work of contemporary theology.

A.   Survey of competing interpretations of quantum physics.

1. Background. Throughout this century the meaning of quantum physics has been debated by such physicists as Niels Bohr, Albert Einstein, Louis de Broglie, Max Planck, Max Born, Werner Heisenberg, David Bohm and many others. Here it is essential to distinguish between physical theory and its interpretation, since, while the theory is not directly in question, its interpretation is a continuing subject of discussion. Does the uncertainty principle, for example, imply that natural processes are intrinsically indeterministic? Or is it an epistemological problem arising out of the concurrent use of classical concepts like space, time and causality? Or does it represent an epistemological limitation due to the experimental basis of physical theory? Is it a prescription holding for all possible further physical theories, or is our present theory merely incomplete, leaving indeterminacy to be circumvented in some way? Do the terms used in modern physics refer to objective physical reality, or are they merely book-keeping devices for cataloging the results of experiment?

Each of these questions, and others as well, led to a different interpretation of quantum physics. For the purposes of discussion I will suggest grouping these interpretations into three categories, related to the measurement process, the process under observation, and quantum theory.[5]

Related to the measurement process of quantum properties:

i) In classical physics, dynamic properties such as position and momentum were thought to be inherent attributes (or primary qualities) of the systems being studied. According to Niels Bohr, however, these properties are not inherent to quantum systems. Instead they are relations between the systems and the measuring device; they belong to "the entire measurement situation." (Note, however, the measuring device is treated as a classical system.) Bohr frequently stressed the holistic aspect of quantum physics and the interconnection of observer and observed through the irreducible quantum of action exchanged in any measurement process.

ii) Among Bohr's followers, some argued that since we chose which properties to measure, the process of measurement in this (weaker) sense creates the properties involved (cf. iv). Moreover, since the logistics of instrumentation precludes simultaneous measurements of certain properties, such as position and momentum, it becomes physically meaningless to attribute both simultaneously to the quantum system or to ask whether they exist before measurement.

iii) Werner Heisenberg, at one point, suggested that the properties of quantum systems are real, but only as Aristotelian potentialities, until measurement actualized them.

iv) John von Neumann argued that the measurement problem can be resolved by appeal to human consciousness. Since even the macroscopic apparatus must in principle be understood quantum mechanically, only the conscious observer can actualize quantum properties and, in this (strong) sense according to von Neumann, consciousness creates the objective world.

Related to the process under observation:

v) During the early decades of quantum theory, Albert Einstein and others argued with the direction being taken by Bohr and Heisenberg. However, after the debates surrounding the paper by Einstein, Rosen and Podolsky in 1934, Einstein took a different approach. He agreed that quantum physics was correct as far as it goes, but that it was incomplete: there are causal factors which quantum physics does not include, and these factors are responsible for indeterminacy. In 1951, David Bohm published the first consistent theory based on such "hidden variables," presumably lying at the subnuclear level.

vi) Finally, according to the proposal of Everett, during each quantum process, all possible outcomes are realized by a bifurcation of the universe (quantum many worlds theory).

Related to quantum theory:

vii) Bohr also stressed the epistemological implications of quantum physics in what became the standard interpretation of quantum physics: his celebrated principle of complementarity. According to this principle it is no longer possible to admit the classical epistemological assumption that causal explanation is compatible with spacetime description. Bohr also stressed the need for alternative conceptual models, such as waves and particles, in every full account of quantum data.

viii) Others believe that the indeterminacy in predictions using quantum formalism arises from its basis in classical (two-valued, distributive) logic.

2. No difference in predictive power to date. To date none of these interpretations offers a direct experimental test which would 'prove' it and 'disprove' the others. Some interpretations, however, do suggest directions for research into more general theories which could conceivably replace existing quantum theory; yet to date none of these directions have been predictively advantageous. Local hidden variables, for example, have never been found even with current measurements at the quark level (where "local" means consistent with special relativity). Theories using alternative (multi-valued or non-distributive) logical systems are still at a speculative stage. New ontologies arising specifically from quantum research, such as Bohm has more recently suggested (in terms of an "implicate order") have not been developed into the type of broadly coherent philosophical systems which could be compared satisfactorily with classical metaphysics, nor have they led to predictive advances within science. Conversely, current, fully-developed "post-modern" metaphysical systems such as process philosophy, have not yet been fruitful in producing a new scientific theory with predictive power to rival standard quantum physics.

3. Changes since Bell's theorem (1964). In 1964 a theorem of profound consequences brought the discussion into much greater clarity and tightened the boundaries on any possible direction for research (please see Addendum B). As Nick Herbert writes in *Quantum Reality*, "What Bell's theorem does do for the quantum reality question is to clearly specify one of deep reality's necessary features: whatever reality may be, it must be non-local...No local reality can explain the type of world we live in."[6]

Given Bell's theorem and its empirical success in recent years, we know that though quantum phenomena (experimental data) as such are without exception local, the underlying processes which they manifest are non-local. This result poses a staggering conceptual problem for us, if we are to attempt anything more than a positivistic or, at most, instrumentalist interpretation of quantum physics. On the one hand we know that the data in my lab consists of random counts which I could never use to simultaneously 'signal' a colleague at a remote location. On the other hand we know that however we refer to the "material world" underlying and producing this data, its structure must be such as to exhibit the kind of correlations which Bell's theorem has underscored, correlations between data which in principle could be taken simultane-ously and at cosmic distances.[7]   What does this result mean for the interpretations of quantum physics previously advanced?

—   If Bohr's insight is right, that the "entire measurement situation" is involved in each quantum measurement, then the non-local feature of quantum physics implies that for correlated systems the results of a measurement on one part of the system in my lab could depend on measurements taken simultaneously light-years away on another part of the system. Moreover, if the properties we measure 'exist' in part through our choice of instrumentation, then they do so as well on the choice of instrumentation of distant col-leagues. Hence, as Herbert points out, even if properties are relational rather than intrinsic they are inter-relational on a cosmic scale.

—   One thing has been lucidly clarified by Bell's theorem: the local data remain equally random whether or not data is being taken at a remote distance. Correlations in remote data only arise through their subsequent comparison; no informa-tion can be gleaned from one set of data as to whether data is being taken elsewhere. Hence although few stress the role of human consciousness in the measurement process, there is no basis in Bell's theorem for an argument for telepathy or any direct mental influence on a distant observation.

—   Perhaps the most serious challenge from Bell's theorem comes to local realist versions of a hidden variables theory. We now know that, if there are causal factors which ulti-mately determine the outcome of individual measurements in my lab, these factors must be instantaneously connected with other factors occurring in my colleague's lab in such a way as to produce very specific type of correlations between our data. According to Bell's theorem these correlations rule out any classical interpretation of the alleged underlying causal factors. In short, the hidden variables cannot be (merely undetected) entities with classical (intrinsic and local) properties.

Hence it seems one must abandon local realism (classical ontology) in the form developed by Einstein and others (although not realism taken as a broader philosophical commitment to referentiality in science). Our ontological choice might be some form of non-local realism (via non-mechanical entities rather than classical particles and fields).

B.   Why not ignore quantum physics?

How might we bring the implications of quantum physics to the theological table? Too often, the response is to trivialize or ignore the problem at the outset by one of two strategies.

1.   "Only Microscopic." Some philosophers and theologians argue that we need not bother about these issues raised by quantum physics, since they only apply to the microscopic realm. I find this view curious. Certainly the minute value of Planck's constant limits the effects of many quantum phenomena. Nevertheless, from another angle, quantum physics is directly involved in all the 'ordinary' macroscopic phenomena we take for granted within the perspective of classical physics. To name just a few, quantum physics underlies such things as vision and color; taste; expansion of water as it freezes; the properties of chemicals; glowing embers in a cooling fireplace. Without quantum physics we wouldn't have such technologies as electricity (even Ohm's law!), computers, nuclear power, nuclear weapons, solar cells, superconducting magnets or communication satellites. On a cosmic scale, without quantum physics we wouldn't have life in this universe, or possibly even the universe!

It is particularly interesting to me that visual perception, without which classical science wouldn't function, depends on a quantum process: individual photons are produced by a quantum transition in atoms in the Sun or an ordinary light bulb, and a quantum process is involved in the firing of a receptor in the retina, leading to the experience of vision. One could even say that vision itself invokes the whole measurement problem discussed above!

Hence I cannot ignore quantum physics in constructing a worldview which is consistent with even ordinary empirical experience. To put it glibly, atoms may be small but they're simply everywhere — there's no getting around it! More seriously, it is hard to think of examples of phenomena studied by physical or biological scientists today where quantum physics does not play at least an indirect role.

2.   "Remain agnostic."   Others argue that we should wait for the interpretative controversies to be resolved before sorting out what implications quantum physics might have for other fields of thought. I disagree for several reasons:

It is a working assumption of my paper that, until we have a clear basis for choosing one interpretation over another, we cannot rule out any interpretative school *a priori* ; the lessons for theology from any of them may prove in the end to be enormously valuable, though at this point they may seem awkward or unbelievable. Indeed, the alternative of tacitly adopting one interpretation seems to me arbitrary and 'unscientific.' Moreover, the process of taking seriously each possible interpretation of quantum physics can be an instructive discipline for those who are quick to take sides in theology. We must all learn to live within and value diversity as a reality in itself, for it teaches modesty, patience and perspective. Ecumenism in any field, not just in religion, is a valuable exercise.

Secondly, research physics, like theology, always contains competing theories. If we wait for agreement we are limited to historical relics — in either field. Moreover we encounter all sorts of problems: when is agreement really reached? what about reversals after a theory was considered settled? what about the possible incommensurability between historical and contemporary worldviews generated by revolution in theories?

Third of all, the presence of competing interpretations does <u>not</u> mean we know nothing about the overall implications of quantum theory. We certainly know that nature displays an irreducibly statistical character in the data at the atomic level, that correlations between distant data from previously coupled systems are of a specific and striking nature and that the assumptions of classical epistemology have been radically challenged, including the simultaneous use of causal and spatio-temporal modes of analysis. We have reason to believe that either classical logic, classical epistemology, or classical metaphysics is inapplicable to quantum problems. And we know that these quantum problems are directly or indirectly a part of all supposedly classical phenomena and hence ordinary experience.

Finally, as I said at the outset of this paper, I believe that science has always played at least an implicit role in the formation of theological theories ("doctrines"), and perhaps vice versa. Therefore to assume that as theologians we can choose not to engage with scientists until their issues are settled is, in my opinion inconsistent: we already have. Rather than see theology and science as two separate conceptual fields which can interact in one way or another, I would prefer to view theology and science as pragmatic designations for two fields which in large measure already include the discoveries, visions, and commitments of one another, both intentionally and inadvertently, even in their classic sources.

C. Quantum nature in theological perspective.

Hence I would like to suggest two options for creatively relating quantum physics to theology: as an epistemological argument and as an ontological clue.

1.   Bohr and complementarity. In 1927 in an historic address to the International Congress of Physics at Lake Como, Niels Bohr proposed the principle of complementarity, which soon became the accepted school of thought for most physicists and philosophers. According to Bohr the "claim of causality" and its "space-time coordination" must be reinterpreted as "...complementary but exclusive features of the description, symbolizing the idealization of observation and definition respectively."[8]

Quantum physics thus represents a radical shift in epistemology, if one follows Bohr's interpretation. Not surprisingly, Bohr's views have been incorporated into a diverse spectrum of philosophical positions including subjectivism, neo-Kantian idealism and positivism. For our purposes, I will focus on the view most frequently advocated: that complementarity is based on the inevitable occurrence of contradictory models in physical theory. Hence, though quantum data display wavelike and particlelike features and though these features are manifestly contradictory, both must be included in a complete description of the data. Quantum complementarity is thus an epistemological limitation underscoring the role of paradox in scientific language.

How might this argument be relevant to theological epistemology? Ultimately we will have to think this problem through systematically by examining our doctrine of God, the problem of Christology, the relation of faith and works, and other theological issues for potential areas of epistemic complementarity. In my opinion key topics in contemporary theology include Karl Barth's profound analysis of the perfections of God; Paul Tillich's analysis of the categories of finite existence and the relation of personal and impersonal language about God; Dietrich Bonhoeffer's insistence on the dialectic of belief and obedience; and Hans Kung's discussion of the paradox of Resurrection, with his specific citing of quantum complementarity.[9] In historical theology an important topic is the logic of Patristic Christology, especially the Chalcedonian formulation with its duality of human and divine in hypostatic union.[10] Numerous others come to mind as well, including such topics as nature and grace, justification and sanctification, the Two Books (Scripture and nature), etc.

Can we generalize epistemological complementarity further? Some suggest that the relationship of various disciplines may be interpreted in terms of complementarity. Yet using complementarity either within theology or for the relationship between disciplines can be problematic. In his brilliant book, *Myths, Models and Paradigms*, Ian Barbour offers a very insightful analysis of these uses of complementarity and adds a word of caution which I endorse. He argues that the extension of the idea of complementarity beyond physics should be "analogical not inferential." Moreover, such extensions should be evaluated via the criteria of the new domain of usage, such as theology, where they must independently prove their fruitfulness. Barbour also insists that complementary models, such as wave and particle models in physics, must be of the same logical type and should refer to a common entity, such as electrons. It is on this basis that he criticizes arguments about Christological complementarity or proposals to view God and the world or science and religion as complementary. Barbour also urges that complementarity not "veto the search for unity" nor be seen to rule out a critical realist interpretation of theories, a view which I strongly support.[11]

One direction in which these goals could be pursued would be the move to an alternative interpretation of quantum physics, and it is to that of Heisenberg that I now turn.

2.   Heisenberg and ontological indeterminacy.   Werner Heisenberg and others have taken a different tactic. In their opinion, the statistical feature of quantum implies that nature is inherently indeterministic, that chance is an actual feature of atomic processes. Heisenberg adopted an Aristotelian interpretation of potentiality when analyzing quantum indeterminacy. By extending this approach, quantum physics can offer a preliminary sign of, and stand as a prerequisite for, the kind of openness, novelty and freedom which we see nature eventually producing in the biological and psychological domains.

It is this approach which Arthur Peacocke has, in my opinion, so fruitfully explored in his work on the doctrine of creation.[12] Rejecting both reductionist materialism and dualistic vitalism, Peacocke views the world in terms of emergence. God is involved "in, through and under" the evolution of the universe, creating new and emergent levels of organization through the open processes of this world, including quantum indeterminacy, irreversible thermodynamics and biological evolution. Against those who see chance in nature as either antithetical to divine purpose or as a reason for denying divine existence, Peacocke takes both chance and law as instruments of God's will. Recognizing that this view could seem deistic (although of a dice-playing rather than clock-making variety), Peacocke stresses the presence of God in the processes of the world (immanence) as well as the utter difference between God and the world (transcendence).

I agree with Peacock's important argument that the presence of disorder in nature need not be a compelling reason against Christian faith in God the Creator. Moreover I greatly value his insight that the new scientific picture, with its intimate relation of chance and law in thermodynamics and biology, can lead to a theological model for both God's participation in and transcendence over the whole of creation. Clearly these areas of science provide fertile ground for *creatio continua*, Irenaean theodicy, and a critical realist epistemology, as well as for *creatio ex nihilo*.

Yet the statistics of quantum physics are radically different from classical statistics, as Bell's theorem has so forcefully demonstrated. Quantum chance is simply not ignorance of hidden variables or random juxtapositions of causal streams. Especially for those like Peacocke and Barbour who adopt a realist philosophy, the difference between quantum and classical (thermodynamic and biological) chance is no longer avoidable.

Hence the non-local implications of quantum physics, however they are understood, seem particularly problematic. It is still possible that we can view God as working through 'law and chance,' and this option is certainly a more adequate approach than the traditional picture of God as a god of order opposed to chaos. Rather it is the kind of chance

God works through which poses a radical challenge to theology. We must ask how events which seem entirely random in isolation form a pattern, not just over time and in large numbers (as in classical statistics) but on an individual, one-to-one basis at 'simultaneous' (i.e., spacelike) cosmic separations, and then we must ask what this means for us theologically about God working "in, through and under" these processes.[13]

It seems that quantum physics, if taken to have ontological significance, will force us to rethink the whole question of God and with this the meaning of creation, christology, eschatology, and the rest. What would it mean, for example, to follow Karl Rahner and others in identifying the economic and the immanent Trinity in light of the theological complementarity of Trinitarian language? How shall we interpret the *creatio ex nihilo* tradition and its relation to *creatio continua* if we view the universe in terms of quantum correlations? Surely whether we start from 'within theology' and work outwards, or whether we allow our scientific perspective to suggest new theological insights (at least by analogy), the topic of quantum indeterminacy presents a fundamental challenge to us and a ripe area for theological research.

V. CLOSING COMMENTS

Given the complexities of relating quantum physics and cosmology to contemporary theology, it may be that what is needed here is something much more radical than a redesigning of the traditional fabric out of which our theological garments have been sewn. There are signs that contemporary philosophy is moving out of the modern period, which I take to be, roughly, from Descartes to Quine. Protestant theology has by and large worked intentionally within the debates over knowledge and language which have characterized this period, and we see similar questions being addressed in Roman Catholic thought especially since Vatican II. Realism itself can be seen as a modernist problem. What we might now be witnessing, both in physics and in philosophy, is an emerging post-modern climate of discussion. What will this mean for the theological task?[14]

However we answer this, the results will be worked out in the language of the universe which made/is making us and in the context of the sciences which bind us to her in knowledge and wonder. There is an enormous, and I would stress ecumenical, task lying before all of us who take Biblical faith seriously. One thing seems certain: many of the concepts appropriate to the 'reality' of whose 'intimations' we find in cosmology and quantum physics and of its Creator by whom we are grasped and redeemed through the Living Word will be vastly different from the traditional classical conceptions which have worked for so long.

NOTES

1.   By hypothetical-deductive I mean a continuous, iterative process of theory-inducing and testing in our theological method. We must correlate theology and culture while using our experience of the word as norm and guide (i.e., operating via *fides quaerens intellectum*).

2.   For more details see Robert John Russell, "Creation, Cosmology and Contingency" in *Cosmos and Creation* edited by Ted Peters.

3.   Ernan McMullin, "How should cosmology relate to theology?" in *The Sciences and Theology in the Twentieth Century*, ed. by A. R. Peacocke (Notre Dame: University of Notre Dame Press, 1981) p. 39-52.

4.   See "Quantum Physics in Philosophical and Theological Perspective" in *Physics and Theology*, edited by Robert John Russell, (to be published by the Vatican Observatory).

5.   Much of this presentation is drawn from the excellent books by Heinz Pagels, *The Quantum Code*, Toronto: Bantam Books, 1983, and Nick Herbert, *Quantum Reality*, New York: Anchor Press, 1985. I owe a particular debt to Ch. 10 in particular of the groundbreaking and outstanding textbook by Ian G. Barbour, *Issues in Science and Religion*, New York: Harper & Row, 1966. At a more technical level see Max Jammer, *The Philosophy of Quantum Mechanics*, New York: John Wiley & Sons, 1974.

6.   Herbert, *op. cit.*, p. 245. A "local" theory is a theory which forbids instantaneous action-at-a-distance (i.e. a theory which is consistent with special relativity).

7.   Again, though we knew this in a sense from the outset of quantum physics, Bell's theorem has forced the issue in a truly explosive way.

8.   Niels Bohr, "The Quantum Postulate and the Recent Development of Atomic Theory," *Atti del Congresso Internazionale dei Fisici, Como, 11-20 Settembre 1927*, (Zanichelli, Bologna, 1928, Vol. 2, pp. 565-588.)

9.   Küng, Hans, *On Being a Christian*, 974, translated by Edward Quinn, Garden City: Image Books (Doubleday & Company) 1984, p. 350.

10.   See Christopher Kaiser, "Complementarity and Christology," *Religious Studies*. Ian Barbour agrees in large measure, as do I but with more reservations, with William Austin's criticism of this type of argument as discussed below. See Barbour, Ian G. *Myths, Models and Paradigms*, New York: Harper & Row, 1974, Ch. 5.

11.   Barbour, Ian G., *op cit.*, 1966, pp. 292-294; Barbour, Ian G., *op. cit.*, 1974, pp. 77-78.

12.   Peacocke, A. R., *Creation and the World of Science*, Oxford:

Clarendon Press, 1979; and Peacocke, Arthur, *God and the New Biology*, San Francisco: Harper & Row, 1986.

13.   Perhaps Peacocke's imaginative language about God as composer would be a helpful metaphor here. We might imagine that we are each a single voice in a universal orchestration. The individual melodies of a single voice move at random, but the voices are correlated harmonically at each beat of the rhythm. Still this sort of image seems deistic to me, although the distant god evoked by it is more a jazz musician than a clock-maker.

14.   See the fine article by Jim Miller on post-modernism in this volume.

Addendum A

THE BIG BANG: A BRIEF LOOK

In his special theory of relativity (1905), Albert Einstein took the first step in establishing modern cosmology. In this theory, space and time are put on an equal footing, combined as a four-dimensional continuum called space-time. With the new arena of spacetime our intuitive notions of the simultaneity of events and of the lengths of objects are altered. Here space or time measurements alone, such as the size of a soaring rocket or the rate at which a moving watch ticks, lose their individual meaning, blending together in a deeper spacetime whole. Like the shadow of a rotating ruler, they seem to contract and expand — though the ruler does not.

Einstein's subsequent work, the general theory of relativity (c. 1915), is a theory of gravity. For Newton gravity was a force exerted between masses as they moved about in space. Einstein took a radically new approach. Whereas the spacetime geometry of special relativity was "flat" (or pseudo-Euclidean), in general relativity theory, space is allowed to curve. Instead of particles being forced into curved paths by the force of gravity as Newton suggested, Einstein depicts the natural motion of particles by the naturally bent paths of curved spacetime. What determines the curvature of spacetime? For this Einstein turned back to matter and created a 'closed circuit' between the two great ideals of natural order: form and content. In Einstein's view, the structure of spacetime, its size, shape, and texture, is dependent on the distribution of matter, while the motion of matter is determined by the local curvature of spacetime. In the phrase of Misner, Thorne, and Wheeler: "Space tells matter how to move; matter tells space how to curve."

Given general relativity, what sort of predictions could be made about the nature and history of the universe? Imagine trying to describe a universe of a trillion trillion stars with one or two simple equations — yet this was precisely what scientists did early in this century. They returned to the mathematics of Einstein's theory and explored two different models which could apply to the universe as a whole. Both of them are expanding in time from a singularity of zero size and infinite density at t=0 (where t is physical time). In the so-called "open" model, a saddle-shaped surface, <u>infinite</u> in size, expands forever, while in the "closed" model, a spherical-shaped surface, <u>finite</u> in size, expands up to a maximum radius, then re-contracts to the final singularity.

But these are just mathematical models. How can we relate them to the data astronomers give us? First off, we shouldn't miss the fact that even the visible portion of our universe is <u>enormous</u>: there are at least one hundred billion stars in our galaxy alone and easily a hundred billion such galaxies within the limits of present-day telescopes. Still, astronomical observations show that galaxies are grouped in the form of clusters, each containing on the average 100 million million stars, and that these clusters are distributed <u>evenly</u> through spacetime! Moreover in the 1920's, Edwin Hubble discovered that light from these galactic clusters is redshifted, and hence that these galactic clusters are <u>receding</u> from us and from each other. The expansion of the <u>universe</u> had been discovered.

This is a staggering fact! Modern cosmology depicts the universe as radically historical, evolving from an initial point 15-20 billion years ago. Moreover its expansion is slowing down. If the closed, finite model is correct, the slow-down will continue until the universe reaches a maximum size, after which contraction will begin until the universe is once again arbitrarily small some 50 - 100 billion years from now. If, however, the universe is open and infinite in size, as most evidence currently suggests, it will continue expanding forever, growing steadily colder and more dilute.

Addendum B

A NOTE ABOUT BELL'S THEOREM

Bell's theorem can be appreciated through the following thought experiment: An atom in an excited state decays, emitting two photons in opposite directions. I measure properties (like polarization) of one of the photons as it travels through my lab, while my friend measures similar properties of the other photon as it travels through her lab. These measurements are taken simultaneously to assure that no interaction could transpire between labs, influencing the results (i.e., the data are "local"). We repeat the experiment many times, using the same kind of excited atom, measuring the same kind of properties of photons.

The results are as follows: The data I took looks entirely random to me, as does the data my friend took. However, when we compare data, we find striking correlations between them. Moreover, the precise nature of these correlations lead to the following paradox: to explain some of our (apparently random) data we must assume the properties of certain pairs of photons were identical, yet to explain other sets of (equally random-appearing) data we must assume the properties were unrelated to each other. We can find no consistent way to assign properties to individual photons such that a correct account of all the correlations in data is given, yet the correlations are not random enough to suggest that all pairs of photons are intrinsically unrelated. It seems as though the measurements made in one lab influenced the measurements made in the other, but since the measurements were made simultaneously, this is impossible. How can we explain the data without recourse to a strictly positivist interpretation?

Theology and Biology

Benjamin A. Reist

Stuart Professor of Systematic Theology
San Francisco Theological Seminary
San Francisco, CA

Two disclaimers are in order at the outset of this discussion. It is as a systematic theologian, not as a biologist, or even a theologian/scientist, that I write. Moreover, such knowledge of biology that I can claim is entirely derived from the work of those for whom the two disciplines indicated in the title of this paper overlap.

Perhaps the word "disclaimer" is misleading. The fact is that everything going on in the context within which theological reflection unfolds is theologically significant. Such reflection is always listening to its world, as well as speaking to it. The context of theological inquiry has a normative significance for the inquiry itself. But note well, it has only a normative significance. The biblical word or words, and the tradition, confessionally oriented and liturgically ordered, also have normative roles to play. And these three components are intertwined in the hermeneutical complex that the continuing proclamation of the gospel of Jesus the Christ both presupposes and extends.

The contextual issues that are before us are theologically urgent. Limited or not we are reflecting on things that we know, and know that we know. To ignore or evade them is to deepen an irresponsibility that is present wherever the bearing of cosmological considerations on theological discourse concerning its primary subject matter, the doctrine of God, is set to one side. In this light I emphasize that the title of this paper is "Theology and Biology". I intend to reflect upon the intersection indicated in such a way that it will become clear that I dwell within it, and am increasingly persuaded that I am not alone.

As theologian I am struck by the fact that the beginnings of the emergence of post-modern science, that is, science on this side of Descartes and Newton, transcending while presupposing those decisive breakthroughs, began with Darwin, not with Einstein or Heisenberg. The advent of reflection on theories of evolution as irresistible and necessary antedates the breakthroughs concerning relativity and indeterminacy. In saying this I presuppose the quite obvious fact that we have moved far beyond the ground initially won by Darwin. By now there is a clear consensus on the basic contention, and I am instructed by Arthur Peacocke as to the best epitomization of this. It comes from the hand of "the French Nobel prize-winner Francois Jacob":

There are many generalizations in biology, but precious few theories. Among these, the theory of evolution is by far the most important, because it draws together from the most varied sources a mass of observations which would otherwise have remained isolated; it unites all the disciplines concerned with living beings; it establishes order among the extraordinary variety of organisms, and closely binds them to the rest of the earth; in short, it provides a causal explanation of the living world and its heterogeneity. The theory of evolution may be summed up essentially in two propositions. First, that all organisms, past, present or future, descend from one or several rare living systems which arose spontaneously. Second, that species are derived from one another by natural selection of the best procreators."[1]

Peacocke insists that a formulation such as Jacob's "is not in dispute among biologists" and he epitomizes this consensus with his own concise statement: "...all forms of life, current and extinct, are interconnected through evolutionary relationships" (Peacocke, 1986:35). The theological question this generates is not whether it is so, but whether the process to which it points is intentional. To respond in the affirmative is to discern the decisive issue before this present line of reflection: How, not whether, shall we confess the first article of the creed given what we know, and know that we know, about cosmology? That is to say, what does it mean to confess "I believe in God the Father Almighty, Maker of Heaven and Earth" now?

I have alluded to Darwin, but I shall not begin with him, for the tortuous conversation generated by his thought is both well known and well charted. Where I shall begin is with Pierre Teilhard de Chardin, and I shall move from there to Charles Birch, and then on to the figure I have just cited, Arthur Peacocke. This line is my own construction, and it does not exhaust the purview a discussion entitled "Theology and Biology" suggests. But it will focus the agenda such a spectrum of concerns generates, and it will disclose promising leads in the thought of those who wonder, from within the context of faith, about how these two disciplines interrelate.

Pierre Teilhard de Chardin

Teilhard de Chardin was not a biologist, he was a paleontologist. The range of his thought, however, was not confined to his specialty, it touched both biology and theology in a way that is decisive for the discussion I seek to develop.

As Teilhard worked out the extended range of his treatment of the human phenomenon, moving from the realm of beginnings yielding molecular aggregates to the human envisioning of the ultimate omega point he found that he could not evade or suppress wondering about what he called "the within of things." He was aware that he was shaped, as most of us still are, by the fact that "The apparent restriction of the phenomenon of consciousness to the higher forms of life has long served science as an excuse for eliminating it from its models of the universe." (Teilhard de Chardin, 1955:55) In the face of this he contended that "Things have their within; their reserve, one might say; and this appears in definite qualitative or quantitative connections with the developments that science recognizes in the cosmic energy." (54) This contention is one of the central elements in the dynamic of Teilhard's creative attempt to understand the human phenomenon within the context of cosmic reality as a whole.

We cannot reckon with Teilhard's fascination with "the within of things" without coming to terms with his idea of the suppression of the evolutionary peduncles. (Teilhard de Chardin, 1955:120) This recurrent phrase is to be found wherever he is attempting to account for the move from one strata of development to the next. It is strikingly similar to the vexatious question of the so-called missing link that plagued evolutionary thought until the marvelous breakthroughs of our own recent decades, but in the case of Teilhard's thought a daring suggestion could not be suppressed. This has to do with the contention that the emergence of the new is always marked by a fragility that will be eclipsed as the new develops. Here we must listen to him:

> Nothing is so delicate and fugitive by its very nature as a beginning. As long as a zoological group is young, its characters remain indeterminate, its structure precarious and its dimensions scant. It is composed of relatively few individual units, and these change rapidly. In space as in duration, the peduncle (or, which comes to the same thing, the bud) of a living branch corresponds to a minimum of differentiation, expansion and resistance. What, then, will be the effect of time on this area of weakness?

> Inevitably to destroy all vestiges of it.

> It is the same in every domain: when anything really new begins to germinate around us, we cannot distinguish it—for the very good reason that it could only be recognized in the light of what it is going to be....In biology, in civilization, in linguistics, as in all

things, time, like a draughtsman with an eraser, rubs out every weak
line in the drawing of life....Except for the fixed maxima, the
consolidated achievements, nothing, neither trace nor testimony,
subsists of what has gone before. (Teilhard de Chardin, 1955: 120-
121)

Since the new can only be recognized in what it is going to be, the
suppression of the evolutionary peduncles is automatic, in the sense that it is
inevitable with the passage of time. Accordingly we can only understand the
past in the light of what has come to pass as the result of the myriad
developments that have gone before. Here then we behold the humanistic
affirmation so central to Teilhard's reflections. We can no longer think of
humanity as the center of all things, but we must think of it as the clue to what
has been going on:

Man is not the centre of the universe as once we thought in our
simplicity, but something much more wonderful—the arrow pointing the way to the final unification of the world in terms of life. (223)

There are two dimensions to this astonishing formulation. First of all it
points toward the past, insisting that the past makes sense in the light of the
present. Quoting a memorable insight from Julian Huxley, Teilhard then adds
his own considered insight:

Man discovers that he is nothing else than evolution become
conscious of itself, to borrow Julian Huxley's concise expression.
It seems to me that our modern minds (because and inasmuch as
they are modern) will never find rest until they settle down to this
view. On this summit and on this summit alone are repose and
illumination waiting for us. (220)

If this is so humanity is not only caught up in the meaning of the present,
it is also the clue to the primordial depths from which it has sprung. The "arrow"
was launched in the infinite reaches of that beginning. Is it still going? Yes!
So Teilhard would argue. Whatever Huxley may have meant by his words, on
Teilhard's lips they become a doxology.

This points inexorably toward the second dimension of the issue at hand.
The humanity that is the clue to the past is indeed also the clue to the future. And
Teilhard cannot conceive of this in terms other than those evoked by his faith.
This is what he meant by speaking of an omega point yet to appear. The most
succinct expression of his real confession of faith is to be found in the brief
"Turmoil or Genesis?", an article written in 1947. Here he expresses four

theorems which will later receive their massive elaboration in *The Phenomenon of Man*:

    a.   Life is not an accident in the Material Universe, but the essence of the phenomenon.

    b.   Reflection (that is to say, Man) is not an incident in the biological world, but a higher form of Life.

    c.   In the human world the social phenomenon is not a superficial arrangement, but denotes an essential advance of Reflection.

To which may be added, from the Christian point of view:

    d.   The Christian phylum is not an accessory or divergent shoot in the human social organism, but constitutes the axis itself of socialisation. (Teilhard de Chardin, 1959: 214-215)

       I must go further than Teilhard de Chardin did, staggering though that assignment is! We all must. We know more about what he considered than he did. And at least some of us will wish to locate the explicitly theological dimension at a different point in the progression than he does, true as he is to his Thomistic training and purview. But however that may be our debt to his efforts defies calculation. If his interpretation of Huxley's insight carries, as it most certainly does for me, then is it the case the humanity is the way, or one of the ways, the universe thinks? Is humanity the way, or one of the ways, the cosmos prays? I must answer Yes to these questions, and then ponder what it means to do so. Theology in the tradition of Anselm and Barth, theology, that is, as faith seeking understanding, is always driven to efforts of this sort.

Charles Birch

       There is help on this task. Much of it focuses in the remarkable work of Charles Birch, just now retiring after his distinguished career as Challis Professor of Biology at the University of Sydney. Here our beginning point is on the biographical front, and happily we have Birch's own account of the decisive turning point, in an article published in 1975 under the title, "What Does God Do in the World?" This occurred in the midst of the deepening research demanded by his study of biology, the discipline to which he committed his life:

       Theology was initially more important to me than science. It gave me an interpretation of much that I valued most in my experience of growing up... It seemed to me that there was an eros, or reaching forth in life, which met a response from beyond myself. And when I stumbled upon that question asked last century at the height of the Darwinian controversy by T.H. Huxley "Is the universe friendly?" I knew that it was; God was pressing in on all sides blocked only by us. My theology drew solely from the personal. (Birch, 1975:78)

Crucial in this paragraph, simply because it is likely to be overlooked, is the word "solely." The problem Birch encountered, and he is surely not alone in this, had to do with the fact that his theology "drew solely from the personal." As we shall see this would prove to be as much a questioning of the prevailing use of the term "personal" as it was the discovery of the limits of a received theology. But the full force of this would dawn later, at the culmination of Birch's work to date. What was happening at the moment in question was the discovery that his theology no longer made sense:

I did not know [my theology] was false until science became part of my experience. My undergraduate science did not really affect my ideas at all. It was not until I became a research student in an active laboratory that I began to try and relate science to my concept of God, challenged as I was on every count by my laboratory colleagues. Whilst God as personal influence was as strong as ever, I had no intellectual defense for my beliefs at all, particularly my simplistic and orthodox view of God as creator. It threw no light, only confusion, on the scientific world-view that I was rapidly assimilating. My God had nothing to do in my new world of science. There was a breach between my experience of "God as redeemer" and my understanding of "God as creator." (Birch, 1974:79)

Why believe in a God who has nothing to do? That question is heavy enough. But it is tame when related to the question it inexorably generates: How can God do the work of redemption if this same God has nothing to do in the world in which redemption must occur?

Providentially, I would say, in the name of the God who does have something to do as both Creator and Redeemer, at just this moment Birch read Whitehead. And as he records it, at this same time, in 1946, he went to the University of Chicago to do research in zoology only to discover there "the richest collection of Whitehead scholars in the land." (Birch, 1975:79) This encounter would lead him to understand that "God participates in the world as it evolves," (83) but it would push him even further, astonishingly enough. It would lead him ultimately to the drastic claim that the human is the clue to nature itself, as well as the context within which alone faith in God as participant could heal the breech between God the Creator and God the Redeemer which his laboratory integrity relentlessly forced.

"Can Evolution be Accounted for Solely in Terms of Mechanical Causation?"—this is the title of an article Birch wrote in 1977, in which we can discern the key move in developing the claim that humanity is the clue to the natural as a whole. His point of departure is Whitehead's observation that "It is orthodox to hold that there is nothing in biology but what is physical mechanism under somewhat complex circumstances..." (Whitehead, 1925:102) In Birch's shorthand form, "...biology has an orthodoxy; it is mechanism based on physics." (Birch, 1977:13) Biology under the dominance of this idea cannot ponder evolution "in a comprehensive way" since it ignores the contention that "there is a qualitative side to evolution which escapes interpretation that is solely concerned with mechanical causes." (ibid.)

It would seem to be the case that this orthodox biology is the predomi nant view among the practitioners of the discipline, and that, given the astonishing advances in this discipline since Whitehead's day, the stranglehold of this orthodoxy is even more unrelenting. But Birch was not completely alone in his central concern, and the list of those who were concerned with the qualitative side of evolution included illustrious names indeed: Theodosius Dobzhansky, Sewall Wright, C.H. Waddington, B. Rensch, and W.H. Thorpe. (Birch, 1977:13)

The basic contention Birch advances can be simply stated. If humanity is the result of all that has gone before, humanity is not only dependent upon the prior process, it is also the clue to its dynamism. If humanity is epitomized by consciousness, then this capacity carries with it the irresistible hunch that what has yielded humanity had and has consciousness implicit within it. This is tantamount to insisting that the simplicity that generates complexity must be understood in the light of the resulting complexity itself. Birch's illustration is illuminating:

> Whitehead reversed the situation of the mechanist.... We do not start with knowing all about atoms and molecules and then seem to understand the phenomena of biology. It is from observed phenomena in biology that we have to start....It is from these we work back to construct models of similar entities....To use an example of Waddington...sodium chloride molecules exhibit properties which we cannot observe by studying sodium and chlorine atoms in isolation. When the compound sodium chloride is formed, it is not that something entirely new is added to sodium and chlorine atoms, but rather we know something more about the nature sodium and chlorine atoms than we did before. (Birch 1977:14)

The central contention is clear. Subsequent development always discloses what could never have been known concerning the components involved had the subsequent itself not have emerged. Birch is willing to take this contention to its inexorable conclusion:

> Similarly with the phenomena of life. When certain arrangements of atoms of carbon, nitrogen, hydrogen, oxygen and so on exhibit properties which we recognize by the name of enzymes, or other combinations are able to conduct electrical impulses as in nerve cells, *it is not that something new has been added to these atoms. We have discovered something about the nature of these atoms that we did not know before.* (Birch 1977:14, my italics)

We are now at the very nerve center of Birch's creativity and contribution. The insight before us has a momentum that drives beyond known frontiers with compelling cogency. If it is the case that the process indicated discloses something about the nature of the atoms in question that could not have been known before the process itself unfolds where then should the study of atoms themselves begin? With the functioning of the atoms directly involved in putting the question!

> We discover that when atoms are organized in particular ways they reveal aspects of their nature not revealed in isolation. Atoms and molecules organized in brains reveal the potentiality of atoms organized in particular ways to give rise to entities with subjective experience to which we give the name mind or consciousness. Atoms that can give rise to brains that think must be different from hypothetical atoms that could under no circumstances have done this. (Ibid.)

The case with Birch is similar to that with Teilhard de Chardin. The implication of his line of reflection is doubly valanced, suggesting both an incisive understanding of humanity's place in the vast sweep of evolution, and a yearning question concerning the ultimate question for theology, the doctrine of God.

The former of these turns on updating evolutionary theory, particularly significant for those who come to reflection on the concern of this paper, Theology and Biology, with little or no formal training in the latter of these disciplines, and it bears heavily on a remark noted above. We do indeed have before us the results of a crucial breakthrough that Teilhard did not have at his disposal. We know something about the DNA molecule.

There were three phases in the development of the theory of evolution by natural selection. The first was the bold outlines in Darwin's <u>On the Origin of Species</u> in 1859. The second had to wait until 1930 when quite independently three brilliant geneticists developed the genetical theory of natural selection. These were R.A. Fisher and J.B.S. Haldane in England and Sewall Wright in the USA. This phase was first highly theoretical. It came to earth in the studies of Theodosius Dobzhansky and his students on natural populations, especially of fruit flies. The third phase had its origin in the unraveling of the structure of the DNA molecule by Watson and Crick in 1953. This opened the door to the interpretation of mutation and selection in molecular terms. (Birch and Cobb, 1981:53) [2]

Teilhard himself was quite clear on the initial implication of the second of these developments. For him, as for Birch, the emergence of humanity is the emergence of a group, not an individual. (cf. Teilhard de Chardin, 1955:185) But he died in 1955, within two years of the breakthrough wrought by Watson and Crick, and thus he could not know that horizons only dimly seen would disclose remarkable corroborations and extensions of reflections such as his. It is the note of concreteness, as over against intuitive speculation, that marks the advance of Birch's insights beyond the frontier discerned by Teilhard. Building on the work of Dobzhansky, and then Waddington, he argues that we are beyond the impasse of "the hit and miss element of simple models of natural selection." (Birch and Cobb, 1981:55) For him Waddington's experiments with flies led to an astonishing conclusion:

> If there are genetic mechanisms that tend to fix these changes genetically then we have a much closer relationship between environment and genetic constitution than a simple reading of Darwinism would give. The theory becomes much more credible. Natural selection is not, as is so often stated, the selection of the genotype. It is not even the selection of the phenotype. It is the selection of the *developing phenotype*. (Ibid., 55-56, my italics)

In this light Birch makes common cause with Teilhard: "We cannot measure evolution by comparing one individual today with a forebear some-time back."(63) But he is able to go further, in two steps. First,

> The biological understanding of human history is that the decisive qualities that made the difference between the human and the pre-human did not appear first in one individual at a specific moment in history. No such moment and no such individual could have existed. A threshold had to be crossed. But it was no mere hop, step and jump but two or more million years wide. (62-63)

The second step brings into play Birch's own specialty, population ecology:

> ... a population made the journey. Mutation, recombination of genes and natural selection are phenomena that happen to populations The human gene pool does not belong to any one individual. It belongs to the total population of human beings alive at any one time.... What happens in evolution is not that the type suddenly changes but the mean of the population in many of its characters gradually moves. The species takes a trip.... Despite the incompleteness of the fossil record of human origins there is a continuum of transitions between early ape-like creatures, Australopithecines, Homo erectus and Homo sapiens. The 'missing link' is no longer missing.(63)

Thus we are tied even more securely with the emergence of life yielding us than Teilhard's intuitive insights suggest. Do we quite literally think for the universe, pray for the cosmos? Such questions stretch our linguistic and conceptual capacities. This is the real theological contribution of Birch's efforts. What does God do in the world? His answer is that "God participates in the world as it evolves..." (Birch, 1975:83) That he is building directly on Whitehead in saying this is obvious. But his own creativity informs his assertion. What is at stake is "a vision of the world in relation to God [that] is not provable. It stands or falls by its adequacy to account for and illuminate our experience. But it requires imagination to see it....For the scientist it is not a case of metaphors or no metaphors. It is a case of which metaphor." (Ibid.)

This imaginative task is one on which Birch is actively engaged. The most far-reaching of his own suggestions is the following:

> Some events have much more significance than others. This is not because God intervened in these events and not in others. To interpret significant events as special acts of God is to turn God into an agent of mechanical causation. It is to replace persuasive love by fiat, acting in accordance with some preordained plan. Significant events are significant because they happen to open up a new realm of possibility heretofore closed. The history of the Jews is rich in such events. The life of Jesus is such an event; it opened up for mankind new possibilities of compassionate understanding, creativity, and human brotherhood.

> But creation is not merely something which has already happened. It is not a doctrine about past events. It is a doctrine of the present. (Birch, 1975:84)

Just as a biological orthodoxy that adheres to the metaphor of mechanism must be challenged because of the facts of the case so a theological orthodoxy that can only speak of an <u>intervening</u> God must be questioned. Birch's theological suggestion is fascinating. From his point of view the longstanding emphasis upon the God who <u>intervenes</u> in the affairs of humanity makes the same error that biological orthodoxy does. Such metaphors now have a mechanistic ring that robs them of the power they once possessed. This suggestion merits prolonged consideration, but one thing is now beyond question. On this side of the rise of mechanism they have become profoundly misleading. A few years later, in the midst of a major address to which I shall return presently, Birch sharply focused the issue at hand:

> One might have expected Christian theology to resist the mechanistic interpretation of the world and all that is in it. On the contrary. Indeed, mechanism's most famous metaphor of the universe as a clockwork with God as the clockmaker was given it by a bishop, the Frenchman Nicole Oresme in the 14th century. Theology found it easy to accommodate itself to the mechanical conception of the world with the human being curiously detached from the rest of nature and with a clockwork God outside it as a <u>deus ex machina</u>. (Birch, 1979:260)

If humanity is indeed part of the evolutionary process in the manner Teilhard de Chardin and Charles Birch insist to be so then only a <u>participating</u> God can be heard within that same process. This is how that ultimate presence effects the persuasiveness of inexhaustible love. For only so can this presence <u>speak</u>. The <i>deus ex machina</i> is speechless.

Toward this metaphoric horizon theology is driven if the theologically informed biologists among the faithful are given the attention that is their due. A pronounced urgency attends the advent of this possibility, for it is not an option but a necessity if the issues are truly grasped. Birch gave one of the most significant of the addresses at the Conference on Faith, Science and the Future, held at M.I.T. in Cambridge, Massachusetts, in 1979 under the auspices of the World Council of Churches (indeed, he was one of the guiding spirits in the planning of this consultation). His address, entitled "Nature, Humanity and God in Ecological Perspective," explored eight theses. The final two of these are as follows:

> 7.   The new partnership of faith and science that is emerging acknowledges the unity of the creation, that is the oneness of nature, humanity and God. It takes seriously both the insights of science and the special characteristics of the human.

8.   This ecological view of nature, humanity and God implies a
life-ethic which embraces all life as well as all humanity in an
infinite responsibility to all life. This new ethic and the new vision
provides a foundation on which to build the ecologically sustainable and socially just global society. (Birch, 1980:62)

The summons to building the ecologically sustainable world is thus
equated with the struggle for a socially just global society. This is the urgent
yield of the theologically profound and genuinely incisive biologist, Charles
Birch. He is not the only such figure that insists on considering nature,
humanity and God together. Precisely this same passion informs the work of
Arthur Peacocke. As I turn to his insights, the final words of Birch's address
ring in my ears:

We have been warned as Noah was warned. Sceptics laughed and
ridiculed then as they do now....But this time the ark cannot be built
of wood and caulking. Its foundations will be a new awareness of
the meaning of life, of the life of all creatures, both great and
small...We do not have to be the victim of circumstances. In the
ecological view the future is not predetermined. It is radically open.
Through its openness to the lure of God the self becomes freed from
total preoccupation with itself. Its concern becomes the world.
That is still possible for each one of us. (Birch, 1980:72-73)

Arthur Peacocke

The issues that emerge from listening to Teilhard de Chardin and
Charles Birch are intensified when the work of Arthur Peacocke is taken fully
into account. His 1986 volume, *God and the New Biology*, carries further
reflections begun in earlier essays, and developed in his well known *Creation
and the World of Science*. Moreover his own specialty takes shape in the midst
of the very center of creativity in today's advances in the field of biology:

My own scientific work has been in the borderline between physical
chemistry, on the one hand, and biology and biochemistry, on the
other—on the structure of biological macro-molecules (e.g., DNA)
and genetic function. (Peacocke, 1986:1)

Peacocke speaks from within the realm of his own competence in
delineating the decisive controversy generated by the advent of molecular
biology, its seemingly inexorable gravitation towards reductionism:

In brief, and with reference to biology, the form of ontological reductionism, which asserts that the laws of physics and chemistry fully apply to all biological processes at the level of atoms and molecules, seems scarcely in dispute; but strong ontological reductionism, which, in asserting that biological organisms are 'nothing but' atoms and molecules, seems to be implying that a physico-chemical account of their atomic and molecular processes is all there is to be said, is widely regarded as inadequate, and is much disputed. (Peacocke, 1986:13)

At hand in this formulation is the position caricatured by one D.M. Mackay as "nothing-but-ery." (cf. Peacocke, 1986:6, 12) Clever though this is, it cannot easily counter the critical issue involved, namely, the issue of interpretation.

[The reductionist view] is often expressed ambiguously, for it is also concerned with explanation. This leads naturally to a consideration of the 'something more' that has to be said over and beyond purely physicochemical accounts of living organisms. (Peacocke, 1986:13)

Peacocke's 'something more' resonates with Teilhard's the 'within of things', and converges with all that is central in the concerns of Charles Birch. Like Birch he states his affinity with Dobzhansky. (cf. Peacocke, 1986:32-33) But he must go further than this, probably simply because he knows the world of molecular biology as a specialist. That is to say, 'holistic' though he is, Peacocke knows that the reductionists have a point that must be taken seriously. Of the many indications of this in his work, the most significant for this present discussion shows his understanding of why, and where, we must move beyond Teilhard de Chardin:

The need for clarity here is provoked by the proposal that there is a connection between 'complexity' and consciousness. This has been strongly urged and gained wide currency through the writings of Teilhard de Chardin who calls this his 'law of complexity-consciousness. This 'law' is certainly an impression, though an imprecise one (what kind of complexity is to be correlated with consciousness?), that is given by the broad sweep of evolution, but Teilhard's pan-psychic assumptions give grounds for doubting such a sweeping generalization. Until we can quantify 'complexity' better it is unwise to promote our impressions into a 'law' that can then tempt us into applying it to the, undoubted, complexity of intra- and inter-communicating societies. (Peacocke, 1986:52)

Peacocke knows how this needed quantification of Teilhard's complexity must be understood. This involves what has come to be known as the <u>central dogma</u> of molecular biology, and in citing this those who are not professionally involved in the study of biology need to know that the development of this theory ranks as one of the two major breakthroughs in biology in the postmodern era. In this connection Peacocke quotes G.S. Stent's observation: "I think it fair to say....that there have been two great theories in the history of biology that went more than a single step beyond the immediate interpretation of experimental results: these were organic evolution and the central dogma." (Peacocke, 1986:171) With this in mind we are ready for Peacocke's crucial formulation:

> The publication of the structure of DNA by Watson and Crick in 1953...led to a veritable explosion in 'molecular biology'....This phase...which lasted approximately until 1963, was dominated by the 'central dogma' of molecular genetics...that DNA replicates its unique sequence of units (nucleotides) autocatalytically by copying one of its two intertwined chains and also acts as a template for single RNA chains, which then control the synthesis and amino acid sequences of proteins. (Peacocke, 1986:58)

The theologically significant word in this formulation is the word "autocatalytically." Recall Peacocke's own specialty, the experimental study of "the structure of biological macromolecules (e.g., DNA) and genetic function." Ponder then what it means for a theologically adept biologist to wrestle with the <u>fact</u> that the creative process leading to the production of protein is <u>intrinsic</u> to the DNA structure itself, and that it functions <u>on its own</u>. That is, no external principle of explanation is needed to understand this process. To grasp this is to cross the threshold into the depth of what must already fire the imagination open to listening to Peacocke, having first heard Teilhard de Chardin and Birch:

> I have already presented the overwhelming evidence for the interconnectedness through time of all living organisms originating from one of or a few simple primeval forms. The 'gaps' in the scientific account of this evolution of the multiplicity of living forms that scientists yesterday thought they detected continue to have the habit of being closed by the work of scientists today—and those of today will, no doubt, share the same fate tomorrow. *The 'gaps' for any intervening god to be inserted go on diminishing.* For we see a world in process that is continuously capable, through its own inherent properties and natural character, of producing new living forms—matter is now seen to be self-organizing. (Peacocke, 1986: 53-54. My italics)

The gaps are really gone! We have been thinking this for some time, so much so that to bring the matter up now is deja vu in the extreme. But is it? The real impact of the new biology on theology has to do with the fact that the death of the God-of-the-gaps is even more undeniable than we had thought. The seemingly bizarre dream of the computer age that artificial intelligence can indeed be produced pales in comparison to the fact that we know, and know that we know, that molecular creativity is, in a profound sense, intrinsically automatic. Now the real frontier comes into view. With whom is Peacocke going to argue, having quantified Teilhard's deep hunch in terms now available? None other than the celebrated F.H.C. Crick himself, the master proponent of the reductionism Peacocke combats. At the very outset of *God and the New Biology* Peacocke sets out the decisive quote:

> Francis Crick ... has ... been quite explicit in affirming that 'the ultimate aim of the modern movement in biology is in fact to explain all biology in terms of physics and chemistry'. (Peacocke, 1986:1)

It would be a mistake to say that the truly polemical dimension of our effort is now unavoidably before us. This is true, and the issue would be even more clear if we stopped to deal with the fact that it is the sociobiologists who carry biological reductionism to its extreme conclusion. (cf. Peacocke, 1986: 108-115) But the polemical issue is superficial when compared with the deep point at hand. For us, this has to do with discerning the arena into which theological creativity is now irresistibly drawn.

> Does the triumph of molecular biology really imply the long-term demise of all 'holistic' approaches and the final victory for a reductionist interpretation of biology...?

> ... Certainly Crick thought so and prefaced his 1966 *Of Molecules and Man* with a quotation which, judging by the subsequent contents, as indeed by Crick's well-known attitudes, leaves us in no doubt that it is meant to be taken ironically. The quotation is from Salvador Dali: 'And now the announcement of Watson and Crick about DNA. This is for me the real proof of the existence of God.' The irony arises because Crick identifies belief in God with vitalism—the view that living organisms have some special added entity or force over and beyond non-living matter—for, as Crick saw it, molecular biology had triumphantly demonstrated the molecular basis of the most distinctive feature of living organisms, their ability to reproduce, and thereby rendered all such proposals of vitalism null and void. (Peacocke, 1986: 59-60)

How does a theologically adept holistic biologist, one who gives reductionism its due without selling out to it, deal with the specifically theological issue now before us? Watch carefully what Peacocke immediately goes on to say:

> This equation of vitalism with theism is, I think, simply false, though understandable because Christian apologists have unfortunately had, and still do have, a tendency to attempt to insert 'God' into the gaps of biological explanation. (Peacocke, 1986:60)

This formulation epitomizes the theological yield of Peacocke's work. Two steps are needed to see this:

1) Peacocke is as holistic in his theological thinking as he is in his biological research. This is the root of his rejection of the de facto equation in Crick's reflections. Vitalism does not equal theism for Peacocke because vitalism does not exhaust the understanding of ultimacy. For him the name for ultimacy is not vitality but God. The basic reason that this is the case for Peacocke manifests his affinity with the thought of the celebrated Anglican prelate, William Temple—nature, humanity, and God must be understood together. At a key moment in his discussion Peacocke focuses his rejection of reductionism with a striking claim:

> ... the physics and chemistry in terms of which living systems are being interpreted is 'physics' and 'chemistry' so profoundly modified by the incorporation of characteristically biological concepts that it is as much a question of whether physics and chemistry have been taken into biology as whether biology has been 'reduced' to physics and chemistry. (Peacocke, 1986:27)

Since this is so can the process of expansion be arrested until ultimacy itself is encountered? Peacocke is sure that it cannot since for him "'reality' is...what the various levels of description and examination actually refer to." (28) And since this is the case ultimacy itself inexorably comes into view.

> We can, I would argue, go further. I refer to that most complex and all-embracing of the levels in the hierarchies of 'systems' namely the complex of nature-man-and-God. For when human beings are exercising themselves in their God-directed and worshipping activities they are operating at a level in the hierarchy of complexity which is more intricate and cross-related than any of those that arise in the natural and social sciences which are in the province of the humanities. For in his 'religious', i.e., God-related, activities man

utilises every facet of his total being....For religion is about the
ultimate meaning that a person finds in his or her relation to all-that-
is. (Peacocke, 1986:30)

Now note carefully just how holistic this formulation is. There is not a
trace of the God-of-the-gaps here. No intrusions of ultimacy are necessary. For
ultimacy is the term that denotes the human involvement in "all-that-is". It is
thus already within the context of human reflection. Moreover, this involvement in the all-that-is is liturgically and confessionally ordered. It is not a
matter of intellectual speculation. It may not be reduced to an equation of any
sort. Vitalism does not equal theism, because "God" is neither the result of a
syllogism nor the minuscule particle at the end of a reduction. God is the
focusing term for this sense of ultimacy; theology is reflection upon this.

'Religion is a relation to the ultimate' and that ultimate is usually
denoted, in English by the word 'God'....Theology is concerned
with the conceptual and theoretical articulation of the processes and
characteristics of this subtle unity-in-diversity and diversity-in-
unity which we call 'religion'. It therefore refers to the most
integrated level or dimension we know in the hierarchy of relation."
(Peacocke, 1986:30)

2)   Theology, as Peacocke understands it, has to do with reflection on
the ultimacy present within the context that has evoked human existence. Its
subject matter, that is, transcends that which is immanent within the created
realm. Here there is a necessary progression in thought, since to move the other
direction, from transcendence to immanence, inexorably falls into the trap of
at least sounding like a god-of-the-gaps maneuver. Informing this way of
understanding the task of theology there is an important judgment regarding the
recent history of reflection on theology and biology. As has already been noted,
Peacocke has been strongly influenced by the work of William Temple.
Temple is a key figure (he mentions others, notably, F.R. Tennant, L.S.
Thornton, and Charles Raven [cf. Peacocke, 1986:84]) in what Peacocke calls
the "'immanentist' tradition of Christian theology in Britain." Peacocke
observes that the strength of this tradition "may help to explain why the ideas
of Teilhard de Chardin and of Whiteheadian 'process theology' have been
generally less significant for an indigenous tradition that was already integrating science and religion, but not under the sway of one dominating metaphysic." (Peacocke, 1986:84-85) The same cannot be said for the situation in
the United States, where far more attention has been paid to Whitehead, at least,
if not to Teilhard as well.

What has just surfaced may well prove to indicate a curious limitation
to the theological incisiveness of Peacocke's reflections on God and the new

biology (though elaboration of this will take us beyond pondering just Peacocke's conclusions). This is at least ironic, given Peacocke's own high estimate of Temple's great *Nature, Man and God*. (Temple, 1935) A case can be made that William Temple was the first major theologian to respond to the thought of Alfred North Whitehead. That he did so without being confined within Whitehead's metaphysic can be demonstrated. In this light Peacocke's theological insights would have been even more incisive had he followed into the depths the reasoning of Temple, and thus pondered the necessity of thinking theologically in process modes of thought. What Peacocke himself demonstrates is far beyond the horizons of Temple's massive undertaking. Given what is going on in the new biology we have no option but to cast theological reflection in process modes.

Conclusion

Just as it was necessary to begin this discussion with a disclaimer so it is important to preface its conclusion with a significant alert. As I see it, there are five parameters that will be discernible in all serious theological reflection on this side of the rise of the new biology. These are vectors which will shape the conversation from this point forward. More than this present discussion, though, is necessary for the full cogency and scope of these implications to be reckoned with at depth. Theology has more to do than listen to the context. It must also address, continually, the biblical witness in which it is rooted, and the confessional tradition by which it is nourished and to which it must make its own additions. To be sure, all of these vectors have been in operation in the thought of each of the figures before us, since each of them have been or are full fledged participants in theological labors of the first magnitude. Even so, the following five formulations will demand more than this discussion for their full force to be brought into play. Given this, we may proceed.

1)   *Creatio ex nihilo* is out and *creatio continua* is in—in fact, *creatio continua* is the only option for those who would confess the first article of the creed on this side of the emergence of the new biology. The central affirmation of the *creatio ex nihilo* (the phrase itself has been around since the intertestamental period (cf. Brunner, 1949:11), and it has informed Christian conviction clear up to our own century) is not simply "creation out of nothing" but "creation once-and-for-all." To be sure the idea that creation occurs initially "out of nothing" may be find a new currency with the advent of the "big bang" theory of the origin of the universe. But it is instructive that throughout the tradition the opposite of "creation out of nothing" has not been "creation out of something" but "continuing creation."

The prevailing consensus regarding evolution is non-negotiable among serious biologists today. We know this, and know that we know it. Intrinsic to this consensus is the assumption that the evolutionary process continues. The sole sense, then in which we may confess "I believe in God the Father Almighty, Creator of Heaven and Earth" affirms that the creative process itself is still underway. Never ever again will we be able to deny this. The question for theology, then, is simply this: How do we understand our confessional conviction that the God of Jesus of Nazareth confessed to be the Christ is still creating all that is becoming?

2)   Theological inquiry on this side of the rise of the new biology will invariably move from immanence to transcendence. Only so will it avoid landing in the cul-de-sac of sounding as though it serves the *deus ex machina*. This may well prove to be one of the most evident and decisive characteristics of theology as it now must move, and the forcefulness of it will be particularly severe on the present generations working at the tasks of theology. All of us have been shaped in the conviction that the good news of the gospel is that the radically transcending God is in fact in our midst. This is good news indeed, but it not only looms up as the only possible conclusion, it now becomes a liability. For the proponents of such a view now sound more and more like the deists of a by-gone day!

Theology in touch with the new biology must take up that task of unmasking the crypto-deism rampant in the churches. This is one of the most basic reasons informing the alert sounded at the outset of this concluding section of the present discussion. If the only tools for this unmasking are drawn from listening to theologically alert biologists the effort will be smashed by those who will claim that the proponents of new points of departure have simply sold out to the newest fad. All too often the systematic theologians have left the scientists sharing the faith alone in facing this charge. This must not happen now.

The full armament of the entire theological arsenal must be brought into play now. I, for one, have no trouble in asserting that I am thoroughly Barthian and Anselmian in taking the position I am now affirming. I did not get my faith in the Creator from either a metaphysical syllogism or a laboratory experiment. I got it from the confessing church. But I have come to understand that faith seeking understanding today must listen long and hard to the faithful who have struggled for metaphysical clarity and/or disciplined experiment. Our collective task now is to find out what it means to say that the immanent ultimacy in our midst, whom we have been taught to name Yahweh, the God and Father of our Lord Jesus Christ, is indeed the transcending ultimacy that is creating even now.

3)   How is this immanent transcendence to be understood? One thing is clear. We now know how it is <u>not</u> to be understood. Interventionist metaphors may have spoken in the past, even in the very recent past that has spawned the theological curiosity of most of those now at work on these issues. But they speak no longer. The *deus ex machina* is mute. A voiceless ultimacy probably does not hear. This is the negative side of the powerfully positive point that follows, but before proceeding to that elaboration there is a crucial qualification of the point at hand.

What I am calling "interventionist metaphors," following out the logic of observations already before us from Birch's reflections, are not to be confused with the dimension of <u>confrontation</u> that is so central to the Biblical witness as a whole. One of the truly abiding themes of the Bible is the intertwining of the judgment of God with the mercy of God. This is so central that it will never lose cogency. Remove the dimension of judgment and the Biblical witness as a whole will be misunderstood simply because the dimension of mercy will be sentimentalized. The redeeming love of God has nothing to do with sentimentality. Neither the Law nor the Prophets of the Old Testament can be understood this way, and the justification by faith through grace of which Saul-become-Paul spoke cost the cross and the risk of affirming the resurrection. So God's confrontation of the creature remains.

The problem is that we have become so accustomed to blending this note of confrontation with the assumption of the intervention of divine power into the affairs of humanity and the working of the cosmos that we cannot have the one without the other. It is this that yields the deistic overtone to our understanding of God, and it is this that cannot abide the scrutiny of those whose theology willingly reckons with the insights of those of the faithful whose dedication to biology has yielded knowledge that cannot be denied. The confrontation of humanity unfolds at the hand of the God who is in the midst of the context within which humanity struggles to believe. This God is on the same side of an unfolding future that we are.

4)   Nature, humanity, and God must be understood together. Temple was right, even more profoundly than he could have known. On this side of Teilhard de Chardin, Birch, and Peacocke there is no question about whether this is so. There is only the inexhaustible question as to what it means, for the meaning at hand refuses any final formulation.

The problem of the right metaphor, of which we have heard Birch speak, is far more complicated than it may seem. Is there a *theologia crucis* to be reckoned with in the realm where theology and biology overlap? May we rest content with reflecting on variations on Teilhard de Chardin's fourth theorem, and thus say that the decisive issue is that of the <u>fulfillment</u> of the evolutionary process of which humanity is intrinsically a part? Does an affirmative answer to the first question dispense with Teilhard's eloquent vision? Questions such as these will intensify when the spectre of genetics engineering is added to the capacities of a humanity that can perpetrate the holocaust of the Nazi era. And with that intensification will resound new affirmations of the ancient credo, by faith alone shall we be saved. But how shall this be said now?

5) Theology on this side of the rise of the new biology will find itself inexorably drawn to expressing its central concerns in process modes of thought.

Here I must immediately indicate that this is not a new case for so-called process theology. Process theology is explicitly and rigidly a philosophical theology. It insists on moving within metaphysical systems rooted in Whitehead and developed by Charles Hartshorne. That it has had, and will continue to have, much to say on the issues being addressed here is both obvious and to be welcomed. But however that may be, process theology and theology in process modes of thought are not one and the same thing. Here I am completely in accord with a pivotal remark made by Ian Barbour in his extremely significant 1974 volume, *Myths, Models and Paradigms*:

> ... the theologian should be cautious about identifying religious beliefs with any closed metaphysical system.... The theologian must adapt, not adopt, a metaphysics; many of the process insights can be accepted without accepting the total Whiteheadian scheme (Barbour, 1974:170)

Only a theology open to this kind of appropriation or adaptation of Whiteheadian language will be able to do justice to Charles Birch's haunting question. What does God do in the world? God participates in the very evolutionary process the creativity of ultimacy has yielded and in the midst of which it operates—even now. What we must now understand is that we are summoned to respond to this immanent creativity with a creativity of our own. Can we do this apart from the presence that summons us? I doubt it. More than that simple doubt, though, is my continuing awareness of the fact that our own creativities, powerful though they are, are self-contradictory apart from the infinite transcendence of a creativity that is redemptive. To be involved in the involvement of God in what God is making is to discover that the theology of the cross and resurrection is even more far-reaching than we have yet known. We become as we become because God becomes as God becomes. Only so can our own living spirits confess faith in the living God. So to confess, though, is to know that in the deepest sense God is at risk too in the cosmos of which we are a part. And in seeking to understand this we will encounter, in new ways, an ancient insight. Easter is the answer of the God who was present though silent in Gethsemane, at the cost of the cross. Faith, then, has to do with involvement in the involving ultimacy we recognize as Yahweh, the God who raised Jesus the Christ from the dead, and who summons us into a future still shaping for ultimacy as well as for ourselves.

NOTES

1. Peacocke indicates the source of this citation to be F. Jacob, *The Logic of Living Systems* (Allen Lane, London, 1974), p. 13. (Peacocke, 1986: 33, and 167, n. 2)

2. This passage is from a remarkable volume that is the result of collaboration between Charles Birch and the process theologian, John B. Cobb, Jr. Birch is responsible for the biological side of the discussion, though the text as a whole is the result of scrutiny by both authors.

WORKS CITED

Barbour, Ian G., 1974. *Myths, Models and Paradigms: A Comparative Study in Science and Religion*, New York, Evanston, San Francisco, London: Harper & Row, Publishers, 1974.

Birch, Charles, 1975, "What Does God Do in the World? *"Union Seminary Quarterly Review*, Vol. xxx, No. 2-4, Winter-Summer, 1975, pp. 76-84.

Birch, Charles, 1977, "Can Evolution be Accounted for Solely in Terms of Mechanical Causation?" in *Mind and Nature*: edited by John B. Cobb, Jr. and David Ray Griffin, Washington, D.C.: University Press of America, 1977.

Birch, Charles, 1979, "Nature, God and Humanity in Ecological Perspective" *Christianity & Crisis*, Vol. 39, No. 16 (October 29, 1979), 259-266. "This article is abridged slightly from a paper presented at the World Council of Churches conference on Faith, Science and the Future," held at the Massachusetts Institute of Technology on July 12-24. Copyright (c) 1979 by the World Council of Churches, Geneva, Switzerland." (259).

Birch, Charles, 1980, "Nature, Humanity and God in Ecological Perspective", in *Faith and Science in an Unjust World: Report of the World Council of Churches' Conference on Faith, Science and the Future*, Massachusetts Institute of Technology, Cambridge, USA, 12-24, 1979, Volume 1: Plenary Presentations, ed. by Roger L. Shinn, Philadelphia: Fortress Press, 1980.

Birch, Charles, and Cobb, John B., Jr., 1981, *The Liberation of Life: From the Cell to the Community*, Cambridge: Cambridge University Press.

Brunner, Emil, 1949, *The Christian Doctrine of Creation and Redemption*, (Dogmatics: Vol. II), tr. by Olive Wyon, Philadelphia: Westminster Press, 1952 (Preface to German original dated August 1949)

Peacocke, Arthur, 1986, *God and the New Biology*, San Francisco: Harper & Row, Publishers, 1986

Teilhard de Chardin, Pierre, 1955, *The Phenomenon of Man*, tr. by Bernard Wall, with an introduction by Julian Huxley, London: Wm. Collins Sons & Co., Ltd., and New York: Harper & Row, Publishers, Inc., 1959; (Harper Torch Book Edition, 1961) Title of French original: Le Phenomene Humain.

Teilhard de Chardin, Pierre, 1959, "Turmoil or Genesis?": The position of Man in Nature and the Significance of Human Socialisation (dated 20 December 1947), in *The Future of Man*, tr. by Norman Denny; New York and Evanston: Harper & Row, Publishers, 1964

Temple, William, Archbishop of York, 1935, *Nature, Man and God* (Gifford Lectures, University of Glasgow, 1932-33 and 1933-34) London: Macmillan & Co., Ltd., 1935.

Whitehead, Alfred North, 1925, *Science and the Modern World*, New York, The Free Press, A Division of Macmillan Publishing Co., Inc., 1967 (originally published in 1925, by The Macmillan Company) The Lowell Lectures, 1925.

Consultation Summation*

Ian Barbour

Carleton College
Northfield, MN

This has been a rich and varied consultation which would be impossible to summarize briefly. I will ask only about the relation between science and religion which seems to be assumed by each of the speakers we have heard. I hope I can point to some general patterns without oversimplifying what are subtle and complex issues. I have drawn up a framework to look at four ways of relating science and religion, with two variants of each (see Table I).

Table I

Ways of Relating Science and Religion

I. **Conflict**
    1. Scientific Materialism
    2. Biblical Literalism

II. **Independence**
    1. Contrasting Methods
    2. Differing Languages

III. **Dialogue**
    1. Boundary Questions
    2. Methodological Parallels

IV. **Integration**
    1. Doctrinal Reformulation
    2. Systematic Synthesis

The Dialogue alternative deals with methodology and it can be combined with either Independence or Integration. There seems to be a common ground among many of the speakers concerning Dialogue. We did not reach

*This presentation was a response to the addresses and discussion during the consultation to this point, ratrher than a paper prepared in advance. In editing the tape recording of my comments, I have kept the informal style of the spoken version. The outline I used and the concluding section have since been developed in my forthcoming Gifford Lectures, *Religion in an Age of Science* (Harper & Row, 1990), Chapters 1 and 8.

a consensus in this consultation, but I think that even the defenders of Independence were sometimes looking for at least limited areas of Dialogue.

I. CONFLICT

It may at first seem strange to put scientific materialism and biblical literalism together. In many ways they are at opposite poles of the theological spectrum. But they do share a number of common features. They both claim that there is a conflict between certain areas of science and certain theological ideas. Each is to some extent a reaction to the other, as Langdon Gilkey pointed out. They also both seek a sure foundation for knowledge — that of empirical data in the one case, that of infallible scripture in the other. They both claim a culture-free knowledge, without any cultural relativism in their interpretive categories. Finally, they both look on religious statements as literal statements about the world which might conflict with scientific ones.

1.   Scientific Materialism

I take scientific materialism to involve two assertions: first, in terms of method, the scientific method is the only reliable path to knowledge; and second, in terms of metaphysics, matter (or matter and energy) is the fundamental reality in the universe. Langdon Gilkey did a beautiful job of analyzing some of the components of scientific materialism. He talked about naive realism among many scientists. I would say that physicists tend to be more positivistic. Physicists often see quantum theory as merely a calculating device for making predictions. I've seen that among some of the scientists this week. Astronomers and biologists may tend to be naive realists because what they're studying seems to be really there. I would want to work out a middle position here, a critical realism which holds that theories are in some way a reflection of the world, but never totally so. Theories are always selective, they are always partial.

The other component of scientific materialism to which Gilkey pointed was reductionism, and that has come up a number of times in our discussions. This is the tendency to look at the lowest level as the most fundamental, reducing all things to physics. He pointed out this tendency in several prominent cosmologists. Another form of materialism is scientism, the assumption that science is the only reliable path to knowledge. Gilkey mentioned Carl Sagan as an example. The *Cosmos* TV program was a wonderful popularization of astronomy. However, about ten percent of each program was Sagan's atheistic philosophy and his attacks on religion, in which he stepped out of his role as scientist to present a form of naturalism. Here he was sitting at the console, the new high priest showing us the mysteries but also telling us how we should live. I have a lot of sympathy with Sagan's ethical convictions about war and ecological disaster, but I don't think we can totally rely on science to be the source of our ethical concern.

We did not have a living example of this viewpoint in our consultation. Eric Chaisson at some points seemed to be adopting a kind of evolutionary naturalism. But it wasn't reductionistic. He talked about the emergence of genuinely new higher levels, from matter to life to intelligence. Although in the first part of his paper he did rely exclusively on science, when it came to a global ethics for the sake of survival he recognized that he was going beyond science. I would want to include other goals besides survival in a global ethic; what about justice, what about freedom, as other goals along with survival? When Chaisson came to his conclusion, he favored an amalgam of science, philosophy and religion. The common element he found in all three fields was evolution, which seems to draw more from the scientific side than the religious. I wasn't clear just what religion contributed to the amalgam. At any rate, I don't think he quite fits into the materialist position, and certainly his ethical concerns are of great interest to all of us, and he felt that they transcended science.

2.   Biblical Literalism

Phillip Spieth indicated some of the problems which biblical literalism has presented to the scientific community. We should note that the revival of the creationist debate in the last 20 years has had a new element. It isn't just a rehash of the Scopes trial, because the new approach is to claim that there is scientific evidence for creation, not just biblical evidence. This is the grounds for passing laws requiring that it should be taught in science classes in the schools. Most scientists find this very dubious. There are a lot of things I could point to that make it clear that the motivations of the movement are not really scientific (for example, creationists have not submitted papers to scientific journals, but one has to accept scriptural inerrancy to belong to the Creation Research Society). I think the creationists have raised some valid objections to the evolutionary naturalism which often gets promoted as if it were part of science. But I think they err in assuming that evolutionary theory is inherently atheistic, and thereby creationists perpetuate the false dilemma of having to choose between science and religion.

The whole controversy also reflects the fragmented character of education. Clergy are very seldom willing to take on issues that seem controversial; they don't feel well enough prepared. Many clergy and scientists have not thought much about alternatives apart from naturalism and biblicism. Perhaps we could encourage the Presbyterian-related colleges and seminaries to help their students see that there are other alternatives. This should be included in the education of clergy. When did you last hear a sermon dealing with science?

II. INDEPENDENCE

The second major option is Independence. A way to avoid conflict is to put science and religion in totally water-tight compartments. They can't interact creatively, of course, but they can't conflict if they are in autonomous and independent spheres. Each has its own distinctive domain and its characteristic methods, which can be justified in its own terms. There are two jurisdictions, and each party must keep off the other's turf. Each must attend to its own business, and avoid meddling with the other. Such a position would obviously have avoided the Galileo conflict and the creationist conflict. Each area of inquiry is selective and has its limitations. This separation is motivated by the desire not only to avoid conflict but also to be faithful to the true nature of each field — so that the distinctive character of its life and thought may be preserved.

1.   Contrasting Methods

One example would be the neo-orthodoxy of Karl Barth. We heard about his refusal to meet with scientists in Germany. He really didn't have much interest in science. According to Barth, God can only be known as revealed in Christ and acknowledged in faith — the wholly Other, unknowable except as self-disclosed. For Barth, natural theology is very suspect. Religious faith depends entirely on divine initiative, and not on human discovery of the kind which occurs in science and in natural theology. Theology and science have very different methods. The sphere of God's action is history, not nature, so scientists are completely free to carry out their work without interference from theology. Their subject matters are totally dissimilar. There is a clear contrast here: on the one hand, human observation and reason; on the other, divine revelation.

In this view, you take the Bible seriously but not literally. It is the fallible human record of events that are revelatory. The locus of revelation is not the book, not the dictation of the words; the locus is events in the history of Israel and the life of Christ — events which are later recorded and interpreted in the continuing community. There are diverse interpretations of these events, and we have to acknowledge the human and cultural limitations of our understanding.

We heard this kind of distinction in Douglas Knight's paper, which suggested that we can distinguish the theological content of Genesis from its particular cosmology. In the last part of his paper, he said that it is primarily the assessments of the cosmos from which we can learn today. The world is good and orderly and purposeful, that is the central message. There is a late apocalyptic view that the world is divided and conflicted, but the dominant biblical idea is that the world is good and orderly. This assertion is independent of both ancient cosmology and modern cosmology.

The second major movement that has insisted on a separation of independent spheres is existentialism. Here there is a strong contrast between the subjective involvement that religion requires and the detached objectivity typical of the scientist. Rudolph Bultmann is an exponent of this position. Now Langdon Gilkey in his testimony at the Arkansas creationist trial, as well as in some of his earlier writings, made this kind of separation. At the trial, a strategy emphasizing Independence was a good response to the creationist attempt to dictate the content of science classes in the schools. He said that the doctrine of creation is not a literal statement about the history of nature, but a symbolic assertion that the world is good and orderly and dependent on God in every moment of time. He held that this is a religious assertion essentially independent of both pre-scientific biblical cosmology and modern scientific cosmology.

Now after the trial Gilkey added chapters to his book, *Creationism on Trial*, in which he pointed to dialogue about boundary questions: the ultimacy of the commitment to truth in science, and the presupposition of orderliness that lies behind the scientific enterprise. In other writings and in his talk here he has raised similar questions. So I suggest that Gilkey really belongs in the third group, about which I will speak in a moment. But he also has at times stressed the Independence of science and religion. Perhaps we could say that he combines the second and third options.

Some of the scientists in our consultation have strongly defended the Independence view. There was a very interesting exchange last night between Harold Nebelsick and Jim Maher. Again this morning Jim urged us not to intermingle science and religion. Don't tie theology too closely to the science of any one generation. Bob Griffiths also urged us not to look for theological insights in quantum physics; physicists disagree, and new theories may develop. Both of these scientists accept the limitations of science. Perhaps it is also significant that both of them come from religious traditions that have a very strong view of revelation, tradition and authority: in the one case, the Catholic Church, and in the other, a scripturally-based Reformed Protestantism. So they don't see much need for the reformulation of theology. For them, science and religion can be separated because theology does not need to draw on anything outside of the revealed truth.

Nebelsick also has a strong doctrine of revelation, but for him revelation is always interpreted within changing categories of human thought. Previous interpretations reflect cultural assumptions which may have to be rethought. I think the question of how one understands revelation may encourage or discourage the idea of scientific and theological autonomy. Tom Torrance's

early writing put a strong stress on Independence. In some of Nebelsick's ideas
I detect a slight echo of the early Torrance, who said that science and theology
have totally different subject matters or objects of inquiry. Torrance himself
has moved from stressing this contrast to a greater concern for boundary
questions. In his recent writing, for example, he says that contingency and
order are characteristics of the world which are revealed by both science and
theology. And Nebelsick mentioned some areas of fruitful dialogue about
methodology.

2.   Differing Languages

Jim Miller referred to Wittgenstein and the language analysts, who talk
about the diverse functions of language and the differences among "language
games." Although Jim valiantly tried to include Wittgenstein and Whitehead
in the same post-modern outlook — and they do have some themes in common
— he recognized that Wittgenstein didn't have much use for metaphysics while
Whitehead did. The language analysts describe the differing functions of
religious and scientific language. Science asks carefully delimited questions
in order to predict and control natural phenomena. Religious language, by
contrast, is used to recommend a way of life, to elicit attitudes, and to encourage
allegiance to ethical principles. It is often tied to the rituals and practices of the
worshipping community. It may also express and encourage personal religious
experience.

I think we have a lot to learn from the people who analyze religious
language. We have a tendency to look only at religious beliefs, as if creeds and
doctrines were the center of religion. We need to be reminded of the importance
of other aspects of the life of the religious community, and these are related to
what religion does in our lives. Religion is a way of life, and the aim of religion
is the transformation of the person. Central in Christian life is the liberation
from guilt by forgiveness, the overcoming of anxiety by trust, the transition
from brokenness to wholeness.

Creation stories are concerned about the significance of human life, not
the description of events in the distant past. Where do we fit into the cosmic
scheme? This is the central point of creation stories in all cultures. In our
recommendations we might also say something about the value of liturgies that
have to do with nature. John Turpin's opening worship and Dan Little's
morning service were an important part of this week. We don't often use hymns
that relate to nature, or liturgies that celebrate the natural world.

Again, religion has to do with ethics. For many people in our congregations it is technology and applied science, even more than pure science,
which impacts daily life. This afternoon we will be looking at technology, and

that's where the action is for many people. So some sense of the totality of the religious life is crucial. The religious community is our context — not the theologian reflecting by himself. As Ben Reist said, the theologian always works within the life of the community. We can then acknowledge the diverse functions of religious language — functions very different from those of scientific language.

There is a lot to be said for the Independence school. Science and theology are indeed selective, and each has its limitations. Every discipline abstracts from the totality of experience the features in which it is interested. This position is a good first approximation, and it avoids the dangers of the Conflict views. Religion does have its characteristic methods, questions, attitudes, functions and experiences, and they are different from those of science. But I see some serious difficulties. The Independence option tends to make the sphere of nature religiously insignificant.

For Barth, as Ben was just saying, nature is the unredeemed setting for redemption. Barth does have a doctrine of creation, but he is much more focussed on the doctrine of redemption, and nature is really secondary. Nature participates in the eschatological fulfilment, but it's not religiously important now.

Existentialism also leaves out the natural order. It strongly contrasts the sphere of personal existence with the impersonal sphere of nature. If science deals only with nature, and religion deals only with self and God, who can say anything about the relation between God and nature? It's not surprising that existentialists tend to adopt a mechanistic view of nature. Moreover, they have had little to say about the exploitation of the earth in a day when ecological devastation is so widespread. They do not provide a strong theology of nature. They portray a sharp contrast between nature and history. But nature is historical, and history is embedded in nature.

Nor can we live with two totally unrelated languages. If God is the Lord of our lives and of the whole universe, we can't separate out an isolated religious sphere. We experience life in its wholeness and its interdependence, so I don't think "Independence" can be the last word. It is significant that many people who earlier adopted this view have moved towards seeing interrelation-ships. Most of those in this consultation who talked about Independence ended up by saying that we don't want a total dualism or absolutely water-tight compartments.

III. DIALOGUE

1.   Boundary Questions

Consider first the dialogue which can occur about boundary questions. Historians have argued that the doctrine of creation made an important contribution to the rise of modern science. The Greeks had a strong conviction that the universe has a rational structure. But their reasoning was mainly deductive, starting from first principles. Mathematics and geometry were well developed, but there was not much interest in observation. The Christian view also saw the world as orderly, but it said that the world's order is contingent; it didn't have to be the way it is. The only way to find out about it is to observe it. This combination of order and contingency provided a setting in which the flower of modern science could grow. It didn't blossom in the Middle Ages, but the roots were there. A lot of other forces were involved, including the Renaissance rebellion against Medieval structures. But it is significant that modern science arose only in the West. Where it has grown in the East, it has been mainly as a transplant. Yes, there was some good Chinese science. Arab science was pretty well developed, but that was also within a monotheistic context. Modern scientific development occurred primarily in the West with its heritage from Greek and biblical thought.

Let me turn now to contemporary authors. Tom Torrance has done a lot with this theme of contingency and intelligibility as presuppositions of science, and he has developed it very nicely. It has been strong in the Roman Catholic tradition. Karl Rahner, for example, talks about the infinite horizon and the conditions which make knowledge possible. David Tracy focuses on boundary situations, and argues that the intelligibility of the world requires an ultimate rational ground. Gilkey said quite a bit about the presuppositions of science — not explicit presuppositions, but the assumptions that are required concerning the order of the universe and the uniformity of nature.

I think that the Big Bang does raise limit questions. They go beyond any particular theory. As Jim Maher was saying, some of the limit questions would be there even if the Big Bang theory is disproved. We would still ask: Why is there something rather than nothing? I don't believe this question is adequately answered by the vacuum fluctuation theory which Joe Silk presented, because one still has to ask: Where do the physical laws come from? Where does the vacuum and the spacetime framework come from? Why the laws of physics? Why is there something rather than nothing? The theory does provide answers on one level, but not to all the questions one can go on to raise. These are not questions that occur within the content of theology, or the content of science, but have to do with limit questions, boundaries, and presuppositions.

2. Methodological Parallels

Discussion of methodology is another kind of Dialogue that is not yet about questions of content. In my own writing, I have given some attention to the role of metaphors, models, and paradigms in scientific thought — and comparable features of religious thought. The theory-laden character of scientific data, to which Nebelsick was referring to last night, is developed in Thomas Kuhn's writing. In a similar way, conceptual frameworks in religion influence our interpretation of experience. Jim Miller talked about new work in the philosophy of science, including that of Kuhn, Stephen Toulmin, and Michael Polanyi. Langdon Gilkey referred to all three writers. In contrast to positivist empiricism, these new views emphasize the role of the community. They examine the ways in which conceptual structures influence what we select as data. All of our thinking has been shown to be paradigm-dependent.

Some theologians have picked this up and have talked about paradigm shifts in theology, as in Nebelsick's paper last night. Nebelsick at this point has a real dialogue going with science that I greatly respect. He emphasizes that this dialogue is methodological and not ontological. It's not dealing with the content of science. Like Bob Russell this morning, he pointed to the complementarity of wave and particle models in physics, and the impossibility of having one unified model, though we have a unified mathematical structure that gives probabilistic predictions. Considering the concept of complementarity, one can see parallels in the two fields.

Nebelsick talked last night about personal involvement in both fields, as compared to the detachment often assumed to be characteristic of science. He spoke of the involvement of the observer in the process of observation. Here I agree with Jim Maher's interpretation: in quantum physics, we are not talking about the involvement of the subject as a conscious mind, but rather about the ways in which the observing process always interacts with the observed system. In the Einstein-Podolsky-Rosen experiment, you have to write the wave equation in such a way that it includes reference to the experimental apparatus as well as to both the particles, even though they are far apart.

For me, the lesson is one of holism and inter-connectedness. You can't deal with a part isolated from the whole. The message is inter-connectedness rather than the pervasiveness of mind. We heard reference to John Wheeler's view that it is conscious mind that has to intervene in nature before there can be an observation. But Maher replied that we could have an automatic recording device and not look at it until next year.

We have had some discussion of Polanyi with his emphasis on personal judgment and the role of community in knowledge. He tried to fit subjectivity and objectivity together by saying that all claims to knowledge are made with universal intent and with a reliance on the community of scientists; science is personal but not private. The same thing can be said about religion. It's personal but not private. The role of the community is being recognized by people in both the philosophy of science and the philosophy of religion, and this is another topic of fruitful dialogue.

IV. INTEGRATION

1. Doctrinal Reformulation

Let me turn to the last of the options, Integration. There are various ways that you could seek Integration. As Bob Russell was saying this morning, you could look for metaphors by which suggestive ideas in science may help you express the ideas you already have in theology. That would be an apologetic use of science in theology. But I think most people in this room, including Bob, want to go beyond that.

You might want to go in the direction of natural theology. I didn't hear a lot of support for that. Some people have tried to use the Anthropic Principle as a new kind of natural theology. They are impressed by all those amazing coincidences in the fine-tuned constants in early cosmic history. I think Joe Silk answered correctly that many of these apparent coincidences, producing conditions which were just right for life, will turn out to be requirements of a more basic theory. But I would say that the more basic theory itself is pretty amazing if it comes out with all these conditions just right for human life. I think there can be grounds for a kind of reformulated argument from design. I'm not so much interested in that myself. I think those of us in the "Integration" school are seeking, not a natural theology, but a theology of nature derived from two relatively independent sources which nevertheless overlap at certain points.

We don't derive our religious ideas mainly from science. Our religious ideas come mainly from the traditions in which we are nourished. But there are certain crucial points where science and theology overlap. The doctrine of creation, the doctrine of providence, and the doctrine of human nature are areas where there is overlap and there is something to be learned from science. A theology of nature, then, would not be based primarily on science.

But if religious beliefs are to be in harmony with scientific knowledge, there may be some adjustments or modifications needed in theology. We may have to change our formulations, particularly concerning God's relation to the world. Now I would say, agreeing with Jim Maher, that we have to be careful not to use too detailed a theory that may be changing next week or next month or next year. But at least certain broad characteristics of nature are relevant. We can accept Jim Miller's claim that there are significant broad changes characteristic of 20th century science.

Nature today is understood to be the product of an evolutionary process with a long history of emergent novelty, characterized throughout by chance and law. Today we see ecological interdependence and a multi-levelled structure. These characteristics will affect our representation of God's relation to the world, and of our relation to non-human nature — which in turn will have implications for how we treat nature. If we view our relationship to nature in these new terms, we won't see ourselves as sharply separated from the rest of nature, as we once did.

Arthur Peacocke is the person that most adequately develops this view. Ben Reist has a whole section on him in his paper, and we heard references to him this morning. Peacocke is a biochemist and Anglican clergyman who holds that chance and law have a positive role in theology. God creates in and through the natural process. Peacocke gives some vivid images for talking about God's action in a world of chance and law. Chance is God's radar sweeping through the range of possibilities. Artistic creativity is another image that combines novelty and open-endedness with purposefulness.

I would suggest that the classical idea of God's omnipotence requires reconsideration if we are going to allow for chance as well as evil, suffering and human freedom in the world. At least we need to talk about God's self-limitation. God's omniscience also needs to be reconsidered. If we say the future is genuinely open, then it can't be known even by God. There are valiant attempts by some theologians to show that predestination and omniscience are consistent with freedom and novelty, but I don't find them altogether satisfactory.

2.   Systematic Synthesis
The last school is systematic synthesis through a metaphysical system. I agree with the people here who said metaphysics shouldn't be a dirty word. Theologians have always drawn from philosophers: Augustine used Plato, Aquinas used Aristotle, Protestant theologians used Kant extensively. The Thomistic framework continues to be a very live option. It talks about primary and secondary causality in a way that preserves the integrity of science. However, it tends to be deterministic, if everything that happens is God's work. It also preserves dualisms of spirit and matter, mind and body, eternity and time, which I would question.

Some Christian theologians have made extensive use of the process metaphysics of Alfred North Whitehead. Miller and Reist both mentioned the process idea that reality is a dynamic web of interconnected events. God is the source of novelty and order. Instead of the idea of divine omnipotence, the cross is taken as the manifestation of the power of love. Rather than starting with power, we would start with love. Process thinkers have given helpful analyses of chance, human freedom, evil, and suffering. Reist's paper cited examples from Teilhard de Chardin, Charles Birch and John Cobb.

I have myself been trying to combine the Dialogue option with the Integration option, making cautious use of process philosophy. The experience of redemption is at the center of the Christian community and one has to start there. I want to avoid any kind of natural theology. The healing of our brokenness and the experience of new wholeness, that's where we start. The existentialists and the linguistic analysts rightly point to the primacy of personal and social life in religion. Neo-orthodoxy rightly reminds us of the centrality of Christ.

But I think we can go on to remember that we are bound to the rest of the created order, and so we need to work out a theology of nature. Christianity can not be equated with a metaphysical system, but perhaps we can use elements of a metaphysical system to express it. Such systems always run the danger of distorting the rich diversity of experience; there is a tendency to force reality into one's set of conceptual categories.

Let me close by indicating some features of 20th-century science that might be relevant to theological reformulation. I will refer to some of the scientific contributions in this consultation. We can see the changes if we compare three periods, which correspond to the three periods in Jim Miller's paper (see Table II).

Table II
Views of Nature

Medieval	Newtonian	20th Century
Fixed Order	Change as rearrangement	Evolutionary, dynamic, emergent
Teleological	Deterministic	Chance and law
Substantive	Atomistic	Relational, ecological, interdependent
Hierarchical, anthropocentric	Reductionistic, mechanistic	Systems and wholes, organismic
Dualistic (spirit/matter)	Dualistic (mind/body)	Multi-leveled

The Medieval world was basically static. To be sure, there was change, but the basic forms were held to be unchanging. It was teleological in that things were explained in terms of purposes, both built-in purposes and the purposes of God. It was substantive in that the basic realities are independent substances, which require nothing but themselves in order to exist. It was hierarchical: God/man/woman/animal/plant, etc. This heirarchy was a fixed order in which the lower serves the higher.

The natural order was basically anthropocentric; lower beings are here for the purpose of the higher, and there is a sharp line between human and non-human. The earth, of course, was the center of the cosmos. Other creatures are here for our benefit. There is an absolute distinction between humanity and other creatures. The Medieval world was dualistic in that there are two sharply contrasting elements in it: immaterial spirit and transitory matter. The purpose of the material is to serve the spiritual. The goal of this life is to prepare for the next.

In the Newtonian synthesis, which we heard about in Jim's paper, change was the rearrangement of unchanging fundamental particles. It was a world which is deterministic rather than teleological; mechanical causes, not purposes, determine all events. The future is predictible from adequate knowledge of the present. It was atomistic in taking separate components rather than substances to be the basic reality. Its theory of knowledge was objectivism or classical realism (naive realism). The approach was reductionistic and mechanistic rather than heirarchical. Physical mechanisms at the lowest level were thought to determine all events, except those in the human mind. It was dualistic, though the division differed a bit from that of the Middle Ages.

Newton, we have heard, accepted the Cartesian dualism of mind and body. Human rationality, he said, is the mark of our uniqueness, even if we are no longer the center of the cosmic system. But with the 18th-century Enlightenment, the mental side was increasingly ignored, and the whole of reality was encompassed in the world machine whose operation could be explained without reference to God. In such a materialistic world there is no place for consciousness or inwardness except as subjective illusion. Moreover, if nature is a machine, it has no rights; it is an object which can be exploited for human uses.

In the 20th century there has been a significant change in these assumptions. In place of immutable order, or change as rearrangement, there is a thoroughly evolutionary, dynamic, and historical picture of all reality. We heard it first in Eric Chaisson's magnificent picture of the evolutionary character of all the sciences, projected also into the future. Joe Silk illustrated the historical character of cosmic evolution, and Phil Spieth described evolutionary biology. Because of the element of chance, you can understand the cosmos only by studying it historically. You couldn't have predicted it. It is what it is because of its history. Basic types have changed radically. New types of phenomena have appeared at successive levels of organization in matter, life, mind and culture.

Next, in place of determinism, there is a complex combination of chance and law. We saw this in Bob Russell's paper and in Jim Maher's, including the portion on non-equilibrium thermodynamics. In cosmology, quantum uncertainty has a role because the very early universe was so small. Then there were random mutations in evolution. The future is open. It can't be predicted from the past, even in principle.

Thirdly, nature is understood to be relational, ecological, and interdependent. Reality consists of events and relationships. The observer is involved in the process of observation: again, note the relational character. Nature is a community, not a machine. To be sure, the reductionist analysis of things into their parts is still very fruitful, and much of science follows that route. But there is more attention given now to systems and wholes, more willingness to recognize that there are distinctive concepts used to explain the higher-level activities of systems, from organisms to ecosystems — an ecological view of reality, if you will. Jim Maher referred to layers, a multi-level view. There are various ways of looking at mind-body issues today, but most of them avoid extreme dualism. The contemporary outlook is less anthropocentric, though obviously humanity is in many respects unique. But scientists see human beings as strongly rooted in nature. In an interdependent world, our treatment of other creatures has far-reaching repercussions.

What models of God might go with these views of nature? Any view of God is not just derived from looking at nature. For the Christian, it is always derived primarily from the biblical witness. But there is a diversity of images in the Bible. Our view of God is also derived from religious experience. Remember Nebelsick's point: we always understand God in relation, not God-in-God's self. We also have to think about God in relation to nature, and here we are inescapably influenced by our understanding of nature.

It's not surprising that in the Middle Ages, with a hierarchical and anthropocentric universe, a monarchial view of the God-world relationship was dominant. This is also a biblical model, but there are a lot of other images in the Bible, too. The stress on God's omnipotence and immutability, all the "omni's" that got such a good run for their money in Aquinas, certainly are much indebted to Greek thought. The God of the Bible was not impassive and unaffected by the world, as Aquinas held. But this ruler-subject model fitted well with the Medieval world.

On the other hand, if the world is a clock, then God is the clockmaker. And so the deistic God, who designed and started the clock and then went out to lunch, became a dominant image. As Nebelsick said, Newton's God had to readjust the clock occasionally, but after Laplace that wasn't necessary and God was on the unemployment list.

There are various models that are especially appropriate today. The process view pictures a cosmic society — not a democratic society, because God is still the supreme member, though God's power is limited. Where the classical view emphasized transcendence, I think that one has to give greater emphasis to immanence today. The Calvinist tradition has been very strong on transcendence. It speaks less often about immanence. A sacramental way of representing immanence is certainly one possibility. One can also develop metaphysical categories, and this is where process thought seems helpful.

There is a crucial question in understanding God's power. The Medieval model emphasized God's absolute power and freedom; it was expressed in the ex nihilo doctrine, which was not an explicit biblical concept. Doug Knight said the Bible doesn't start with nihilo, but with a primeval watery chaos. Also the Bible sometimes uses the present tense; it talks about God creating the grass now (Psalms 104). Doug gave a couple of other examples. We were also hearing about the "continuing creation" tradition from Ben Reist. The ex nihilo tradition was developed in the early Church as an antidote to the Gnostic view that the world is evil. Ex nihilo was a way of saying that the world is good; both form and matter are due to God. The Gnostics said this is a world of evil from which we escape as quickly as we can to the world of spirit, and the early Church rejected that view.

So what do we do with continuing creation? How do we rethink God's power in a way that doesn't make God powerless, and that preserves transcendence? The process God is transcendent as well as immanent. Perhaps process thought goes too strongly to the side of immanence. Certainly, it isn't pantheism, as I heard somebody say. Hartshorne has a dipolar concept of God, unchanging in essence and purpose, but changing in knowledge and interaction. God's action in the world is a topic that one could spend a whole conference on; I think that's a very crucial question.

What about miraculous intervention? Ben is right that one doesn't want to talk about intervention if God is already here. The process God works in the unfolding of every event, so it's not a God-of-the-gaps. We all know that the latter has not worked historically, since science gradually closes the gaps. I think we have promising answers from a number of directions. I'm very much impressed with Thomism as a live possibility in many ways. The primary and secondary causality scheme does a lot to give the scientist freedom. If you say God is the primary cause, the scientist is free to investigate the secondary causes. The distinction between these levels is also made by Luther, Calvin and Barth. It doesn't involve sudden intervention because God is acting through all natural causes.

However, the idea of primary and secondary causes has difficulty dealing with human freedom, evil, and chance, because it implies that everything that happens is God's will — including that AIDS virus we heard about this morning. We have to avoid compromising God's goodness in the interest of defending God's power. We don't want Deism, where God acts only in setting up the machine and letting it run. If we don't want a God-of-the-gaps to intervene, how do we represent God's action in the world? That's part of the theological agenda that we need to address.

Personal Faith in the Context of Contemporary Science

Ronald Cole-Turner

Memphis Theological Seminary
Memphis TN

In Steven Weinberg's frequently quoted words, "The more the universe seems comprehensible, the more it also seems pointless."[1] As our understanding of the cosmos advances, our sense of cosmic purpose and personal significance dimishes. If we find ourselves nevertheless affirming that there is both cosmic purpose and personal significance, we do so in faith.

Yet we are troubled. As whole persons who strive for intellectual integrity, we seek to inhabit intellectually a single world. We are not comfortable with a faith contradicted, not merely by a specific scientific theory or model, but by the general movement of modern science as a whole. This movement, which we might describe simply as the elimination of final cause or purpose in science, makes the idea of a purposive God unnecessary if not doubtful. While it is true that the question of purpose in science is not settled, modern science taken as a whole has been methodologically opposed to explanations of natural phenomena in terms of final cause or purpose.[2]

The retreat from the idea of cosmic purpose in the arena of science leaves us, if we in faith affirm cosmic purpose, holding the last echo of divinity in a world long since gone quiet. The cosmos of human understanding is pointless, and human life itself almost completely meaningless: "The effort to understand the universe is one of the very few things that lifts human life a little above the level of farce, and gives it some of the grace of tragedy."[3] Ironically, if we could not understand that the universe is pointless and that we ourselves are virtually without meaning, then we would be utterly without meaning. Perhaps Weinberg is right; perhaps we people of faith, by persisting in our belief in cosmic purpose, have shut ourselves off from the one discovery—namely cosmic meaninglessness—that brings any dignity at all to our human existence.

Is there any grace beyond the "grace of tragedy"? Any meaning to human life beyond our discovery of meaninglessness? Any faith—not delusion, not projection, not blind leap, but faith through which cosmic purpose and personal meaning may dawn upon us?

In this paper, we will consider faith as a possibility in the contemporary world. We will begin by considering how the word "faith" has been used in biblical and Christian tradition. Second, we will consider what faith is for us, and how it is personal. Finally, we will briefly explore three issues which, for many in our time, pose concerns relative to personal faith. These include the question of cosmic purpose, the meaningfulness of traditional Christian faith language, and the sense of divine presence.

I

Like hope and love, faith has many meanings. It can mean a hunch, an opinion, a groundless feeling. It can be a second-rate way of knowing, one that requires external authority for its warrant. For some, in the absence of such a legitimate authority, it is a leap in the dark, a desperate attempt to give meaning to a meaningless life.

The New Testament words for faith—the verb *pisteuo* and the noun *pistis*—are drawn from general literature. In both general and biblical litera-ture, these words mean trust. As a noun, generally it means trust or confidence in God. Less frequently, it means the body of Christian belief, as in "the faith." Usually, this use of the word occurs in later New Testament writings. As a verb, *pisteuo* means to believe or to trust in something or someone.

One of the problems of translating into English is that our language lacks a verbal form of our noun "faith." While "faith" is used for the biblical noun, "believe" is used for the verb. But "believe" has its own English noun (belief) and it carries other meanings, some from everyday usage and some from philosophic discourse. In the New Testament, the use of the verb *pisteuo* outweighs use of the noun *pistis*, so the effect in translation is that the Greek stem *pist*- takes on the senses of the English word "believe" (and, by implica-tion, belief) more than the word "faith." For example, in John's gospel, the verb appears 96 times while the noun is missing; in translation, we have "believe" but not "faith."

Additional difficulty arises because "believe" and "belief," in contem-porary English usage, convey more of a sense of assent to truth than trust in a person or a thing. While the personal dimension of "belief" is not entirely missing from contemporary usage, it is not the primary sense of the word. However, as Wilfred Cantwell Smith points out, the earlier sense of the words "believe" and "belief" is intensely personal and, to that extent, are appropriate translations for the Greek stem *pist*-. "Literally, and originally, 'to believe' means 'to hold dear'." We can see this readily, Smith notes, when we compare English with German: "*lieben* is the verb 'to love'....*Belieben*, then, is to treat as *lieb*, to consider lovely, to like, to wish for, to choose."[4] While this original meaning of believe is different from faith or trust, it is (like them) intensely personal and relational.

In both its predominant biblical usage and in the etymology of the words "believe" and "belief," the words "faith" and "believe" are not primarily associated with knowledge but with trust. As such, their meaning is fundamentally personal and has to do with personal trust or confidence in God. Emphasis is not placed on believing or assenting to certain propositions about God, but rather placing one's confidence in God.

Through the centuries, however, faith has been a primary category of theological epistemology. How do we humans come to knowledge of God? In various ways, theologians have described faith as a source of knowledge about God, or at least as the way in which such knowledge is affirmed as true. Accordingly, faith is seen primarily as knowledge rather than trust.

It is impossible to separate knowledge and trust, and it is not our intent here to do so. But it must be noted that where biblical usage emphasized trust, later theology emphasized knowledge.

In the Reformation, the trust aspect of faith was reasserted with vigor. This is important to note, especially since the key theme of the Reformation was "justification by faith," or, more precisely, "justification by grace through faith." For both Luther and Calvin, God justifies guilty and idolatrous human beings by graciously creating faith within them. Faith is not a human accomplishment, and emphatically not a form of human knowledge, either inferior or superior to other forms. It is, rather, a gift of God, created graciously by the Holy Spirit in those who hear the gospel. Through this faith, the gospel is believed and made effective to salvation.

So conceived, faith is primarily trust that God will be gracious, not belief in God's existence or in any particular religious truths. Indeed, the important thing for the reformers was not that God's existence be believed (since practically no one doubted it) but that God's graciousness in Christ be trusted as the sole basis for our salvation. Such faith involves explicit beliefs about God—that God is trustworthy, gracious, and capable of saving us. But these beliefs are given little attention outside the implicit context of trust in God.

In the era of Protestant orthodoxy, however, the knowledge aspect of faith is emphasized. Through faith, the believer assents to the truth of scripture's propositions. These propositions are systematized (the task of systematic theology), and they must be believed *in toto* for salvation to occur. While faith is the primary way to assent to saving knowledge, many theologians of Protestant orthodoxy thought it desirable to aid faith by developing philosophical arguments for God's existence and by arguing, in various ways, for the trustworthiness of scripture, portraying it as literally dictated by God. For the ordinary believer, then, faith became a matter of believing what the theological expert could largely demonstrate. Faith as personal trust in God became secondary.

For orthodoxy, the propositions of scripture, all of which faith believed, involved many claims about the natural world and about humanity. Their idea of faith committed them to a great many explicit beliefs about God and the world. As these beliefs were challenged by the emerging natural sciences, faith was lost or became (over time) fundamentalism.

In the crisis of faith, the pietism of the eighteenth century recovered the personal dimension of faith as trust. With Schleiermacher and nineteenth century theological liberalism, this recovery continued. Indeèd, faith or religious experience became foundational, and theological doctrines are derived from the basic experience of faith rather than merely affirmed by faith. But here emerges a tendency which links such disparate theological movements as liberalism, existentialism (as in Rudolf Bultmann), and neo-orthodoxy (as in Karl Barth). This tendency is to emphasize properly the trust element of faith but to disengage faith from the natural world as it is experienced in other ways or is described through the sciences. Such a faith is protected from any change in scientific theory, for it is compatible with any view of the natural world. But that protection is bought at the price of making faith irrelevant to science and vice versa.

II

In this section, we want to develop a view of faith that emphasizes the element of personal trust, but does not thereby isolate faith from other dimensions of human life. We want, in other words, to see faith primarily as a trusting, open response, but as including explicit beliefs or convictions about the cosmos and about ourselves as human beings.

We reject a faith that includes nothing of explicit belief about the cosmos or about humanity, and is therefore compatible with everything. The meaning of such a faith is purely arbitrary and self-created. By contrast, we affirm a faith which includes some explicit beliefs. Our faith will not be nearly as detailed in its explicit belief as the faith of an orthodox Protestant or a fundamentalist; but at least we share with them the understanding that faith does include explicit beliefs about the cosmos and about humanity.

Before attempting to say what beliefs faith properly includes, it is important to consider how faith is (and is not) personal. There are at least two meanings of the word "personal" that we do not wish to attach to our understanding of faith. We need to identify these and state reasons for rejecting them, and then affirm how faith is personal.

First, we are rejecting personal as individualistic. The primary reason for rejecting an individualistic personal faith is that it relies upon a mistaken notion of persons. Persons do not exist in individualistic isolation; rather, "person" is fundamentally a social reality, for it is in relationship with other persons that personhood arises. Culture, language, meaning, and beliefs are social or interpersonal, never individualistic. Even private thoughts or beliefs are held in socially-created language and in constant reference to the thoughts or beliefs of others. Persons are constituted by social relations, and if faith arises it is engendered by those relations.

Second, we reject personal as privatistic. Religious faith does not pertain to some private realm of subjective taste or whim. It does not have to do with some peripheral sphere of value, sealed off from the real world of fact. It is not a coping device for softening the horror of meaninglessness, as if we by faith could create private value and meaning in an otherwise valueless and meaningless cosmos. Faith may be able to discern meaning or purpose, but it cannot create it.

In contrast to individualistic and privatistic faith, we are searching for faith that is socially engendered and significant for all aspects of life. In faith the believer affirms there is purpose in life that is not a privately created or arbitrary purpose but one that is believed to be found in life (indeed, in the cosmos) itself.

As socially engendered, faith arises within a community and becomes part of the general consciousness of persons reared within the community. Typically in Christianity, this community is the Church, especially at worship. As important as the question of the engendering of faith is, it is not our primary concern here. Instead, we are concerned with the question of what explicit beliefs are included in personal faith, and how these beliefs interact with other sources of human understanding.

Personal faith includes explicit beliefs or convictions that bear upon other values and understandings which we humans hold. Indeed, these beliefs do not merely bear upon other areas of thought and action; as religious beliefs, they draw other values and understandings together into a personally meaningful whole. In this way, religious faith gives coherence to all other aspects of our lives. Far from being peripheral, faith is at the center or core of our way of understanding the cosmos, the meaning of our life, and our basic values.

What explicit beliefs are included in personal faith? In other words, what are the beliefs or convictions which inevitably arise from personal faith? For Luther and Calvin, as noted earlier, faith includes explicit beliefs about God's trustworthiness, graciousness toward us, and power or ability to save us. For them, these beliefs could not have been denied without betrayal of their trust in God.

For us, faith includes explicit belief in some sort of coherent ultimate purpose for the whole of creation, in reference to which all things (including humanity in general and our lives in particular) find their meaning.[5] Further, it includes the belief that this ultimate or transcending purpose is communicated, perhaps in many ways, to the cosmos. These explicit beliefs arise when we reflect upon what it means to have personal religious faith or trust. Their denial would seriously alter what we mean by faith.

Personal faith, then, is trusting ourselves to this ultimate, cosmic purpose; seeking to find the meaning of our lives in reference to it; opening ourselves to become aware of it; and orienting our values and our relations with all other creatures in reference to it.[6]

This view of faith is indebted in several respects to John Haught's *The Cosmic Adventure*. In that book, Haught observes that "faith is an attitude of acknowledging the limits of comprehension and of opening ourselves to being comprehended by that which transcends us."[7] Haught's understanding of the cosmos is that it is hierarchical, and that higher levels comprehend and integrate lower levels, but not vice versa. Human intelligence is capable of comprehending (and therefore influencing) lower levels; but if there is a higher level transcending human intelligence, it is beyond comprehension. While we cannot comprehend the higher or influence (much less control) it, we can open ourselves to being comprehended, integrated, and influenced by it. This opening of ourselves to the transcendent is faith. "Faith, in the context of an emergent universe, is simply the stance that we at the human level of emergence would take when we surrender ourselves to being influenced by whatever higher field there may be encompassing the cosmic hierarchy."[8]

Understood in such a way, faith is not a knowledge or a comprehension of truth, but a trusting openness to what ultimately transcends us. This openness is not a knowing like other human ways of knowing; but it can be seen as a listening or a receptivity to what cannot be known through normal means of investigation, critical analysis, or experimentation.

While all creation (to the extent that it is creation) is receptive to this transcending purpose, human beings in faithful worship or prayer focus intently and consciously on that purpose. "In man, physicality has become capable of reading those meanings in existence which are the immanence of the transcendent God in the whole cosmic process."[9]

In this sense, personal faith, if it has any validity at all, is arguably the most important phenomenon in the entire cosmos (allowing that if intelligent life exists elsewhere, something like personal faith exists there, too). The reason for its importance is simply that there alone, to our knowledge, does the creation consciously focus in on the cosmic purpose, opening feeble but sustained consciousness over millenia through historic communities. All creation responds to transcendent purpose, but we are able consciously to discern and reflect upon its meaning. Because of faith, there is within creation a place of conscious listening to that which embraces and orders the whole creation. This changes the relationship between the creation and the creator.

Such awareness is not for our manipulation or control, as if we could exploit transcendent purpose for our private ends. It is instead for us to participate in what transcends and surrounds us, consenting to it and seeking to be defined by it. This involves trust. Even as the reformers themselves recognized, faith is trust in God to define the meaning of our lives, to give them whatever validity or worth they have, and finally to "justify" them. For Luther and Calvin, this was justification by faith.

For us, faith is also justifying in the sense that through faith, we open our lives to a meaning which is defined outside us, in a transcendent purpose. In faith, we decline any longer to define the meaning of our lives for ourselves, seeking instead a definition consonant with the ultimate purpose. Over centuries, devout people have sought "the will of God" for their lives. However badly they may have perceived it, and whatever monstrosities they may have committed as God's will, nevertheless they sincerely searched for a meaning for their lives in a will or purpose that transcended their own. They opened themselves to be comprehended or integrated by what transcended them. Their life meaning, goals, and ultimate justification lay in conformity to what was beyond.

III

In this final section, we want to give brief attention to three challenges to the kind of personal faith that has just been described. We will barely do more than identify the challenge and suggest where answers may be found.

The first challenge is the one with which we began the paper, namely the question of the legitimacy of even thinking any more about cosmic purpose. In our description of personal faith, we have said that faith includes the explicit belief in some sort of a coherent, ultimate purpose for the cosmos. In saying this, we mean that faith includes an explicit belief about this same cosmos or natural world that science and other disciplines attempt to comprehend. Consequently, the question of natural purpose in science, and analysis of it in philosophy of science, bear directly on our understanding of faith.

That being noted, we must point out that faith relies upon a coherent, ultimate purpose. While philosophy of science might consider whether such a coherent, ultimate purpose has any standing, science itself does not examine the question directly, nor can it. It is a metaphysical question, and as such it is beyond the methods of science.

But science is not irrelevant to its consideration. For certainly, the natural sciences offer the appropriate way to consider whether there is purpose in nature—not a coherent, ultimate purpose, but phenomena which are best described as purpose-like. It is at least arguable that certain natural phenomena are best described in terms that include purpose. The perplexing question for personal faith is the relationship between these purposes within nature and the coherent, ultimate purpose that faith confesses.

At stake is the question of God and nature. If God and nature are held together, some convergence between purposes in nature and divine purposes will be affirmed, even to the point of natural purposes (discerned by science) providing a clue to divine purposes. James Gustafson can be seen as an example of such a holding together of nature and God. He writes, for instance, that "evidences from the sciences not only indicate that there are powers on which we are radically dependent; they also indicate that there is an order and ordering of natural processes and developments."[10] And then: "I believe that we can discern through experience (not simply in terms of sensationism or phenomenalism) and through our knowledge of life in the world what some of the divine purposes are for the creation. Some of these have already been introduced: ordering, creating conditions for possibilities, and so forth."[11]

He may be right. Faith in an ultimate purpose, however, does not require such a close bringing together of divine and natural purposes. The ultimate purpose faith affirms may be seen as more transcendent, certainly working through natural purposes but sometimes at cross-purposes, so that one would always be reticent about generalizing from partial knowledge of natural purposes to what may lie behind them. Transcendence, of course, can also be overdone. If divine purposes have nothing to do with natural purposes, and if natural purposes and processes offer no clue about divine creativity, then we have backed ourselves into faith affirmations that are disengaged from this world.

Second, we want to ask about the meaningfulness of traditional Christian faith language. Traditional discourse about God arose in different ages and within the context of different cosmologies. To what extent is it meaningful and helpful today?

Negatively, we need to recognize how cosmologies and cosmogonies shape language and concepts. The ultimate frame of reference, from which concepts and images are drawn for metaphoric use, is structured by cosmology. A concept or image used metaphorically in one cosmology may mean something radically different in the next. Or it may become meaningless because it has been dislodged.

Positively, however, we are discovering how thoroughly our theological understanding takes place through metaphors. Terms or images drawn from one context are transferred to another, transferring some (but not all) of the meaning from a familiar context to a less familiar context, and in that transfer stimulating new meaning on both sides. Theology necessarily does this, for there is no other way to imagine or conceive of God, creation, and the relationship between them.

The task of Christian theology in our age is to work from the personal faith of thoughtful people, ranging from scientists to poets, and to draw together the metaphoric images which their faith suggests, bringing these into new clusters or doctrines. This would be a radically new theology, at least potentially. No doubt traditional metaphors would remain; some of them have, for centuries, served to focus the experiences of faith in meaningful ways. To the extent that they continue to focus contemporary faith experience meaningfully, they will remain. But it is the task of theology always to test how far this is true and continually to search for new ways to draw together the metaphors and images that are meaningful to believers in our time.

This leads us to a third concern, the experience or the sense of divine presence. For many, such an experience or sense is absent. If there is a coherent, ultimate purpose that is present at all times to the whole creation, there ought to be some possibility of experiencing that presence consciously. But to bring such an experience to explicit consciousness requires, once again, metaphors and images. As a matter of faith, we might believe that there is a divine presence which does indeed surround us and sustain us at every moment, without ever experiencing it consciously. It is only when we have adequate metaphors or images which focus the divine presence and convey it to explicit consciousness that we experience God in a religiously significant way. All creation experiences God; only religious people, who focus that experience through adequate metaphors capable of bringing that experience to focused consciousness, are aware that they experience God.

The embarrassing absence of God in our world may be due to inadequate and outmoded metaphors and doctrinal clusters of metaphors. If so, then the task of discovering and clustering metaphors which speak to us of God today is a crucial task. Metaphors arise from faith and must be faithful to it, but metaphors also nourish faith. If traditional theological metaphors are empty in our age, we should expect that faith will languish and God will remain out of focus.

NOTES

1. Steven Weinberg, *The First Three Minutes: A Modern View of the Origin of the Universe* (New York: Basic Books, 1977), p. 154.
2. Cf. Charles Birch, "Chance, Necessity and Purpose," in *Studies in the Philosophy of Biology*, ed. by Francisco Jose Ayala and Theodosius Dobzhansky (Berkeley: University of California Press, 1974), pp. 225-239; and Philip R. Sloan, "The Question of Natural Purpose," in *Evolution and Creation*, ed. by Ernan McMullin (Notre Dame: University of Notre Dame Press, 1985), pp. 121-150.
3. Weinberg, op. cit., p. 155.
4. Wilfred Cantwell Smith, *Faith and Belief* (Princeton: Princeton University Press, 1979), p. 105.
5. The word "purpose" may be troublesome here to many, in that it is not only anthropomorphic but perhaps rather western and modern. Whether "purpose" necessarily implies personal intent (therefore entailing belief in a personal God) is not, however, a foregone conclusion. Use of anthropomorphic language will be defended briefly later in this paper, including the value of personal metaphors for picturing cosmic purpose. I do not want to say, though, that these metaphors are entailed by faith.
6. On this final point, cf. James M. Gustafson, *Ethics from a Theocentric Perspective*, 2 vols. (Chicago: University of Chicago Press, 1981-84).
7. John F. Haught, *The Cosmic Adventure: Science, Religion and the Quest for Purpose* (New York: Paulist Press, 1984), p. 11.
8. Ibid., p. 96.
9. A.R. Peacocke, *Creation and the World of Science* (Oxford: Clarendon Press, 1979), p. 145.
10. Gustafson, op. cit., vol. 1, p. 262.
11. Ibid., pp. 270-71.

Genesis, Procreation, or Reproduction: Cosmology and Ethics

Abigail Rian Evans

Director, National Capitol Presbytery Health Ministries
Senior Staff Associate, Kennedy Institute of Ethics
Georgetown University, Washington, D.C.

> Nay the same Solomon the king, although he excelled in the glory of treasure and magnificcnt buildings, of shipping and navigation, of service and attendance, of fame and renown, and the like, yet he maketh no claim to any of those glories, but only to the glory of inquisition of truth; for so he saith expressing, "The glory of God is to conceal a thing, but the glory of the king is to find out." As if, according to the innocent play of children, the Divine Majesty took delight to hide his works, to the end to have them found out, and as if kings could not obtain a greater honor than to be God's play-fellows in that game." Francis Bacon, *The Advancement of Learning* [1605][1]

Introduction

First, let me beg the indulgence of my readers for the broad sweep of philosophy, anthropology, science, and theology by reducing thousands of years of human history into three *Weltanschauung* (world views): theocentric, anthropocentric, and technocentric. I am not suggesting that at any given period of history only one *Weltanschauung* exists but rather that one may dominate. There have always been prophets and gadflys who force us to step back and examine our cosmologies. These world views are not monolithic systems but rather they create a backdrop for our ethical reflection and behavior.

My thesis is that our *Weltanschauung* influences our understanding of human nature, hence our values and ethics. This is clearly illustrated in the current shift of how we understand the creation of human life. A particular world view may encourage the development of certain ethical theories in which one type of ethics dominates, though not to the exclusion of all others. There has been a shift in western civilization from the Judeo-Christian concept of a theocentric universe to the nineteenth century rationalism of an anthropocentric universe and now, in the late twentieth century, to a techno-centered world view. This shift in our cosmology—here I am using the word in a slightly different way—is illustrated by the descriptions we use for the creating of human life. We have moved from talking about genesis (to begin) which the Greeks used to connote the springing forth of new life, to the word procreation with its reference to man's co-operation with a creator God, to using the term reproduction, a metaphor of the factory.[2]

The three world views I will contrast are theocentric, anthropocentric, and technocentric which foster different ethical theories—teleological, egoistical and utilitarian. In the first, ethics is guided by absolute, objective principles grounded in God. In the second, morality is based on man's reason, intuitive or experience. In the third, practical and legal contracts for the society as a whole define morals. In a theocentric view universal truths, transcendent values, revelation, and (for those in the Thomistic tradition) natural law form the centerpiece of our ethics and morals; grounding ethics in God's existence is the starting point for ethics. In an anthropocentric universe, autonomy, rights, reason, and right and wrong rather than good and evil are the primary emphases; man becomes the measure of what is moral. In technocentric universe, utilitarianism, allocation of resources, efficiency and pragmatism form the heart of ethics. This more mechanistic view leads to either determinism or libertarian views of man. Nihilists and existentialists led the way for the shift from the man-centered to a machine-centered universe. In this latter view, our ultimate fears are realized through the creation of computers which become our nemesis; popularized paradigms of this are seen in movies such as *War Games* and *2001: A Space Odyssey*.

I will argue in this paper that a technocentric *Weltanschauung* threatens the very nature and destiny of humankind. The basic struggle that we encounter between the scientific and theological views of the world should not center on questions of evolution versus creationism, biology versus theology, or spirit versus mind. Rather the heart of our debate should be how the harnessing of science to technology in particular arenas may strike at the fundamental questions of how we understand our world and man/woman's place in it. The real threat to theology is not the new science, but the harnessing of science in the service of technology without a transcendental reference. Technical knowledge of select elements of our universe is outstripping our ability to craft a new theological synthesis which would provide a view of the whole and from which we could derive our ethics. We need the insights of theology and ethics to asist us in applying our knowledge wisely.

In criticizing a technocratic world view, I am not following some romantic, Rousseauian dream of an unspoiled primitive world or the counter-culture's idyllic back-to-nature movement, but rather raising questions about the dehumanization and fear of the future that is an outgrowth of this particular world view.

Brave New World is here—our worry may not be so much what the future holds but will there be any future. We have bombs not only to wipe out cities, but civilizations. While the bomb has not caused modern anxiety it is the occasion for it. Modern men and women realize that this is the time in which it is possible for us to destroy not only life but also the possibility of rebirth, not only men and women but also humankind, not only periods of existence but also history itself. The future has become an option. The possibility of nuclear war has caused us to lose our naive faith in technology. The same power that enables us to create new life carries the potential for self destruction.

Henri Nouwen, in *The Wounded Healer*, recounts an old tale of ancient India which captures this problem of technology destroying us:

Four royal sons were questioning what specialty they should master. They said to one another, "Let us search the earth and learn a special science." So they decided, and after they had agreed on a place where they would meet again, the four brothers started off, each in a different direction. Time went by, and the brothers met again at the appointed place, and they asked one another what they had learned. "I have mastered a science," said the first, "which makes it possible for me, if I have nothing but a piece of bone of some creature, to create straightaway the flesh that goes with it." "I," said the second, "know how to grow that creature's skin and hair if there is flesh on its bone." The third said, "I am able to create its limbs if I have the flesh, the skin, and the hair." "And I," concluded the fourth, "know how to give life to that creature if its form is complete with limbs."

Thereupon the four brothers went into the jungle to find a piece of bone so that they could demonstrate their specialties. As fate would have it, the bone they found was a lion's, but they did not know that and picked up the bone. One added flesh to the bone, the second grew hide and hair, the third completed it with matching limbs and the fourth gave the lion life. Shaking its heavy mane the ferocious beast arose with its menacing mouth, sharp teeth, and merciless claws and jumped on his creators. He killed them all and vanished contentedly into the jungle.[3]

Many of us feel that the lion of technology has in fact turned on us. What Brave New World have we entered where our knowledge and scientific advances have in fact outstripped our ethics and values. Our modern angst towards nuclear age reflects itself in a general dis-ease about technology's achievements which spills over into areas of health care and hi-tech medicine; no where is this more apparent than in the area of reproductive technologies.

In order to understand our current approach to procreation, I will discuss three world views, their accompanying ethics and conclude with a discussion of the ethical issues involved in the new reproductive technologies. The points that I will discuss in analyzing my central thesis are as follows:

I.   Science and religion should be linked by a common pursuit of truth.

II.   A theocentric world view emphasizes teleological, objective ethics.

III. An anthropocentric world view fosters a rationalistic, subjective and situational ethics.

IV.   A technocentric world view reflects a utilitarian, legalistic and pragmatic ethics.

V.   Our cosmology and accompanying ethics determine how we understand the creation of human life as genesis, procreation or reproduction.

I. Science and Religion Should be Linked by a Common Pursuit of Truth

Any conference on the subject of theology and cosmology should first address the question of knowledge and its relationship to truth, not in the sense of what constitutes our epistemology but rather how we regard knowledge— fear, reverence, joy, pursuit or avoidance.

As Christians, Jesus Christ charges us to love God with our minds as well as our bodies and hearts. Religion and science should be united in a single pursuit of truth. Knowledge and faith are responses to two fundamentally different questions. Scientific knowledge talks about the relationship among various phenomena as perceived by the senses. Faith refers to the perception of one's self in the context of the whole creation—past, present, future, i.e. who is God and what should I do in light of His existence and commands. Knowledge does not undermine faith, but rather illuminates the areas of mystery.

Paul's words to the Corinthians are appropriate here, "Brethren, do not be children in your thinking. Be babes in evil, but in thinking be mature." (1 Corinthians 14:20) Paul challenges us to a clear and reasoned faith; to mature thinking; to unity of mind and spirit so that God's power may be real in our lives and we may give a clear and powerful statement of our faith.

Theology should assist us in developing a unified view of ourselves— body, mind, and spirit—as well as of our world. The Christian life is more than a mental exercise but a person whose mind is unfruitful is not true to his or her Christian calling. Albert Schweitzer, troubled by the disposition of contemporary Christianity to keep the mind in cold storage, wrote, that a renunciation of thinking is a declaration of spiritual bankruptcy. Christianity cannot replace thinking, it must be founded on it.

Karl Barth refers to the illumination of knowledge by faith. In Jesus Christ *gnosis* and *pistis* should not be separated but be enriched by one another. We should rightly look to science to illuminate our understanding of the world in which we find ourselves. However, attempts to make theology a science are generally ill-founded. The orthodox Protestant did not want to confer anything he could not prove, so he devised a 'scientific theology' that could prove everything, according to Herbert Hovenkamp. Unfortunately, what we saw happening was a stripping of religion's authority, a pseudoscience whose "facts" could not hold up the more convincing"facts" of biology or geology. Religion of humanity and a social Gospel dominated the late nineteenth century.

The distinction between special and natural revelation is really part of this same problem; another nuance of the debate. Emile Cailliet criticizes Barth for his strong reaction against natural revelation which Barth traces to the radical nature of sin. Here Barth follows in the tradition of Augustine over Aquinas with a tinge of the former's conclusion that Athens has nothing to do with Jerusalem.

Unfortunately, many theologians have attempted to create a dualistic understanding of knowledge, i.e. knowledge by the use of reason and knowledge that flows from faith. Although theologians such as Reinhold Niebuhr generally have a robust view of the pursuit of knowledge, even he concludes that although man's reason is part of his freedom which enables him to see pattern or intelligibility, it does not reveal the ultimate meaning of life.

However, there may be a new rapprochement between science and religion in their mutual pursuit of truth as reflected in post-Newtonian science. Scientists such as Richard H. Bube at Stanford University put it this way, "What we all need is constant integration... To see that there is good science and bad science, good biblical theology and bad biblical theology and to take the best from both and see them both as ways that God guides us."[4] Theologians as well recognize that theology is not only no longer the queen of the sciences but is not a science at all and certainly does not contain all the knowledge about God. As Paul wrote, "We see through a glass darkly and then face to face. Now I know in part; then I shall understand fully, even as I have been fully understood." (1 Corinthians 13:12) Theology should be in constant dialogue with the other disciplines to understand God's world and human nature.

When science and religion do clash it generally occurs when they trespass their realms of proper jurisdiction. Each discipline has its own sphere. Struggles emerge when science attempts to provide ultimate answers to the questions it raises and when religion attempts to use theology to explain how the physical world functions.

When science makes statements about purpose it steps out of its realm. An illustration of this is Bertrand Russell in *A Free Man's Worship* when he comments on God from the basis of a mathematical philosophy. Some of science's optimism and *hubris* was reflected as well, in the words at the founding of the American Association for Advancement of Science in Boston: "To nourish the incremental spirit, the democracy of facts against the genteel tradition of 'natural philosophy', general science, and the search for scientific panaceas against that 'modified charlatanism' which makes merit in one subject excuse for asking authority in others."[5]

Where science and religion should have one of the greatest co-operative searches for truth and knowledge, i.e. in the field of health care, unfortunately they have often been at odds. The medieval Roman Catholic Church resisted the study of anatomy and scientific medicine as a threat to orthodoxy. Both science and the reformation were born from a rebellion against the Aristotelian philosophy. Science was neither encouraged or discouraged by the church and theology still reigned supreme at mid-nineteenth century.[6] However, generally they established a friendly relationship with the scientific revolution from 1600 to 1850. American Protestants had a supernatural view of health and sickness which especially flourished in Puritan New England, and later led to a dualism, assigning the care of the body to medical science and the care of the soul to the Church.[7] This dualism still exists today though movements towards integrated approaches to health care are gaining ground. We will note the unfortunate consequences of the separation of theology and science when we examine the area of reproductive technologies where the begetting of life is no longer a family celebration, or an extension of God's covenant love, but a medical event with third party involvement.

II. A Theocentric World View Emphasizes Teleological and Objective Ethics

Let me state at the outset, in describing a theocentric world view I am basing it on Judeo-Christian theology not religion in general, admitting there is great divergence even in that theological tradition. In a theistic framework, God is the author and source of life, as well as lord over life and death. By the divine word, life is brought into being. There is no necessary conflict between a God who said "let there be light" and a God who, in his pronouncements, worked out his creation through a gradual evolution of the universe or a universe created by a "big bang." Even Darwin wrote that his views should not shock the religious feelings of anyone because there is a grandeur in this view of life since the creator is behind these patterns of life. Creation is by God's Word which began the universe and which then became flesh in Jesus Christ, the *logos*, the power, the vehicle by which God displays the divine power. (John 1:1) The central tenets of this perspective are God's eternal existence, prior to matter and His bringing it into being; God's ongoing involvement in the universe, described as *heilsgeschicte*; and God's omnipotence over the course of the world and all the galaxies. Here Christian theology would contrast with, e.g. Plato's demiurge where rather than creation *ex nihilo* God gives form to formless matter. (There is not total agreement among Christians on this point as process theologians do not accept a creation *ex nihilo*.) God's creation where He pronounced the world as good and entrusted it to our care forms the basis for our stewardship and reverence toward life in all its forms as well as the physical world.

Christianity is rooted in the history of God's interaction with man and his world. For example, Judaism bases its holy days on historical events from the calling of a chosen nation, the covenant, Exodus and Passover, the receiving of the Ten Commandments and the feast of Purim, etc. Christianity as well is oriented by the birth and death of Jesus. All events are accounted from Anno Domini—the coming of the Savior. For this reason, early Church historians such as Eusebius (260-340 A.D.) chronologized events of Chaldean, Greek and Roman civilizations into the framework of Bible; he provincialized the history of the whole world into the history of Christianity.[8]

God in history does not mean that we always see Him fully but as Luther stressed by *Deus Absconditus* sometimes His wrath cloaks God in a mystery which cannot be fully understood by humans. When we confront the questions of suffering, pain, sickness, and death our theodicy questions are never answered, but as Job, we are encouraged to ask them.

A theistic framework does not denigrate man or marginalize him, but rather his full glory is revealed as he/she grasps God's purpose in his/her life.

We are freed from a sense of doom to an assurity of destiny. The Psalmist, when searching for man's place in this amazing universe, describes him as crowned with glory and honor and "a little lower than the angels." (Psalm 8) He is made in God's image, hence is of infinite value and worth. This view translates in ethics into respect for persons based on their inherent dignity and worth where people are understood as ends in themselves not means. As Paul Ramsey writes the Christian starts with people not rules.[9]

In the brief confines of this paper it is not possible to survey all of Christian ethics but rather highlight those facets which provide a contrast to the ethics that derive from an anthropocentric or technocentric *Weltanschauung*.

Ethics in the Judeo-Christian perspective is not only teleological and objective but rooted in history. The honoring of the covenant between God and man is the setting for the ten commandments which are one way of living out that covenant. When they became legalistic, God raised up the prophets to call the nation of Israel back to its transcendent and overriding purpose—faithfulness to God. Morality then sprung from this covenant and its accompanying virtues were fidelity, promise-keeping, and steadfastness. For the Christian, Christ became the fulfillment of the Old Testament prophesies and promises. In the moral sphere, Jesus was not only a teacher but provided the motivation and power to follow a higher morality by belief in Him as messiah/savior. Man's inability by his own reason to follow the moral life was exposed through a soteriology, where confession, repentance, and forgiveness were the first steps towards being a moral being.

Teleological ethics were rooted both in a God acting in history who gives purpose and meaning to the world as well as to our individual lives. Man's purpose in the words of the Westminster Shorter Catechism were "to glorify God and enjoy Him forever."

The central tenet of ethics in a theistic *Weltanschauung* is its grounding outside of man in an objective, transcendent being, i.e. God. Ethics in a theistic framework is prescriptive rather than descriptive, normative and objective rather than situational and subjective. There are absolutes which are given through revelation either in a legalistic from, i.e. the Ten Commandments or spiritual form, i.e. the Beatitudes.

As Paul Ramsey suggests in criticizing Paul Lehman's *koinonia* ethics: What should I do cannot be telescoped into what am I to do? or a notion of what is right be derived from what is good.[10] For Lehman *koinonia* ethics is creating the reality of Christ's presence in the world, but for Ramsey morality should be our response to what Christ has already done.

III. An Anthropocentric World View Fosters a Rationalistic, Subjective and Situational Ethics

The central tenet of an anthropocentric view is the replacement of God by man (used here in the generic sense). The "death of God" was not a phrase invented by G.T. Robinson in his "death-of-God" theology, or even by Nietzsche. Hegel referred to the death of the dogmatic orthodox God and Jean Paul (1976) in *Sieben Kas* shows in a striking passage from this work how atheism, or an anthropocentric universe, is really nihilism. "The whole universe is burst asunder by the hand of atheism and fragmented into unnumerable quick-silver particles of I's which twinkle and roll about, wander, flee together, and from each other without unity and stability, no one is so very much alone in this universe as the one who denies God..Alas, if every I is its own father and creator, why can it not also be its own angel of destruction?"[11]

The *hubris* of man's desire to be a god was also reflected in the early stories of Adam and Eve eating the forbidden fruit of the knowledge of good and evil and Aeschylus' heaven storming hero Prometheus who tried to capture the fire from Zeus.

Throughout history man has crowned himself as king. He has done this by building towers of Babel, glorifying his mind in the Golden Age of Pericles (4th century, B.C.), or Protagoras' 'man is the measure of all things' as his compromise between the Heraclitan change and Parmenides absolute, and by later philosophers' humanistic rationalism. It is generally man's reason which is enthroned as the new king which renders divine revelation, creation, and God himself as obsolete. Anselm (1033-1109) may have been the first theologian who exposed the dangers of this anthropomorphic rationalism.

Bertrand Russell in the twentieth century epitomized the separation of man from a divine creator, where he described him as a product of blind and meaningless causes, origin gross, "the new outcome of a local collocation of atoms."

Descartes provided the passageway to modernity by his "cogito ergo sum," where reason was enthroned; Heinemann furthered this anthropocentric view with his replacement. "Respondeu ergo sum," which substituted experience for reason and foreshadowed the British empiricists and French existentialists.

Modern science further assisted the move toward an anthropocentric universe by answering man's need to conquer the forces of nature and to shape by the power of knowledge his own destiny, i.e. man imposed his will on nature.[12]

A tension exists in this world view about how to regard man. On the one hand, man is viewed as simply an advanced animal in a continuous evolutionary chain and on the other hand, as the epitome of creation. These views can take the form of Darwinian evolution or be Christianized by, e.g., Teilhard de Chardin who describes man moving towards his omega point, i.e. Jesus Christ the revelation of perfect man. An evolutionary view may also take a sociological or moral bend as, e.g. by Plato and Aristotle, when a society has both slaves as 'animated tools' (though actually this phrase Aristotle used to describe doctors) and the philosopher-king who epitomized the "great-souled" man. The distinguishing feature of most evolutionary theory is its belief that man does not represent a completely new creature man created by God. Tyson, e.g. in the 1680's removed man from his unique role and linked him to the animals.

A later addition to the anthropocentric world view was in the development of the science of man by Edward Taylor (1832-1917). The history of man was viewed as part and parcel of history of the nature. He created an archaeology of society. While Darwin made a flank attack on Christian orthodoxy, Taylor's attack was frontal. His 'developmental' view was a menacing perhaps fatal blow to the dogmas of Eden. In this view there were no sudden revelations of a Christian gospel but he believed that the truths of monotheism and Christianity developed gradually out of the whole worldwide human experience. Taylor promoted his science of culture under the name of anthropology. He wanted to break the "Unholy Alliance between Theology, Classical Studies, and old-style Natural Sciences."[13]

The dilemmas for anthropocentric view is man's limited vision and inability to understand a sphere which is beyond his grasp. Barth's critique of Schleiermacher's anthropological theology is illustrative of how the self-consciousness of man replaces the sovereignty of God. Man is allowed to define God from his experiences. However, there is no way from anthropology to Christology. The outcome is a restricted view of man as non-referential.

If man is not grounded outside of himself then we are left with a darkness, the removal of a sense of purpose. As Sartre suggested with the disappearance of God from our *Weltanschuung* we lose ideals, the universe is indifferent to us. We are left with blind forces that rule us. These forces for the Greeks were embodied in the nemesis that caused, e.g. Clytemnestra to kill Agamemnon and Orestes to kill his mother; this view of tragic inevitability is echoed through history and literature and for twentieth century man is starkly captured in Eugene O'Neill's *Long Day's Journey into Night* where the plot unfolds with a sense of fatal necessity.

This modern pessimistic view of man really results from Kant's (1724-1804) destruction of metaphysics since in his system ideas do not refer to real objects. Emile Cailliet blamed Kant for creating an ontological deviation away from the transcendent. This so called liberation was to usher in "man-come-of-age" a term coined by Kant in a pamphlet he wrote by that title, but by really marginalized man.

A loss of religious vision creates a morality which may be nothing more than an expression of our own likes and dislikes. Hobbes reflected this when he wrote that good equals what pleases us and evil what displeases us.

The long shadow of Kant created a vacuum where dogmatism was removed and replaced by ideologies such as Marxism and Communism. Morality substituted religion which resulted in a religion within the limits of reason alone. The categorical imperative required no justification but was simply a fact of reason. Religion then reduces to obedience and adherence to the universal moral law; the only proof of God's existence becomes a moral one where He speaks through man's conscience.

Following in Kant's train were those such as Felix Adler (1851-1933) who founded the ethical cultural society. Here morals are severed from any transcendental reference and absolutes are difficult to develop. Situational ethics is the norm where man's weighing of various factors determines the right of action.

Autonomy is the virtue, and the moral goal is the honoring of rights. Service to others and duties are consumed by an ethical egoism.

IV. A Technocentric World View Reflects a Utilitarian, Legalistic and Pragmatic Ethics

First, I wish to make a clear distinction between a science-centered and a technological-centered *Weltanschauung*. The first scientists were, to a large degree, theologians. They understood their scientific discoveries in the context of a theological perspective. The technological world view employs a science unfettered by awe at the uniqueness of man and devoid of any references outside of itself. This current use of science is a far cry from the work of the first scientists, such as the Greeks, who were as much philosophers as they were scientists, e.g., Aristotle and even those of the Miletian school.

Even with the rise of modern science, many great scientists have recognized the importance of religion. Sir Isaac Newton (1642-1727) devoted the last years of his life to finding ways to use astronomy to confirm biblical history. He refused, for example, to take seriously any date which made the earth older than the biblical date of 4004 BC. Science was used in the service of religion. As Boorstin cites, e.g., "The eminent Polish astronomer Johannes Hevelius had calculated the exact position of the sun in the Garden of Eden at the hour of creation, which he fixed at 6:00 p.m., October 24, 3963 BC."[14] While we would likely have problems with many aspects of Newton's synthesis of religion and science, we should affirm his recognition of the need to do so and his attempts to transcend the narrow constructs of his laws of motion, calculus and many other scientific contributions.

The seeds for a technocentric world view were planted by nihilists such as Nietzsche, determinists, and yes, even Darwinian evolutionists. In a world where the fittest species survive, what could be more fit than a machine which would not be subject to the emotions, foibles or errors of man? It can perform tirelessly tasks to be accomplished without mistakes. There is a growing determination in science to eliminate the human element, substituting machines to test the validity of mental constructs or, in the words of Laplace (as early as the end of the 18th century), natural philosophers should aspire to become omniscient calculators.[15]

Science rejected the old approach through the empirical data of consciousness and substituted it with a series of intellectual constructs of mathematics. The mental pictures that were obtained from them were depersonalized. As mathematical models are applied to the physical world they become more remote from the date of consciousness. Russell's use of mathematics to understand reality eventuated in symbolic logic the principles of which he set forth in *Principae Mathematica* and were further developed by Gottlieb Frege, the father of modern logic. Max Planck, the father of quantum physics, writing about the nature of causality, discussed it as a convenient way of asking questions as a child does. Not only man as a rational being, but man as an experiential being receded into the background. The shifts in philosophy, psychology, and anthropology also led the way to the current technocentered world view.

In a machine-centered world view the ends, the products, overshadow the means. "Efficacy" and "accomplishments" are the measuring rod, whether it is a skyscraper, frostless strawberries, or the perfect baby; how we accomplish these goals is lost in the vision of the outstanding "products." Persons are treated as means not ends, as shown in the use of third parties in birthing, such as surrogate mothers who become vehicles to satisfy others' needs.

The technocentric perspective generates two conflicting views: one of despair and helplessness, the other of an euphoric conviction that all human problems have a technological solution. On the one hand, this world view reflects a sense of doom, a lack of purpose in life captured by Faulkner's dictum that "life is full of sound and fury signifying nothing." There is no cosmic direction. Nihilism forms one side of the technocentric view, believing that neither God nor man reigns supreme, but all is to be doubted. "The new science seemed to doubt the validity of all external observation. But the assault on the basic assumption of western thought was broad as well as deep. Sociologist Allan W. Eister writes, "Not just religious assertions or dogmas (or even quite different kinds of statements such as scientific propositions) have been challenged . In philosophy, in logical positivism, e.g., the fundamental processes involved in conceptualizing experience are now seen to be a matter of social invention, complicated by the presence of non-rational, irrational, and even anti-rational preferences and responses among humans."[16]

The despair of the modern world for philosophers such as Emile Cailliet was traced to a loss of cosmic purpose. Hume's challenge to the views of causality, Kant interpreted as changing all realms of knowledge. Kant, who says he was awakened by Hume from his dogmatic slumbers, concluded that we never know the noumena (things-in-themselves) but only the phenomena.

Paradoxically, on the other hand, there exists a belief that technology can solve any problem from hunger to infertility. We continue to run breathlessly along side of knowledge wherever it leads us. However, we are also experiencing a loss of the nineteenth century euphoric optimism about science which has resulted from our mid-twentieth century social, economic, and military tragedies. Technology has not solved the problems of starvation, war, human greed, and death; yet we cling to the belief that it will. Especially in the area of health care despite tremendous victories against infectious disease, lifestyle related illnesses are killing our youth (alcohol-related car accidents, homicide, and suicide) in record numbers.

This world view generates a value system where what works is prized, and solutions to problems are its goals. There is a depersonalization where if there is an ethics it is a sterile utilitarianism which loses sight of the very people it should serve. John S. Mill's utilitarian of the greatest good for the greatest number has been distorted into a depersonalized pragmatism where no one is honored in the claim to improve life for all.

What is possible becomes what is ethical. Knowledge translated into technology is thought to need no ethical restraints. Knowledge outstrips our ethics in a headlong plunge into a brave new world. As Leon Kass has expressed it, "Thus, engineering the engineer as well as the engine, we race our trains, we know not where."[17]

We may even question if there is an ethics in the traditional use of the term. Science has been enthroned as the new god with the Ten Commandments reduced to algorithms. Technology has added to the demise of a common value system as structures of family and society are turned inside out.

In the absence of a common ethics we turn to the courts to adjudicate our moral problems from broken relationships to broken bodies. Our problems are thrown to judges and lawyers to sort out and a new subset of ethical theory becomes public policy. Without a common value system and an operative ethic we have nowhere else to turn. Once we consulted the clergy, then the doctors, then our elected officials; now it is the lawyer who is the new guru who we ask to solve our moral problems as well as our quarrels with those other once trusted professionals.

V. Our Cosmology and Accompanying Ethics Determine Whether We Understand the Creation of Human Life as Genesis, Procreation, or Reproduction

This section considers the implications of the three world views using the paradigm of reproductive technology. Reproductive technology employs a science severed from a theological synthesis which could provide a context for understanding the consequence of that technology.

Our current practices of bringing human life into being reflect the impact of the technocentric *Weltanschauung* on our lives. As was mentioned at the outset, unlike the early civilizations which stood in awe at the origins of human life or the believers in God's created order where man and woman bore children out of an exclusive covenant of love, twentieth century man is mesmerized by his own creation—the machine that now in turn creates him.

Some very hard decisions may soon be upon us. For it is not obvious that the vague potential of abhorrent misuse should weigh more strongly than the unhappiness which thousands of married couples feel when they are unable to have their own children. Different societies are likely to view the matter differently and it would be surprising if all come to the same conclusion. We must, therefore, assume that techniques for the *in vitro* manipulation of human eggs are likely to be general medical practice, capable of routine performance throughout the world within some ten to twenty years.

The situation would then be ripe for extensive efforts, either legal or illegal, at human cloning...

Moreover, given the widespread development of the safe clinical procedures for handling human eggs, cloning experiments would not be prohibitively expensive. They need not be restricted to the super-powers—medium sized, if not minor countries, all now possess the resources needed for eventual success. There furthermore need not exist the coercion of a totalitarian state to provide the surrogate mothers. There already are such widespread divergences as to the sacredness of the act of human reproduction that the boring meaninglessness of the lives of many women would be sufficient cause for their willingness to participate in such experimentation, be it legal or illegal. Thus, if the matter proceeds in its current nondirected fashion, a human being—born of clonal reproduction—most likely will appear on the earth within the next twenty to fifty years, and conceivably even sooner, if some nation actively promotes the venture.[18]

I will admit to you a certain concern that the way we are choosing to reproduce the human race seems to be moving more and more from the outcome of an act of love between a husband and a wife to bring a child into the world, to a laboratory experiment. Birth has become a medical event instead of a family celebration. Sexual intercourse will no longer be needed for generating new life.

Even an unwanted pregnancy is labeled a disease to be treated. Note, e.g., that the Center for Disease Control in its epidemiological monitoring includes the rate of abortions per 100,000 pregnancies, suggesting that the unwanted child is the product of a disease. Ethicists such as Joseph Fletcher label an unwanted pregnancy as a disease and abortion as its therapy. In like manner, some view infertility as a disease; physicians, as Leon Kass, however, challenge this view on two grounds: it requires two individuals to make it manifest and undermines the bond between child bearing and the covenant of marriage.

There are even those such as Gena Corea, author of *The Hidden Malpractice: How American Medicine Mistreats Woman* and *The Mother Machine*, who blame male physicians and researchers for developing anti-feminist therapies such as the pill and robbing women of motherhood by moving birth from the womb to the lab.

We live in an age where we are losing the distinction between having knowledge and using it. The trend is that if we know a technique or procedure, we are obligated to use it. No where is this more apparent than in the area of surrogate motherhood. It seems as if only now with broken lives and legal suits are we asking what our ethical responsibilities are? Should the only limits to our actions be technical possibilities and financial resources? Are there some areas where moral prohibitions should exist?

In discussing reproductive technologies and how our world view influences our perspective on the creation of human life, we refer back to our early discussion about the important link between science and religion in the pursuit of truth. We should not fear where knowledge will lead us, or even avoid technology based on some anti-rational spirituality. Rather we should struggle to understand the proper application of knowledge in the service of humankind and in honoring our creator God. I agree with Paul Ramsey, "a man of serious conscience means to say in raising urgent ethical questions that there may be some things that men should never do. The good things men do can be made complete only by the things they refuse to do."[19]

We want to be careful in criticizing the reproductive technologies that this not appear as resistance or fear of innovation but rather from conclusions based on moral principles. In other words the new is often frightening as has been reflected by past denials that the world was round not flat, that germs not evil spirits caused sickness, and that man could conquer space without replacing God. Hence, it is with hesitancy that one opposes some of these technologies such as surrogate motherhood which to some appear as yet one more way of assisting an imperfect nature in her job of providing couples with children. There are 10 million infertile couples in the U.S. today.[20] Is resistance simply based on some romantic notion of parenthood and opposition to technology per se or is it rooted in justified moral and religious reservations which cut at the very core of what it means to be human as well as undermining the created order of our world?

We are fast approaching a point where any and all means of reproducing the human race are accepted. Surrogate motherhood as the newest technique in our armentarium is especially alarming; I will use this practice as an illustration of the dehumanization which many of the new reproductive technologies create. One of the underlying issues of surrogacy is the question of technical assistance in procreation. If we take the Roman Catholic position that most technical intervention is prohibited, including homologous AID, or the orthodox Jew's perspective that AID is adultery, then surrogate motherhood becomes a moot question. Even if we do not agree with the Roman Catholic Church, there are many people who have a growing concern about our attitudes toward procreation. We no longer view ourselves as co-operating with a creator God, but with a sophisticated technology which creates babies from its test tubes.

Most of the new reproductive technologies separate love, the conjugal act, parenting and family. Surrogate motherhood carries this separation one step further by introducing a third person, not only the products of another person but a person in her totality. Somehow disembodied elements such as impersonally donated sperm and egg are less intrusive emotionally to the unique relationship between one man and one woman. I am not necessarily objecting to all technical assistance in reproduction, nor are my arguments against surrogate motherhood contingent upon opposition to *in vitro* fertilization per se.

The Vatican paper, "Instruction on Respect for Human Life in Its Origin and on the Dignity of Procreation," bases its primary objection to surrogacy on its opposition to IVF and other reproductive interventions. These are seen as undermining maternal love, breaking the conjugal act as well as reflecting a basic hostility against life. Curiously, the Roman Catholic Church seems more interested in maintaining the unitive and procreative dimension of intercourse than the exclusivity of one man and one woman. Surrogacy certainly undermines the exclusive nature of one man and one woman. This variation of a *menage a trois* bring another woman, if however briefly, into the midst of the intimate experience of a man and a woman, i.e. having a child. Tensions will surely develop between these three in all sorts of combinations of jealousy, feelings of inadequacy, i.e. not being able to bear a child, or exploitation, i.e. bearing one for someone else.

The new reproductive technologies confuse and destroy the parent/child relationship. Who are the parents—the biological or adoptive ones? With more adopted children attempting to locate their biological parents, how much more will this natural instinct be compounded with surrogacy? Will a child be told about his manner of birth? Who are the parents? Here parenthood appears to result from negotiation rather than love. One of the central questions that the use of reproductive technologies raises is whether there is a right to be a parent. There is a tendency to view infertility as a disease with any cure acceptable, but these "cures" are almost exclusively available to the wealthy. We believe that parenthood is not a contract but a covenant, an obligation and responsibility rather than a right. For this reason surrogacy by relying on legal contracts undermines parenthood as a covenant.

There are numerous ethical problems which a technocentric world view fosters by defining the creation of human life in terms of production instead of procreation. First, persons are treated as means not ends. Immanuel Kant made famous the categorical imperative which described both universality as determining the morality of acts as well as their necessary goal of treating persons as ends in themselves and not merely means. The moral dimension of judging an act by its universality is an important criteria in assessing surrogate motherhood or other third party involvement; even its strongest advocates would not recognize this as a desirable universal method of parenting; hence, it fails on Kant's first criterion. The second part of his moral position is grounded in the belief of the inherent dignity and worth of each person. Respect for persons is not based on age, sex, physical, or mental qualities, or quality of life or achievements.

The surrogate mother becomes the means by which someone else becomes a parent and her needs and feelings and womanhood are not valued in and of themselves.

Not only is the surrogate mother treated as a means, but also the baby. The child becomes a possession to be bought and sold—an object of a contract. If "service" rather than the baby is what is being bought, then the host mother has the option to keep the child. It is hard to distinguish this from baby-selling. Furthermore, how can you sell something you do not own? There is bound to be psychological impact on those babies who are birthed by technology.

A cartoon in *The Washington Post* captured this with a drawing of "Pandora's womb." Here were pictured dozens of babies talking to one another:

> "Yeah, the deal's off. They say I'm handicapped"

> "Where were you born?"; "You mean, where was I brokered..."

> "Ten Grand!!!? Mine only got $3,750"

> "I figure by second grade the courts will decide who my legal parents are."

> "My mom's a career woman, so she couldn't make it for the birth..."

> "Who's your agent?"

> "I'm going to a single parent." "You think that's bad, I've got two, but they're both gay..."[21]

Another problem is the "defective" baby. The "defective" baby has no rights. Current surrogate contracts give the biological father the right to request an abortion if amniocentesis reveals congenital abnormalities. Depending on one's view on abortion, this can already violate the unborn child. What "defects" warrant abortion? Would the wrong sex or certain physical characteristics become sufficient grounds? Furthermore, there are some abnormalities which cannot or are not detected in utero; these babies become pawns in debates about duties and obligations. There have already been cases where paternity was disputed and none of the parents wanted the handicapped baby.

A further complication of this act is its effect on the other children of the surrogate mother. If the host mother has other children (required presently to prove her child-bearing capacity) certainly they would experience anxiety that perhaps they would be sold as well; even if this ultimate fear is ungrounded, certainly their view of motherhood would be distorted.

Conclusion

Where we are going in our present technocentric world was captured decades ago in T. S. Eliot's poem "The Rock."

O perpetual revolution of configured stars,
O perpetual recurrence of determined seasons,
O world of spring and autumn, birth and dying!
The endless cycle of idea and action,
Endless invention, endless experiment,
Brings knowledge of motion, but not of stillness;
Knowledge of speech, but not of silence;
All our knowledge brings us nearer to our ignorance.
All our ignorance brings us nearer to death
But nearness to death no nearer to God.
Where is the Life we have lost in the living?
Where is the wisdom we have lost in knowledge?
Where is the knowledge we have lost in information?[22]

The progress of science has performed a considerable service in the history of humankind. It has cleared up many misconceptions, removed illusory sources of fear and groundless superstitions, and helped us to understand the wonder of our bodies and our universe. Technology has removed much of the danger of life and enabled us to conquer the previous limitations and barriers to a full life. All of this, however, has not been an unmixed blessing. By substituting categories of spirit and a transcendent God and Biblical reality with material categories and depersonalized machines, science has left us powerless in the arena of the deeper questions of life—who and what is the purpose of my life and the world and how can I experience love and meaning.

Scientific models and deductions concerning the origin, evolution and destiny of the universe can be incorporated into a new theological synthesis, but they cannot be the whole of the synthesis. What we need is a world view which honors the dignity and worth of each person, the glory of man, the care of the world and all of creation as a gift to be cherished and protected, and a belief in an omnipotent God who is the source of all knowledge, truth and love.

NOTES

1. Daniel Boorstin, *The Discoverers* (New York: Random House/Vintage Books, 1983), p. 1.

2. Leon Kass, *Toward a More Natural Science: Biology & Human Affairs* (New York: Free Press, 1985).

3. J.A.B. van Buitenen, trans., *Tales of Ancient India* (New York: Bantam Books, 1961), pp. 50-51.

4. William Durbin, Jr., "The Return of the God Hypothesis," *Christianity Today*, p. 21.

5. Boorstin, *The Discoverers*, p. 640.

6. David Edwin Harrell, Jr., "Healing in Protestant America," *Health and Healing* (1980), p. 64.

7. Ibid., p. 62.

8. Boorstin, *The Discoverers*, p. 572.

9. Paul Ramsey, *Deeds and Rules of Christian Ethics* (New York: Scribner, 1967).

10. Ibid., p. 46.

11. Jean Paul, *Sieban Kas*.

12. Hartshorne and Holmes, *The Promise of Science and the Powers of Faith* (Philadelphia: Westminster Press, 1958).

13. Boorstin, *The Discoverers*, p. 647.

14. Ibid., p. 601.

15. Stephen E. Toulmin, "The Nature of Scientific Progress," *Science, Technology, Human Values* (Winter 1985), p. 28.

16. Leone and Zaretsky, *Religious Movements in Contemporary America* (New Jersey: Princeton Univ. Press, 1974), p. 72.

17. Leon Kass, *Science* 174 (19 November, 1971), p. 785

18. James D. Watson, codiscoverer of the structure of DNA in his testimony before the House panel on Science and Technology.

19. Paul Ramsey, *Fabricated Man: The Ethics of Genetic Control* (New Haven: Yale Univ. Press, 1970), pp. 122-23.

20. Beth Spring, "What is the Future for Surrogate Motherhood?," *Christianity Today* (1987), p. 42.

21. Benson cartoon, "Pandora's Womb," *Washington Times* 3D (September 4, 1987).

22. T.S. Eliot, "The Rock," *Collected Poems 1901-1962* (New York: Harcourt, Brace & World, Inc., 1970), p. 146.

BIBLIOGRAPHY

The Age of Enlightenment. Isaiah Berlin (ed.). New York: Mentor Books, 1956.

Allen, Diogenes. *The Reasonableness of Faith.* Washington: Corpus Books, 1968.

Barth, Karl. *Protestant Thought: From Rousseau to Ritschl.* New York: Harper & Brothers Publishers, 1959.

Benson. "Pandora's Womb." *Washington Times* 3D, 4 September 1987.

Boorstin, Daniel J. *The Discoverers.* New York: Random House/Vintage Books, 1983.

Cailliet, Emile. *The Dawn of Personality.* Indianapolis: The Bobbs-Merrill Company, Inc., 1955.

Cutcliffe, Stephen H. "Science, Technology, and the Liberal Arts." *Science, Technology, and Human Values.* New York: John Wiley & Sons, 10(1): 80-87, Winter 1985.

The Dialogue between Theology and Science. Paper adopted by the 122nd General Assembly and Commended to the Church for Study. Atlanta: Office of the Stated Clerk, General Assembly Presbyterian Church in the U.S., 1982.

Durbin, William Jr., "The Return of the God Hypothesis." *Christianity Today.*

Eliot, T.S. "The Rock." *Collected Poems 1901-1962.* New York: Harcourt, Brace & World, Inc., 1970.

Ferre, Nels F. S. *Faith and Reason.* New York: Harper & Brothers Publishers, 1946.

Harrell, David Edwin, Jr., "Healing in Protestant America." *Health and Healing* Ministry of the Church, Wheat Ridge Foundation, 1980.

Hartshorne and Holmes. *The Promise of Science and the Powers of Faith.* Philadelphia: Westminster Press, 1958.

Paul, Jean. *Sieben Kass.*

Hocking, William Ernest. *The Coming World Civilization.* New York: Harper & Brothers Publishers, 1956.

Kass, Leon. *Toward a More Natural Science: Biology & Human Affairs.* New York: Free Press, 1985.

Kass, Leon. *Science* 174, 19 November 1971.

Lewis, C. S. *Christian Reflections.* Grand Rapids, MI: William B. Eerdmans Publishing Co., 1967.

Mascall, Eric. *The Christian Universe.* New York: Morehouse-Barlow Co., 1965.

Pollard, William G. *Physicist and Christian.* London: S.P.C.K., 1962.

Ramsey, Paul. *Deeds and Rules of Christian Ethics.* New York: Scribner, 1967.

Ramsey, Paul. *Fabricated Man: The Ethics of Genetic Control.* New Haven: Yale Univ. Press, 1970.

Spring, Beth. "What is the Future of Surrogate Motherhood?" *Christianity Today*, pp. 42-45, 6 March 1987.

Thompson, William Irwin. *At the Edge of History: Speculations on the Transformation of Culture*. New York: Harper Colophon Books, 1971.

Toulmin, Stephen E. "The Nature of Scientific Progress." *Science, Technology, Human Values*. New York: John Wiley & Sons, 10(1): 28-37, Winter 1985.

Utke, Allen R. *Bio-Babel*. Atlanta: John Knox Press, 1978.

What Theologians Do. F. G. Healey (ed.) Grand Rapids, MI: William B. Eerdmans Publishing Co., 1970.

Zaretsky and Leone, *Religious Movements in Contemporary America*. New York: Princeton Univ. Press, 1974.

An Ecological View of Ethics

Garrett Hardin

Department of Biological Sciences
University of California
Santa Barbara, CA

There is a unity among the disciplines of economics, ecology and ethics, and it is this: all three have as their principal concern the allocation of scarce resources. Allocation under scarcity mandates choice. Since my training lies in ecology I will use the language of that discipline to discuss the problems of choice.

A scientist cannot accept the orientation of the first sentence of the book of John: "In the beginning was the Word, and the Word was with God, and the Word was God." No doubt this statement can be interpreted in terms of symbols, parables or myths, but all such substitutes for real propositions are ambiguous. Scientists are more attracted to the motto of the Royal Society of London: *Nullius in verba.* If I were charged with altering Scripture to conform with science I would say: "In the beginning was the *World*, which everywhere and forever envelops us; against this external reality all human words must be measured."

There are many languages, many words — but only one world. The world is primary: words are secondary, and they are always on trial. No word can be its own guarantor. The world, however, needs no guarantor. We can never be sure we have captured its meaning in words. Perhaps we cannot do without words; but neither can we entirely trust them. Though no scientist, Wordsworth expressed the faith of science when he wrote: "To the solid ground of Nature trusts the mind that builds for aye." Though his vocation was tied to language, note that the poet did not presume a "solid ground of Language." Neither should we.

Respect for words led scholars to create the abstraction "literacy." This word generally suggests only printed words, but for our purposes we can broaden it to include spoken forms. Literacy is an important measure of education, but it is not the only one. In the 1950s someone created the matching abstraction, "numeracy," to apply to skill in dealing with numbers, quantities, ratios and rates of change. No one doubts the importance of numeracy in dealing with scientific problems. I shall try to show that numeracy is also important in the investigation of ethical problems.[1]

The armamentarium of literacy includes many words that implicitly deny numeracy. Most of these are cryptic variants of "infinity." We must pay attention when mathematicians tell us that infinity is not a number; that means that the word "infinity" is no proper part of numeracy. Physical scientists insist that no thing of this world is present in infinite quantity. An apocryphal account asserts that medieval logicians used to ask, "What happens when an irresistible force meets an immovable object?" Modern scientists deny that this is a meaningful question, for the operative adjectives imply an infinite amount of force or inertia. When Infinity enters, Reason flees.

It is now fashionable to build ethical theories on the assumption that "Human life is infinitely precious." But when the chips are down, does anyone really accept this theorem? Workmen's compensation insurance assigns finite monetary value to human life; if it did not, either the heirs would have to be paid an infinite amount of money (which is impossible), or no money at all (which would be unsatisfactory).

Then there is triage (a French word for "choosing"). Military physicians, faced with overwhelming casualties after a battle, feel obliged to choose which of the wounded shall receive the severely limited medical attention. Medical triage assumes that all damaged lives are not equally deserving of attention; triage is a recipe for maximizing the number of lives saved. No life is infinitely precious. Under conditions of scarcity rational men feel compelled to evaluate competing lives in a comparative way — and then choose.[2]

"Infinity" is a subterfuge used to escape the discipline of numeracy: so also is "equality." The Biblical injunction, "Love thy neighbor as thyself" implies an equality between responsibility to oneself and responsibility to others. But who is my neighbor? Now that there are five billion people in the world, do I have equal responsibilities to all five billion? How can I possibly carry so enormous a burden of obligations? Must I not rather deny the universal equality of five million obligations?

A commitment to maximize the good leads us to prioritize our obligations. Propinquity, which is relevant to obligations, can be quantified. If my literal neighbor has a need that is no more and no less that of a figurative neighbor twelve thousand miles away, the good of dispersing limited resources can be maximized by giving to my literal neighbor first. (Getting a loaf of bread to someone on the other side of the world may require more energy than there is in the loaf itself.) Traditional advice is numerately wise: "Charity begins at home."

But should charity stop there? Clearly one literal neighbor close at hand should claim more of my attention than a theoretical neighbor thousands of miles away; but what if distant claimants number in the millions? This is a more difficult problem.

To solve this problem we must go beyond intentions and examine consequences — that is, the probable consequences of well-intentioned actions. Trying to do good at a great distance — "telephilanthropy" it has been called — is now very popular.[3] It started with the proliferation of church-sponsored foreign missions during the 19th century. After the Second World War the level of telephilanthropy was raised to new heights by such national programs as AID, the Agency for International Development. Has the amount of good achieved been proportionately increased? The record is at best ambiguous.

The more distant the object of telephilanthropic attention the poorer is our understanding of the situation. Our ability to control the distribution of gifts is also poorer, as is our ability to evalute the results. The last defect, of course, is a great protector of our egos: we often do not know how much harm we do at a distance, and so (tragically) our enthusiasm for telephilanthropy continues uninhibited by experience.

All philanthropy suffers a major defect: it tends to transfer responsibility from the receiver to the donor, thus shielding the recipient from what could be a learning experience. Philanthropy pursued on a small and intimate scale by intelligent donors can minimize this danger; but on the scale of a national effort like AID the danger may be overwhelming. Critics are justified in summarizing the results of billion-dollar telephilanthropy with this bitter judgment: "The helping hand strikes again!"

Except for international aid to Lisbon following the disastrous earthquake of 1755, telephilanthropy is a creation of the 19th and 20th centuries. Technologies for better communication and better transportation made this development possible. Curiously, biology helped create a theory of telephilanthropy by popularizing the model of evolutionary succession.

Late in the 19th century, in *The History of European Morals*, W.E.H. Lecky put the history of ethics on an evolutionary basis. He wrote : "At one time the benevolent affections embrace merely the family; soon the circle expanding includes first a class, then a nation, then a coalition of nations, then all humanity." The postulated evolution seems plausible so long as the language is left pleasantly vague, as in Lecky's words, "the benevolent affections embrace." But his followers were more explicit. Shortly after the First World War a now-forgotten minor poet wrote:

Let us no more be true to boasted race or clan
But to our highest dream, the brotherhood of man.[4]

The belief that humanity is working toward the "withering away of the state," as described by Marx, with its replacement by a single world sovereignty, "One World," is a popular belief. Because such an evolution could bring an end to national wars (and presumably all wars), the One World dream is seductive. But is such an evolution inevitable? Is it even possible?

Let us rank the levels of cooperative action as follows: *Self—Family — Cronies — Tribe — Nation — One World*.[5] Since there's strength in numbers, in a competitive world (and we know no other) the egoistic individual finds that he has a better chance of achieving many of his goals by combining with other egoists. "Other things being equal," the more the better.... But other things are not equal.

In general, joining forces with others entails some sacrifice of individual interests. Consequently it is only reluctantly and with some doubts that the individual does so: unconsciously he keeps his fingers crossed. Sad to relate, there is some level of doubting at which the average cooperating animal will double-cross his associates. Such is animal nature: the study of "cheating" as an inescapable threat of altruism is an active field of research in the new field of sociobiology.

Cheating is also part of human nature; perhaps it merits being called "original sin." If we say that it is his sense of loyalty to the group that keeps a person from winning, we must acknowledge that the larger the group, the less potent is the power of loyalty. The consequence, usually decently kept hidden by taboo, was revealed in a bitter sentence written by the novelist E. M. Forster in 1939: "If I had to choose between betraying my country and betraying my friend, I hope I should have the guts to betray my country."[6]

Here is the dilemma: political power favors evolution toward the largest possible group, while loyalty favors smaller groups — cronies, friends, or (we must admit) mere self. The antagonism of opposing forces makes impossible the ultimate evolutionary replacement of intermediate groups by One World.

This conclusion is strengthened by a thought-experiment proposed by Bertrand Russell.[7] Let us suppose that the impossible happens, that One World comes into being. What then? As Russell wrote in 1949: "A world state, if it were firmly established, would have no enemies to fear, and would therefore be in danger of breaking down through lack of cohesive force." I would strengthen this statement by asserting that the postulated world state *would be certain to break down* sooner or later.

In every group, egos batter against the constrictive walls of group decisions. It takes the threat of enemies external to the group to impose the necessary discipline on egoistic members. Science fiction writers have seen this better than philosophers: repeatedly they have imagined the appearance of interplanetary aggressors who (without intending to do so) unite all the earth's sovereignties into a single world. At that point there is One World, but it is only one world among many in the universe — and Russell's point is confirmed at a higher level.

So long as there are no real interplanetary aggressors we must accept perpetual conflict between competing earthbound units. For the foreseeable future, the largest of these competing units will continue to be nations. This is the reality with which we must make our peace.

What forms will future competition take? I am optimistic enough (or fool enough) to think that national "leaders" will, in time, catch up with their nominal followers and recognize that all-out-war is no longer a survivable mode of competition. Small numbers of human beings— say a few million — might well survive total thermonuclear war; but not civilization itself. I see no profit in trying to devise a post-total-war strategy. So let us examine the less-than-war forms of conflict that we call "peace." What adjustments are required to live under conditions of survivable competition?

The human problem becomes more understandable when we adopt, and adapt, a concept from the management of animal populations. The "carrying capacity" of a territory (for a given species of animals) is defined as that number than can be supported indefinitely without degradation of the territory. If this capacity is transgressed, by even a small amount, carrying capacity in subsequent years is diminished. If transgression occurs every year, the carrying capacity enters a downward spiral from which there may be no recovery, ever. The strip of Africa bordering on the Mediterranean underwent such destruction nearly two thousand years ago, from the effects of which it has never recovered. It is for that reason that the first commandment in a Decalogue of Ecology would have to be this: *Thou shalt not transgress the carrying capacity.*

When we come to consider the human situation we are not content to look at carrying capacity in the simplest sense. We add material meaning to the Biblical statement that "Man does not live on bread alone." We westerners want to have automobiles, television, space heating, fashionable clothing and countless other things that require energy in their fabrication and maintenance. On an energy-rich diet the carrying capacity of a region is greatly reduced. Following the anthropologists in using "culture" to include material things, we want to know the *cultural carrying capacity* of a region.[8]

This capacity is inversely related to the level of the standard of living: the richer the life a human population leads, the lower is the cultural carrying capacity of the territory available to it. Differences between human populations may be great: Americans use 140 times as much commercial energy per person as do the inhabitants of Bangladesh. (The differences in food energy consumed are not so great, even allowing for Western waste; probably a factor of 5 would encompass the difference.)

What allocation problems are presented by international differences in per capita consumption of energy? Karl Marx in 1875 defined the ideal allocation in these words: "From each according to his ability, to each according to his needs."[9] His language echoes that of Scripture (Acts 4:34, 35) — an ironic resemblance, considering the low opinion Marx had of religion. In any case, the Christian-Marxist ideal motivates those who hope to put an end to what they call "global poverty." Is their hope realistic?

I think it is not. I will argue my position from two different viewpoints: first, that of the world as a whole; and second, that of the recipient of charity.

First, Marx's formula creates an unmanaged commons in which resources are held "in common," to be distributed according to need. But who determines need? Given a license to determine their own needs individuals are apt to be too generous to themselves. The Mormons in their early days tried to live by the Christian-Marxist ideal and found that it absolutely would not work because it gave lazy, wasteful and greedy individuals an advantage over those who were energetic, frugal and considerate of others.[10]

Marx's formula is counter-productive; the nobility of its language is no excuse for reiterating it. To say that poverty is global is to lead many to suppose that globe-wide forces produce it, and therefore the responsibility for getting rid of it falls on all the people of the globe.

But the creation of poverty has its immediate cause in very local actions. Where people are poor and wretched it is because their reproductive actions have swelled their numbers far beyond the carrying capacity of the lands on which they live. The correction of such local poverty must also bring into play local actions, and local determination to act. Widespread poverty is not a new fact; only our reaction to it is new. The term "global poverty" directs our attention in the wrong direction. We would do better to speak of "ubiquitous local poverties."

Eighteen centuries ago the Christian father Tertullian wrote: "The scourges of pestilence, famine, wars, and earthquakes have come to be regarded as a blessing to overcrowded nations, since they serve to prune away the luxuriant growth of the human race." No longer are Christians willing to call famine a blessing. Instead they seek to a gentler correction to overpopulation. Among the alternatives put forward are the following.

Immigration. So long as the poor can be moved fast enough to other, richer countries, famine can be averted.

Foreign food aid. Logically this is the same as immigration, except that food is moved to the people, instead of people being moved to the food.

Capital transfers. It is sometimes possible to create new industries in a poor country through gifts (called "transfers") of capital from rich to poor. Production is thus transferred from rich countries to poor.

Free trade. Workers who accept lower wages can, ceteris paribus, produce goods at lower prices than workers who demand higher living standards. Free trade then allows remunerative work to be transferred from rich countries to poor. When knowledge and know-how are shared among all, under free trade low living standards drive out high — a sort of Gresham's Law of Labor.

The threat that poor countries pose the rich does not arise from the sloth, wastefulness or greed of their people. The threat arises from the large numbers and the greater fertility of the poor. The populations of the poorest countries of the world are increasing by 2 to 3 percent per annum, while the native populations of the richest countries are increasing by less than 1 percent per year. If famine and disease are eliminated as correctives to population, commonizing the world's resources in accordance with the Marxist formula will not eliminate global poverty: it will merely universalize it. As long as there are variations in fertility, wealth cannot be shared: only poverty can be shared.

Before considering more acceptable control measures than Tertullian's famines we need to see how a commonistic sharing of the world's food can affect the recipients of charity. Ethiopia presents us with an instructive example. The famine of 1984-85 was partially aborted by massive shipments of food from the rich countries. The donors were proud that they had saved perhaps half a million lives — in the short run. What they did not ask was this: What is the probable long term effect of such a short term gain?

For poor countries like Ethiopia, the cultural carrying capacity need scarcely be considered. Such populations are living so near the animal level that the concept of simple carrying capacity is sufficient for the analysis of their survival problem. Food production is the most important aspect of this problem.

The Ethiopian population manages to survive almost entirely by virtue of three production factors: crop land; pasture land; forest land.

Crop land produces grains and other human food directly. Pasture land produces human food indirectly: grass is turned into animal flesh, which people then eat. There is an almost 90 percent loss of food energy in this transfer, but the inefficiency is nothing for humanity to worry about, because cattle can feed on grasses that have essentially no direct nutritive value for human beings.

The contribution of forest land to human nutrition is more indirect but no less important. The term "forest land" includes land that produces low bushes that are unsuitable for the feeding of cattle. Fuel is needed to cook human food. The fuel of poor people like the Ethiopians includes tree-trimmings, bushes, and animal dung. Ecologically, these fuels are likely to prove ruinously expensive.

Trees and shrubs are needed to hold the soil in place, particularly on steep slopes. Once the vegetation is gone from the slopes the soil is washed away, leaving the slopes less able to support plant growth. Soil in the rivers ends up as silt in such lakes as that behind the High Aswan Dam in Egypt. The more silt deposited, the shorter the useful life a dam-lake built for irrigation and the production of electricity. Moreover, the elimination of the water-absorptive capacity of tree-covered mountain soils greatly increases the destructiveness of floods in the lands below the slopes. As for the burning of animal dung in the cooking of food, this deprives the soil of the nitrogen it could obtain from unburned dung.

Our hearts urge us to send food to the starving poor in a distant country. But our informed heads tell us: Stop and think! Do not risk doing more harm than good. Every poor, overpopulated country has already transgressed its carrying capacity, thus violating the First Commandment of Ecology. Every life saved this year in an overpopulated country adds to charity's burden in subsequent years. Additional lives further weaken the production factors in subsequent years, thus lowering the carrying capacity and increasing the "need."

So even if the long-term effects of food gifts on the total world economy are ignored, if potential donors are concerned with the well-being of the recipients themselves they should usually refuse to give direct food aid to people who have transgressed the carrying capacity of their land. That the transgression may have taken place in innocence or ignorance makes the result more tragic but does not change the prescription for minimizing future suffering.

Ethiopia has 46 million people — far beyond the carrying capacity of the land by any reasonable standards. Ethiopians are increasing by 2.3 percent per year. Every year there are one million more Ethiopians in a land that is already overstressed. Averaging out climatic fluctuations, every year the production factors of crop land, pasture land and forest land are less capable of taking care of the Ethiopians. Tertullian's solution to overpopulation may seem cruel to present-day Christians, but are we any kinder to Ethiopians in the near future when we become a party to the further overloading of an already mistreated land? The short-fall in crops of 1984-85 is being repeated again in this year of 1987. The consequences of charitable intervention extend far beyond the present moment; it is by the total consequences that charity must be judged.

Is there nothing that well-wishers outside an overpopulated nation can do to reduce the suffering therein? Yes, one thing: help the poor nation to reduce its population.

This is not an easy task. If we were dealing with deer on an overcrowded range, shooting the excess would be the fastest, kindest measure to take. But we are dealing with fellow human beings, and homicide is out of the question.

However, over time, population numbers can be reduced by attrition — by seeing to it that the birth rate falls below the death rate. A sustained negative rate of population growth will eventually bring the population level down to the carrying capacity of the environment. How can this be accomplished?

There are two parts to the problem. First, the people must be informed of the available methods of birth control. If their leaders interpose no barriers to education, external philanthropists can help in this effort. The United States has been helping in this way for decades. The amount of money we spend on this is trifling, by our standards; but it does a great deal of good.

However, this is only the easier half of the problem. Given reliable methods of birth control most of the world's people will still have families that are too large to result in negative population growth, *because most people want too-large families*. For attrition, the *average* family must have less than two children. This means that deep-seated ideals must be changed. This is a daunting task, but we are now finding that it is not impossible.

In recent years David Poindexter's group (The Center for Population Communications—International) has had striking success working with native communicators to produce "soap operas" for movies and television that put the small family size ideal into language that is acceptable to native viewers. Obviously this work must be redone for every different culture, using the native language with natives as actors. External philanthropists can furnish money, as well as already existing materials developed for other cultures as models for the natives in creating their own materials. This work has scarcely begun, but already the results are most heartening.

The process of population attrition by acceptable means is necessarily slow. We must have patience: we are in this for the long haul.

The most serious danger I see in any program of bringing population control to other nations is this: that we may fail through trying to impose our choices on them.

Consider China's situation. The largest nation in the world has the world's most successful program of population control. Control is exerted through the women of a "production group," a socio-political entity that has no parallel in our part of the world. Women in a small unit (less than a hundred members, apparently) put pressure on each other to meet national standards. We Westerners, who have been raised in the shadow of John Locke, have a view of individualism that leads us to call the Chinese method of control a form of "coercion." Chinese women call it "persuasion."

Who's right? Who is to say? If the Chinese themselves accept their method of control, have we any business condemning it?

Led by anthropologists, we in the West have made great progress in the past century in freeing ourselves from ethical provincialism. We no longer ridicule other peoples for worshipping different gods and practicing different rites. But some among us still want to control the way other people achieve population control. This dangerous impulse needs to be exposed and discouraged.

In a world of many sovereignties, in the interests of international amity and peace, we must learn to tolerate behavior in other nations that we might condemn in our own. Our principal concern must be that every sovereign nation achieves population control by some means.

Other cultures, other means must be the motto that shapes our attitude towards the efforts of other nations to achieve population control. It would be too much to expect us to be completely indifferent to the means used by other cultures, but we must guard against the growth of a new intolerance in this area of paramount importance to all the peoples of the world.

NOTES

1. Garrett Hardin, 1985. *Filters Against Folly. How to Survive Despite Economists, Ecologists, and the Merely Eloquent.* New York: Viking.

2. Garrett Hardin, 1980. *Promethean Ethics. Living with Death, Competition, and Triage.* Seattle: University of Washington Press.

3. Hardin, *Filters Against Folly*, chapter 18.

4. Thomas Curtis Clark and Esther A. Gillespie, eds., 1927. Indianapolis: Bobbs-Merrill. See Clark's "The New Loyalty."

5. Garrett Hardin, 1982. "Discriminating altruisms." *Zygon* 17:163-186.

6. E. M. Forster, 1951. *Two Cheers for Democracy.* New York: Harcourt, Brace & World. (p.68).

7. Bertrand Russell, 1949. *Authority and the Individual.* London: Unwin. (p. 17).

8. Garrett Hardin, 1986. "Cultural carrying capacity: A biological approach to human problems." *Bioscience* 36: 599-606.

9. Karl Marx, 1875. "Critique of the Gotha program." See R.C. Tucker, ed., 1972. *The Marx-Engels Reader.* New York: Norton.

10. Kari Bullock and John Baden, 1977. "Communes and the logic of the commons." In Garrett Hardin and John Baden, eds. *Managing the Commons.* San Francisco: W. H. Freeman. (Chap. 19).

Notes on the Practice of Christian Asceticism
in Relation to Contemporary Science and Technology*

Carl Mitcham

Philosophy and Technology Studies Center
Polytechnic University
Brooklyn, NY

The following notes begin by sketching four arguments for the inherently technological character of modern natural science. Such arguments provide a basis for proposing a re-appraisal of the practice of an explicitly Christian asceticism in the contemporary technological world. A post-script emphasizes the extent to which a Christian technological asceticism can make common cause with others who recognize the need to delimit modern science and technology in the name of higher goods.

On the Technological Character of Modern Science

The essentially technological character of modern science can be argued on historical, sociological, epistemological, and metaphysical grounds.

Historically, modern science arose both under the influence of the experiences of new technologies (mechanical clocks provided the images for a clock-work Newtonian universe) and out of a desire to conquer and control nature (empiricists such as Francis Bacon and rationalists such as René Descartes agree on justifying the new science as leading to "the relief of man's estate"). A significant aspect of the basic impetus behind the rise of modern science in its classic form has been the pursuit of material power of a specifically technological sort — at both the societal and individual levels.

In the sociology of science, scholars have shown repeatedly how experimental traditions and the interactions with apparatus of various sorts (from clocks to cloud chambers and geiger counters) have been major influences in how scientists have conceptually framed the world. On the more mundane level, modern science would simply not be possible without the technological support of rockets and giant telescopes and computers and particle accelerators, etc. — that is, without the enormous technological and economic base of the

*The central section of this article, "On Technological Asceticism," has been revised from a mistitled and improperly attributed piece in *The Catholic Worker* (March 1987). The piece was co-authored with P. Hans Sun.

modern industrial state. It is also no accident that world-class science is associated with world-class military power, because only the rationale of national self-interest and military competitiveness makes possible the spending of the kinds of funds necessary to support advanced contemporary science on a broad scale. (Note that from the Manhattan Project to the "war on cancer" or the "war on AIDS" the language used to justify spending on science has almost always entailed a military metaphor.)

Epistemologically, scientific theories are regularly judged on their ability to predict the outcomes of certain technological (experimental) manipulations of the world. Resolutions of debates in science -- from nuclear physics and polymer chemistry to genetic biology -- depends on complex technical instrumentation - particle accelerators, laser spectrometers, recombinant DNA techniques. Furthermore, it is technological extensions of the human sensorium that make contemporary science feasible. Without microscopes and telescopes to extend vision, without sensors to detect single photons of light, without probes to test temperatures and pressures far above and below the human thresholds, without sensitive listening devices of all sorts and digital counters to register at speeds beyond human powers, contemporary science would simply not be possible. The scientific call for the creation of a $6 billion plus super-conducting super-collider is a recent dramatic illustration of the epistemological dependence of advanced science on advanced technology.

Metaphysically, science arose and thrives within the experiential world established by a "carpentered world" and a principled rejection of the transcendent. At the same time, modern science has its own metaphysical framework, one which presumes a dualistic distinction between appearance (phenomena of all sorts) and some deeper reality that explains it (laws, atomic or subatomic particles, fields, etc.). This dualistic framework is structurally parallel to and interrelated with that which supports technological action — i.e., the distinction between the way the world is (appearance) and the way I want to make it (in reality).

The issue here is complex, but can perhaps be rephrased as follows. Neither science nor technology is content with the way the world appears, to common sense or common experience. Both want to change the world - and not just the human world. Science aspires to penetrate the veil of appearances to make contact with more basic elements *of nature* (laws, fundamental particles) that are more able to satisfy certain human cognitive demands. Technology aspires to transform appearances to make them more compatible with human demands of a physical sort. What is remarkable, metaphysically speaking, is that both science and technology are not content with the world as it is given and in ways that call not for the transcending of the world or for the transformation of human relationships, but for physical action on material nature.

The historical, sociological, epistemological, and metaphysical arguments sketched above are not, of course, completely separate. They overlap and, it seems, mutually reinforce each other at a number of points. At the same time it is not necessary to accept all facets of each argument in order to be influenced by their collective weight. With regard to public policy questions, surely it is precisely the dominantly technological character of contemporary science that makes such questions overwhelming and crucial. It is, then, on the basis of this inherently technological characterization of modern science that one can consider an appropriately spare argument for technological asceticism on Christian foundations.

On Technological Asceticism

> The problem of getting technology back into the power of man so that it may be used for man's own good is by all odds the great problem of the day .... I think it should be the job of the monk ....
> — Thomas Merton (Letter to Rosemary Radford Ruether, March 19, 1967)

Askesis in Greek originally signified exercise or training for gymnastic games, for military prowess, or in virtue. It occurs widely in Xenophon, Isocrates, Plato, yet is appropriately limited by Aristotle to five isolated uses in the *Nicomachean Ethics* and *Politics*. For the Greek Stoic Epictetus, however, the term takes on spiritual meaning and becomes of central importance. What is the proper ascesis, he asks, by which to realize the good for which one is born? "The highest ascesis," he answers, "is this: Whenever you grow attached to something, do not act as though it were one of those things that cannot be taken away, but as though it were something like a jar or a crystal goblet, so that when it breaks you will . . . not be troubled" (*Discourses* III, xxiv, 84).

The Greek-speaking monks of the Egyptian desert — so named because they lived alone (*monos*) and for only (*monon*) one thing — brought "ascesis" into Christian theology. For Evagrius Ponticus, for instance, "ascesis consists in keeping the commandments" (*Praktikos*, no. 81) and is a spiritual method for cleansing the affective part of the soul (no. 78). "The goal of the ascetic life is charity" (no. 84). For Abba Agathon, "The human being is like a tree, bodily asceticism is the foliage, interior vigilance the fruit"; although all care should be directed toward the fruit, this is realized through the cultivation of a "protective foliage."

Christian asceticism is sometimes contrasted, first, with purification rituals, abstaining from certain foods (say) in the belief that they harbor demonic forces, and, second, with asceticism in Hinduism or Buddhism. In the latter, it is said, asceticism is not so much a means to some higher end as the beginning in this life of that cessation of personal or finite existence that is the actual goal of the spiritual life, whereas for the Christian, ascetic practices are merely ways to subordinate the lower to the higher, a path to charity. Even the commandments, for Evagrius, partake of this instrumental character.

Yet asceticism -- particularly in a liturgical context, the context (say) of Advent or of Lent -- can also be experienced as an imitation of and participation in the life of Christ. Jesus, after his baptism by John, went into the wilderness for forty days, during which he did not eat. At the end of this time he was tempted, and in rejecting the temptations, practiced a further ascesis, an exercise or training for the life that would lead him to the cross — and, through the cross, to resurrection.

According to the Gospel of Luke, the temptations were three in number. First, Jesus was tempted to make food for himself outside the normal order of growing and harvesting, by turning stones magically into bread. Second, he was offered political charge or control of "all the kingdoms of the world." Finally, Jesus was tempted to take himself outside the order of bodily limitation by casting himself down from a high place yet miraculously escaping injury. Setting aside the idea of taking charge of all the kingdoms of the world (which is an unreal possibility for most of us), how can one imitate or participate in the rejecting of such temptations?

Scripture re-presents the world in only slightly less ambiguous terms than the world originally presents itself. Like poetry and the novel — indeed, like a divinely inspired work of art — Scripture calls attention to aspects of our lives which might otherwise be overlooked, suggests paths of interpretation and response, but necessarily leaves the full development of that interpretation and the walking of those paths up to us. The Word of God calls but does not constrain. The struggle for insight, and the movement from insight to action, is fraught with ambiguity, difficulty, temptation — and should be undertaken only in prayer. Monks such as Evagrius read the Bible out loud and on their knees. We work out our salvation with fear and trembling.

In our technological age Jesus' temptations can take on new resonance, and thus suggest special courses of action or perhaps special motivations for action that otherwise has no more than a purely rational basis. Doesn't the idea of making food outside the normal order of growing and harvesting, call to mind our processed and fast-food industry and biotechnological agriculture?

Doesn't the prospect of throwing oneself down from a high place and surviving anticipate the aims of high-tech medicine?

In the Catholic tradition since Vatican II there has been a tendency to take a more "positive" approach to Lent, to shift away from denial ascesis — not to mention the self-inflicted pain ascesis characteristic of Celtic monasticism — toward doing-good ascesis. Fast on Friday, yes, not to mortify the flesh, but in order to give the money saved to the poor. While laudatory, still, it is not clear that such a rationalized asceticism reflects traditional teaching any more than does the idea of fasting to improve one's physical health.

Indeed, there are today many arguments for the delimitation of technological expansion and power: i.e., threats to the environment (pollution) and to privacy (large scale computer networks and data bases), questions of equity between developed and developing countries (technological change that causes cultural disruption), between present and future generations (genetic engineering), anticipations of apocalypse (nuclear weapons). Philosopher Hans Jonas's *The Imperative of Responsibility* seeks an ethical justification for once again practicing the virtues of moderation and circumspection, of heeding the prophetic voice which calls "Beware!" and "Preserve!" Likewise with the political theorist Langdon Winner who, in *The Whale and the Reactor* sees technologies as not neutral means but "forms of life."

Christians are in no way absolved from attending to such arguments and considering their force, but it also may be that they have resources not found in such philosophical texts for promoting new voluntary austerities. Although it is difficult for us to appreciate-- except when jolted by disasters such as Challenger and Chernobyl -- the technological world does have the fragility of a jar or crystal goblet, and we should not act as though it were a thing that cannot be taken away. The truth, according to St. Paul, is that "the form of this world is passing away" (1 Corinthians 7:31). Perhaps during Lent the practice of some technological asceticism could be experienced not so much as making deposits in an alms savings bank or as promoting physical health, but as living out the truth that our technology, too, is passing away—and as a way of imitative participation in the life of Christ.

Is there a Christian technological form of life? Perhaps this Lent we could abstain, not just from meat on Fridays, but from fast or pre-processed food, food flown in from great distances and foreign lands or otherwise dependent on high-tech agriculture. Why not drink water instead of technologically carbonated beverages? Buy products that are recyclable, take our own bags when we go shopping? Choose a book or silence over the TV, movies, stereo, or newspaper? Could automobile commuters turn their car radios off, maybe even take public transportation? Could we walk to the store instead of drive? Couldn't the telephone be turned off at least one day a week? Does one need to wear a watch every day? Maybe a person could on an occasional basis give up electric lights and once again rise and go to bed in harmony with the pattern of the sun.

In many instances Jesus asks his followers to live what feel like impossible perfections — to love enemies, to forgive those who hurt us. During Lent we traditionally make extra efforts to be open to such counsels. Why not, as well, make special efforts to be more open to the teachings of the Church regarding artificial contraception? To consider the implications of a distinction between extraordinary and ordinary means of medical technology? To abstain from the cosmetics of that industrialized vanity that rules the world of modern fashion? Could these not be spiritual preparations for that more general technological asceticism that Jonas and Winner argue must eventually be discovered by our society as a whole?

"Keep the faculty of effort alive in you by a little gratuitous exercise every day," writes William James. "That is, be systematically ascetic ... in little unnecessary points, do every day or two something for no other reason than that you would rather not do it, so that when the hour of dire need draws nigh, it may find you not unnerved and untrained to stand the test." For Christians this need not be for "no other reason than that you would rather not do it," but in order to be one, in some small way, with Christ. And through such daily practice of technological asceticism, the Christian can prepare and reach for the larger goal of technological restraint "when the hour of dire need draws nigh."

POST SCRIPT

By way of post-scripted conclusion it should be emphasized that the idea of technological asceticism is not a wholly religious notion. The founding of the Environmental Protection Agency (1969), the 1970 Senate rejection (by one vote) of the funding of the SST, and the establishment of the Office of Technology Assessment (1972) together point toward a watershed in U.S. science policy history. The key characteristic of this watershed was a willingness to say "No" to some technologies.

The Cambridge astronomer Martin Ryle has gone even further and argued that scientists should say "No" to some technologies (because of their expense, which can only be met by military funding) and even pure research (because of its potential for evil). "Should fundamental science (in some areas...) be stopped?" he asks. "It seems that, in some, the resulting evil now outweighs the good. (We do not have to understand the evolution of galaxies, or the subatomic particles...)."

The churches, too, have a history of being able to say "No" to some technologies or to call for their reformed or selective utilization. The suggestion is simply that this must be expanded in two different ways. It must be carried into our daily lives, practiced personally. And it must not let itself be unduly swayed by the arguments of scientists that science is the noble pursuit of knowledge for its own sake that we must support (to remain competitive in the world). From SDI to super-conducting super-collider and the idea of spending billions of dollars to map and sequence the human genome, science-technology could benefit from a healthy dose of criticism from the pro-asceticism perspective that sometimes "less is more."

SELECT REFERENCES

Peter Galison, *How Experiments End* (Chicago: University of Chicago Press, 1987).

Patrick Heelan, *Hermeneutics and the Philosophy of Science* (Berkeley, CA: University of California Press, 1983).

Hans Jonas, *The Imperative of Responsibility: In Search of an Ethics for the Technological Age* (Chicago: University of Chicago Press, 1984).

Martin Ryle, *Martin Ryle's Letter* (London: Menard Press, 1987).

Langdon Winner, *The Whale and the Reactor: A Search for Limits in an Age of High Technology* (Chicago: University of Chicago Press, 1986).

Science and Christian Faith Today
What They Can Learn From Each Other

Robert Short

408 Central
Wilmette, Ilinois

"Science and Christian Faith"! How are these two related nowadays and how can they help each other?

Well, to go back toward the beginning, they're certainly related in a "family" or historical way. Many thinkers have correctly seen that modern science is one of the many children or results or offsprings of Christianity. Generally speaking, it has been the Christian doctrine of *creation* that's been seen as providing the ideological *basis* for modern science. In other words, the biblical ideas about "in the beginning" were also there at the beginning of science. British theologican John Baillie puts it this way:

> But where did Bacon and Descartes, and where did the first modern scientists whose methods these were attempting to formulate, learn (the inductive method of science)? The answer may be surprising to some, and yet it is an answer given by an ever increasing number of contemporary historians. They learned it from the Christian revelation, and more specifically from the Christian doctrine of creation which teaches that the world is not itself divine but is contingent upon the divine Will.[1]

Carl-Friedrich von Weizsäcker, the Christian physicist whose writings had a profound influence on the imprisoned Dietrich Bonhoeffer, has said:

> ...the concept of strict and generally valid laws of nature could hardly have arisen without the Christian concept of creation. Matter in the Platonic sense, which must be 'prevailed upon' by reason, will not obey mathematical laws exactly: matter which God has created from nothing may well strictly follow the rules which its Creator has laid down for it. In this sense I called modern science a legacy, I might even have said a child, of Christianity.[2]

But now if all of this is true, then Baillie is right in raising the point that — "No doubt it will at once be asked why then the new movement in science had to wait for its beginning until the period of the Reformation."[3]

Or, to more precisely zero in on that part of the Reformation where the major breakthrough of modern science really took place, why did modern science have to wait for 17th Century Puritanism before it really took off? Many good books have been written about this subject, one of the best being Robert K. Merton's *Science, Technology and Society in Seventeenth-Century England*. But Ian Barbour has summarized the general conclusions of all of these careful researchers when he writes:

> Beyond the contribution of the biblical tradition in general, <u>Puritanism</u> in particular seems to have lent support to scientific endeavor. Without belittling advances that occurrred elsewhere, one can say that seventeenth-century England was the turning point in the history of science, and that the Puritans were its chief agents.[4]

So far so good, I suppose. But then the question becomes, why did "Puritanism in particular" provide such an "over the top" boost to the rise of modern science? Well, Puritanism, probably much better than any other movement in the entire history of Christianity, did a good job of holding fast to the four great "*sola*'s" of the Protestant reformation.

Solus Christus		Only Christ
Sola Gratia		Only Grace
Sola Fide	or	Only Faith
Sola Scriptura		Only Scripture

These four great pillars of Protestantism, all of which were especially emphasized by <u>Puritan</u> Protestantism, provided, it seems to me, the strongest possible foundation for the rise of modern science. And at the head of these four is *Solus Christus*, as the three other "sola's"-- or "only's"-- can be seen as branches that necessarily grow out of this strong Christo-centric root or orientation.

From the point of view of science, the first thing this Puritan concentration on Christ did was to "purify" the biblical doctrine of creation. Because although the Old Testament had taught that all the world was God's good creature and therefore natural, still a large place was left—in Judaism and in the Medieval Church—for the <u>miraculous</u> and the <u>supernatural</u>. But by emphasizing that *only* in Christ is the divine revealed, this had the effect of purifying faith from any fear of the semi-divine or the pseudo-divine or the demi-divine. There is now no longer a basis for superstition. With Christ alone as Lord, the demons are driven out. With Christ alone as Savior, there is no longer any need for any other manifestation of the divine—no other miracles, no other supernatural, and therefore no superstition. And hence Puritanism concluded "...that miracles had ceased;" the time of miracles was over. Concentration on Christ alone as God's self-revelation is why in the very first sentence of the Puritan *Westminster Confession of Faith* we are told of "those former ways of God's revealing his will unto his people being now ceased."[5] If we have faith in Christ alone, we no longer need to be afraid of any other gods or supernatural powers. And the truth of the matter is that in Medieval Christianity the natural was so saturated with the supernatural, that superstition rather than science held the order of the day and remained the chief means of controlling the world around us. But with Christ alone as the Truth, this meant that we were then quite free from fear of any other supernatural truths and could safely investigate the natural as merely the natural without being afraid of any lesser truths that we might later discover there. And so also in this sense we can understand the saying of Jesus: "If...you truly are my disciples" (that is, if you trust me alone) "you will know the truth, and the truth will make you free"—that is, free from ignorance and fear of the world and nature. And here again the apple of science didn't fall far from the Christian tree. "In their insistence on truth early Christians and modern scientists have something in common," says Weizsäcker, "differently though they interpret the meaning of truth."[6]

Russian philosopher Nicolas Berdyaev has written:

> However paradoxical it may seem, I am convinced that Christianity alone made possible both positive science and technics. As long as man had found himself in communion with nature and had based his life upon mythology, he could not raise himself above nature...by means of the natural sciences or technics. It is impossible for man to build railways, invent the telegraph or telephone, while living in fear of demons. Thus for man to be able to treat nature like a mechanism, it is necessary for the demonic inspiration of nature and man's communion with it to have died out in the human consciousness.[7]

All of this through "Christianity alone," as Berdyaev puts it. But especially through Puritan Christianity with its purifying emphasis on Christ alone.

Christ alone as Lord also led to the strong Puritan emphasis on grace alone, or *sola gratia*. For if Christ alone is savior, then we do not save ourselves even to the slightest degree. Because the extent to which we save ourselves will mark the extent to which we are our own saviors and Christ isn't. And this of course is idolatry -- idolatry of the self and one's own righteousness. It's literally self-righteousness. Therefore, said the Puritans, we must be perfectly clear that we are saved entirely by God's power alone—i.e. by *grace* alone. The decision for our salvation could only finally be made by God or by ourselves. But if we make it ourselves, then faith becomes just another good "work." It is something we have achieved and merited ourselves. We have become our own masters. But if no one can serve two masters and God alone is master and God alone is eternal, then this decision for our salvation must have been made by God himself from all eternity. This is called "by grace alone" or "predestination." And thus we can see how for the Puritans that "Predestination is...the protector and guarantor of the more important point that justification and redemption are by God's grace alone."[8]

"By grace alone" or predestination also meant, then, that God was "holy" in the sense that he was wholly in charge of everything that happened and therefore wholly responsible for all. Of course this left the Puritans with the problem of evil as a problem they didn't have an answer for. But ultimately this didn't matter for the Puritans' faith. Faith would not be faith if it didn't have evil to contend with. It would only be knowledge. It would be all head and no heart. Faith was precisely a "nevertheless" in the face of evil. It was the assurance had by all those who have faith, or who "love God," that ultimately "all things work together for good."(Romans 8:28)

And so this "working together of all things" was seen as the way God carried out his purposes in history and in nature. And since this working together was of God, it was also seen to be good, to be orderly and trustworthy, and to be a gift from God for people's investigation and use. In other words predestination or "by grace alone" or "all things working together for good" was a sort of God-sponsored determinism. And of course it was only a short step for the modern scientist to leave off the "God-sponsored" part. The Puritans had said "Holy Mother Nature." Their grandchildren, the ones who have become scientists, simply skip the "Holy." But, as Robert Merton has written: "The conviction in immutable law is as pronounced in the doctrine of predestination as in scientific investigation."[9] And it's just for this reason that the Puritan doctrine of predestination helped to pave the way for the rise of modern science.

But now notice what the Puritans did with this knowledge. Did they simply file it away as an interesting bit of Christian theorizing and let it go at that? Nope. Not the Puritans! For them, after theory came practice. They began putting this knowledge to good use and they did it with a vengeance. Why a vengeance? Because for the Puritans there was no salvation without faith in Christ alone; and there was no faith in Christ without active obedience to Christ. So this is where *Sola Fide*, or "*Faith alone*," comes into play in the Puritans' enormous contribution to the rise of modern science: their faith put them to work. And all of this has been carefully researched and is a matter of historical record. As Ian Barbour summarizes—

> Seven out of ten members of the Royal Society were Puritans -- a ratio far out of proportion to the population as a whole: most of the virtuosi [as the English scientists of the second half of the seventeenth century called themselves] were active churchmen, and many of the clergy encouraged or themselves took part in scientific pursuits. Puritan schools put science courses in their curricula...the conviction of Newton and others [was] that the study of nature, the divine handiwork, redounds to God's glory. But the Puritan understanding of *vocation* seems to have provided additional motivation for scientific work.

> The set of attitudes sometimes called "*the Protestant ethic*" (though it was not shared by all branches of Protestantism) was the development of a distinctive viewpoint toward daily work by seventeenth-century Calvinists, especially the Puritans in England. Calvin, like Luther, had rejected the idea that "religious vocations are superior to "secular" ones....

> [But] Calvinism was more activistic than Lutheranism in encouraging "this-worldly" enterprise, holding that work conducted in a rational and orderly way furthers the general welfare and is approved by God. The Christian should glorify God by working with honesty, sobriety, and thrift...[And] the "Protestant ethic" similarly endorsed *scientific* work.[10]

So "Christ alone," then, meant that the natural was *only* the natural: "grace alone" meant that it was an orderly, understandable natural; and "faith alone" meant that this natural was to be obediently *used* in service to God for men's and women's benefit.

But of course the Puritans couldn't hold opinions like this if the ecclesiastical authority they lived under held these opinions to be erroneous. Therefore the Puritans were <u>Protestant</u> Puritans. That is, they had protested against the teaching authority of the Roman Catholic Church and of the Pope, and had substituted for this authority another authority --namely, the Bible. For Puritans, and for Protestants in general, it would now be "Scripture alone" that would be their teaching authority. Well, we can see easily enough, I think, how this kind of protest could free Puritanism from some of a lot of notoriously backward ways of looking at science, views held by Popes and Catholic theologians. But switching to the teaching authority of the Bible was also very effective in freeing Protestantism from the tremendous influence of the bogus science of someone who'd never even been any kind of Christian at all -- namely, Aristotle. For the longest time, and to a large extent, science had been throttled by Aristotle. Now Aristotle was a brilliant Greek philosopher and all; but when it came to natural science, Aristotle wasn't much better than the rooster who thought it was his own crowing that caused the sun to rise every morning. And it just so happened, that early on the Catholic Church had adopted Aristotle to do most of its philosophical thinking for it, including most of its thinking about science. So when the Protestants said Scripture alone would be their teaching authority, this definitely helped free them from all of these debilitating Aristotelian notions about what makes things tick.

"Modern thought may be said to begin with the repudiation of this Aristotelian doctrine [of causation]..." writes John Baillie.[11] And it was chiefly through "Scripture alone" that "Aristotle alone" was repudiated and science was no longer throttled by Aristotle.

What we've presented so far is a thumbnail sketch of the religious presuppositions underlying the rise of modern science, presuppositions so strong and formative that they enable someone like Weizsäcker to call modern science "a child of Christianity." The effect of Puritanism and its four "Sola's" was to so purify this branch of Christianity that in this time and place science was not only freed from religious interference and persecution, but science even had religion's strong blessings and support. And so by this point I hope it's no longer a mystery why seventeenth-century Puritanism and the brave new world of science were off and running together as a happy, enthusiastic team, a team very much resembling a father and his young son.

But now given this background of these strong, original family ties, we now come to the question of what this relationship should be today, and how each of these can help the other give to the world the very best that each has to offer. A lot of water has flowed under the bridge since the days of early English Puritanism. Science and Christian faith have tended to follow their own unique and characteristic ways, just as a father and his son should. But by this time one would hope that both have learned some important and valuable lessons that might be passed along to the other. And it's to those "lessons" that we now turn.

Albert Einstein once said that "...it is just as well to state a thesis starkly and nakedly, if one wants to clear up one's mind as to its nature."[12] I agree with this statement. And in order to formulate a thesis that I'd now like to propose, I'd like to use some famous but stark and naked words of a late sixteenth- early seventeenth-century Englishman, a man who, if he was not actually a card-carrying Puritan himself, did an excellent job of expressing their ways of thinking. I'm talking about Shakespeare and the conclusive warning that

Shakespeare, in <u>Hamlet</u>, puts in the mouth of a father to his son: "This above all", says Polonius to Laertes, "To thine own self be true/And it must follow, as the night the day,/Thou canst not then be false to any man."

That is, <u>science</u> and <u>Christian faith</u> can each help the other best when each is true to its own task, its own genius, its own object and method of working, its own "self," and doesn't try to take over any of these from the other. In the body of humanity, the heart helps the mind best when it sticks to being the very best heart it can be, and doesn't try to take over the functions of the mind. And vice versa. When we express the problem in this way, this might seem to be a lesson that's self-evident. But when we consider the matter more closely, we can see that even today each of these fields of endeavor still hankers to take over a function or two of the other. I say "still" because this problem has always been the central problem between science and faith. The reason Puritanism was successful in giving science its independence in the first place was that it simply purified the church from its illegitimate desire to <u>control</u> or <u>be</u> science itself. If we have learned anything during all of this time it should be that both should stick to their own task and mind their own business. This doesn't mean that one can't help the other. But, paradoxical as it might seem, both help the other best precisely when both are true to themselves and don't try to assume the distinctive character of the other.

"To thine own essential nature be true and it must follow as the night the day thou canst not then be false to any other field of endeavor." If science and Christian faith want to give each other the very best that each has to offer, then each of them should emulate the humble postage stamp: Consider the postage stamp: its usefulness consists in the ability to stick to one thing till it gets there. For example, how can science, in sticking to its own true self, best help Christian faith today?

Well, first of all, science, in its devotion to "objective truth," can also insist that <u>religion in general</u> be true in this way whenever religion claims to be talking about matters of fact and not matters of faith. But in its devotion to careful thinking and analytical reasoning, science can be especially helpful to Christian faith by insisting that this faith be true to itself—i.e., by being true to its own declared object and methods. In this way science can help keep Christian faith honest and free of theological hypocrisy—of openly avowing one thing while denying it in actual practice. And not only can science help to <u>keep</u> faith true to itself in this way, but it can also help faith to become even truer and truer to itself, just as science has done so frequently in the past. So what an amazing development this is, then: the Puritans help to produce something called "modern science," which—as a chip off the old block—has the salutary effect of turning right around to help purify the Puritans. And when it comes to the ways this actually works, it seems that generally there are <u>negative</u> and <u>positive</u> ways in which science helps purify Christian faith.

Kurt Vonnegut is a popular contemporary novelist who has a strong background in the sciences -- especially in chemistry and anthropology. And I think Vonnegut has done a beautiful job of expressing how his kind of "scientific humanism" can use both negative and positive modes for helping faith be better faith. Vonnegut says:

> My only brother, eight years older than I is a successful scientist. His special field is physics as it relates to clouds. His name is Bernard, and he is funnier than I am. I remember a letter he wrote after his first child, Peter, was born and brought home. "Here I am," that letter began, "cleaning shit off practically every-thing."

> My only sister, five years older than I, died when she was forty...Her dying words were, "No pain." Those are good dying words. It was cancer that killed her.

> And I realize now that the two main themes of my novels were stated by my siblings: "Here I am cleaning shit off practically everything" and "No pain."[13]

So first, the <u>negative</u> way that science can help Christian faith.

"Cleaning shit off practically everything" should mean for science's confrontation of religion exactly what it also means for Vonnegut -- i.e., debunking everything that <u>can</u> be debunked. Obviously, this is a much-needed scientific task; but at the same time it's not the kind of thing that most scientists want to get involved in. There's very little money or prestige in this kind of effort, any progress made is difficult to recognize or measure, and you clearly don't make a lot of friends going around being coolly rational while tipping over people's irrational false gods. In biblical and theological terms, what we're really asking is for the scientist to play the part of the prophet or the iconoclast, and this is a role that's just naturally never going to be that popular. So thank heavens it's now true that more and more scientists seem to be realizing that as scientists they have a personal stake in this task. They seem to be more aware "that the recent tide of antiscientific and pseudoscientific irrationalism threatens to drown us in sheer nonsense and may ultimately threaten the social climate within which the pursuit of objective knowledge is advanced."[14]

And indeed we can already see this pursuit drastically weakening. In 1987 in the United States -- "the number of undergraduate science majors [fell] by half since 1960, and in another 10 years the batch of home-grown scientists will have dwindled to crisis proportions."[15]

And so, whether the task appeals to them or not, or whether out of selfish interest or altruism, the scientific community needs to get on with this important job of "cleaning the shit off practically everything." And certainly the community of faith can only gain by this effort. As the Reformers and Puritans were well aware, Christianity itself is in constant need of being reformed and purified. And so whether they realize it or not, the scientific purifiers are among Christian faith's best and most helpful friends. Their efforts can only help clean off what needs to be cleaned off. They can only clean off what is not of faith. The real thing they can never harm. The truth of God has nothing to fear from truth about his world. As Karl Barth can write:

Faith in God the creator frees us from all mythical interpretations of the world and enables us to investigate scientifically the whole of that reality in nature and history which is open to our sense-experience and reason, without falling victim to any ideology of science.[16]

Well, if this is the first way that science can help Christian faith, by acting as this kind of purifier which forces faith to be true to its own Lord and not some other, and if we define faith in terms of the "four sola's" of the Reformation and of early Puritanism, then the question arises as to where it is among these four sola's that tough-minded scientific thinking can be most helpful to faith today. In other words, when people speak nowadays in the name of "the Christian faith," what are they saying and emphasizing that's most easily and manifestly debunkable from a scientific point of view? And from a Christian point of view, what are they saying that has the greatest need for being debunked—scientifically and otherwise.

Well, of course science is going to be interested in that aspect of faith that claims to know about what science claims to know about—namely, the nature of this world and how it works. We would expect science to be most conversant with the Christian doctrine of creation. And that leads us back to Sola Gratia. Because the Reformers and the early Puritans held that it was solely by God's grace, by God's own love and power, that anything comes into being and is sustained in being; and that furthermore it was only by God's grace, working in and through the world—through nature and history, that Christian faith came into being and is sustained in being. In this view, believers themselves did absolutely nothing to help create their own faith. Even when it came to faith,

God remained the sole creator and predestinator. Even here the sovereignty of God remained pure. *Sola Gratia*, God's grace alone creates faith in the world.

"So it depends not upon man's will or exertion, but upon God's mercy" (Rom. 9:16, RSV) says St. Paul.

But now this view of things has never been popular with people. People don't like the idea of not being in charge of their own destinies, especially if their destinies are in the hands of a mysterious and capricious God who is going to send all people either to heaven or to hell, and evidently most of them to hell. And so then most people quite understandably rejected the notion of predestination, and with it *Sola Gratia*, and opted instead for some form of what can probably best be called "Pelagian Christianity."

In Pelagian Christianity I have something called "free will." Which side of God I end up on is finally my own doing, my own choosing, and hence what comes to me as a result will be my own deserving. My will is "free" -- i.e., it is ultimately free from any forces extraneous to it that cause it to act as it does, including the laws or forces of nature. My will is itself the creator of its own responses. And so then Pelagian Christianity would expressly deny Paul's statement that— "By grace you have been saved through faith: and this is not your own doing... "(Eph. 2:8, RSV). Pelagianism instead insists that faith indeed depends on man's will and its exertion, that faith is indeed our own free doing.

Well, this notion of people being their own lords and saviors, the creators and masters of their own destinies, is not only bad theology, as we can see from these statements of Paul's, but is also very bad science. And it's not necessary to be anything close to a trained scientist to see this. In one of his short stories called *A Report to an Academy*, Franz Kafka has an ape who has been transformed into a man, say to his audience something that sounds very much like what St. Paul says to his audience. The ape tells them:

> I fear that perhaps you do not quite understand what I mean by...the word "freedom." I do not mean the spacious feeling of freedom on all sides. As an ape, perhaps, I knew that, and I have met men who yearn for it. But for my part I desired such freedom neither then nor now... "self-controlled movement." What a mockery of holy Mother Nature![17]

The scientist tells us the same thing. To attribute to people the kind of freedom that Pelagian Christianity attributes to them -- "self-controlled movement" -- is, as far as science is concerned, a "mockery of holy Mother Nature"! Albert Einstein says that "the serious scientist" is the scientist who "takes the hypothesis of causality really seriously." And so we guess that Einstein himself was a serious scientist, because he goes on to tell us that -- "...a man's actions are determined by necessity, external and internal, so that in God's eyes he cannot be responsible, any more than an inanimate object is responsible for the motions it undergoes."[18]

Good grief! What a heretic this old bird is in the eyes of Pelagian Christianity (which was itself condemned as a heresy back in the sixth century). But then what Einstein is saying here is true of all science as science. As he says, science wouldn't even be science without taking the hypothesis of causality seriously. And so, as Einstein could also say: "I do not at all believe in human freedom in the philosophical sense. Everybody acts not only under external compulsion but also in accordance with inner necessity."[19]

And it sems to me that this is a statement with which by far the greatest portion of the New Testament would have no trouble at all. What Einstein has said here is simply "only Mother Nature!" Or to use Kafka's term, which is more in keeping with the Christian doctrine of creation, "only holy Mother Nature!" Or, to use the New Testament's word, "only grace."

Now we mustn't suppose that this antiscientific view of man held by Pelagian Christianity is merely a minor problem in the thinking of the churches. Because it's also an anti-Christian view of man. Starting with its attack on grace, this idea then infects everything else in the Church's thinking, including its thinking about Christ and faith and God. You can't weaken one central dogma of Christian faith without weakening all the others, and that means eventually weakening just about everything else in civilization. Luther shows us how this question lies at the very center—and not merely on the outskirts— of Christian faith:

This is my absolute opinion: he that will maintain that man's free-will is able to do or work anything in spiritual cases, be they never so small, denies Christ. This I have always maintained....and thereby will I remain, for I know it to be the truth, though all the world should be against it.[20]

Now it happens that there is practically no end to Pelagian Christianity as it contaminates the churches' thinking today. In one form or another it seems to be found in most present-day Protestant, Orthodox and Roman Catholic theology. It's found among liberals and conservatives of all stripes, whether they be liberal theologians teaching in our best seminaries or fundamentalists handing out tracts on the street. But all of these folks seem to be dimly aware of the "enfeebling inconsistency lurking in the background" to use Whitehead's way of describing the problem. They all seem to be more or less consciously aware that this idea of "free will" is a "mockery of holy Mother Nature" and that it is flatly contradicted by the very nature of science itself. Therefore the Pelagians have long been looking for some sort of gap in science that can act as a basis for Pelagian respectability. Just as the fundamentalists anxiously search for gaps in the paleontologists' records in order to give credibility to something called "creation science," the Pelagians anxiously search for gaps within the realm of scientific theory that can lend support to the Pelagian idea of "man-his-own-creation science."

And guess what! They think they've found it! Now they all bend their knees and bow their heads and thank God for sending them—St. Heisenberg! Bonhoeffer told us that the god of religion was supported in different ages by what were then perceived to be the gaps in human knowledge. But now, said Bonhoeffer, we're running out of gaps and so the god of man-made religion is doomed. The "god of the gaps" is done for. Well, perhaps Bonhoeffer underestimated just a bit the gaps that sin could still come up with. Because the robust, formidable, "god of the gaps" that our own age is now so proud of is the god of the gap revealed by St. Heisenberg—i.e., Heisenberg's so-called "principle of atomic indeterminacy." Now that a physicist like Heisenberg has assured us that we can't always determine what's going to happen among sub-atomic particles, this opens a whole new gap of mystery and uncertainty into which we can conveniently inject God or "free-will" or spirit or anything else that we might like. And the marvelous thing about the "Heisenberg Principle" is that it can be used by absolutely anybody. The fundamentalist out on the street will cite Heisenberg chapter and verse to prove to you that you do have "free will," and therefore if you freely decide not to believe in Jesus it'll be your own damned fault and therefore God will be quite justified in sending you to hell for all eternity. The process theologian can use Heisenberg to elevate human potentiality to its traditionally high status in liberal theology, and can also help us to better understand evil, since not even God himself knows what sub-atomic particles are going to do next.

People like Shirley MacLaine and the New Age dimwits can point to Heisenberg as scientific proof that the entire universe is both materially and spiritually up for grabs. That is, creation is no longer understood as God's good creation, but once more becomes the home of spooks, and goblins and things that go randomly bump in the night.

In John Updike's recent novel *Roger's Version*, Roger Lambert is a present-day Protestant professor of theology who obviously represents a lot of Updike's own views. At one point Lambert practically goes up in smoke when he tells a student: "If there's one thing that makes me intellectually indignant around here it's the constant harping of calf-eyed students on quantum

mechanics and the Heisenberg principle as proof of that hoary old philosophical monstrosity Idealism."[21]

But what could be a better gap for religion—all religion—since science
itself, in the Heisenberg principle, has now proven conclusively that it's no
longer necessary to take science seriously, much less take seriously the grace
of God? So this is the famous all-purpose "god of the Heisenberg gap," the
particular "god of the gap" that our own time has taken so to its heart. Once
more, to use a phrase from *Roger's Version*, we're busily "tying God to human
ignorance."[22]

But even should the "gap" of atomic indeterminacy turn out to be true
(and there's no assurance that it will), this theory in physics has nothing to do
with "metaphysics"; this view about the material has nothing to do with the
spiritual, either from the point of view of science or from the point of view of
the Christian faith. From the point of view of Christian faith, to "prove God"
on the basis of the material simply shows that our faith is really in the material,
since what we finally use to prove something is what we finally have faith in
or trust. And even if our attempts to "prove God" didn't represent a lack of faith
in God, science -- with or without Heisenberg -- is still an essentially deterministic as it ever was. As theologian John Dillenberger can write: "That nature
is no longer to be interpreted in the older causative terms hardly means that ...
there are gaps in nature in the traditional sense of that term. The concept of
causality in a more restricted sense has not been abandoned by physics."[23]

No doubt many people felt that their provable God and their free will had
been given "the old heave ho" when Laplace told Napoleon that his, Laplace's,
thorough-going mechanical and deterministic view of the universe had no need
for a "God hypothesis." But now these same people can be seen gleefully
celebrating. They figure that since science is now talking about something
called "indeterminacy," that this must mean that science not only now needs a
"God hypothesis," but also that science now supports their Pelagian freedom.
But, says Dillenberger --

> This new openness in science dare not be misinterpreted .... It
> is not a warrant for basing philosophical and religious ideas on
> specific conceptions in the new science. There is a great danger of
> filling the gaps in science with theological answers, or of seeing too
> readily the footprints of God in the world, or of assuming ... an
> argument for free will in the concept of indeterminacy ....

> It is extremely perilous to inject theological biases into the
> problems of indeterminacy and into the apparent void created by the
> abandonment of the older notions of rigid causation. Nor is such a

procedure theologically fruitful: it is frankly inappropriate to speak
of God in that way ....

In a world which has lost its sense for mystery, theologians are
tempted to find support for it in science. But the mystery in science
is potentially more open to specific forms of investigation, and
hence transformation, than the essential mystery of revelation. The
mystery of revelation is of another order, even if the mysteries
present in science do not abate.[24]

So here again Christian faith is called back to be true to itself, true to its
own "order," its own norm and basis of revelation, and not to go whoring after
false gods or basing itself on something from another order, even when this
something sounds as impressive as "the Heinsenberg principle of indeterminacy." And for its part, science should be better aware of when its tentative
findings are being illegitimately used like this and hence do a better job of
cleaning the shit off practically everything—including the crap that has
attached itself to science.

And what would happen to faith if it once again began to take the
doctrine of *Sola Gratia* in utter seriousness? Well, for one thing this would
mean that Christians would no longer have any basis for worshipping themselves and their own abilities and possibilities. Nor would they have to continue
making a mockery of Holy Mother Nature in the eyes of science. But wouldn't
this also mean a return to the terrible doctrine of "double predestination," taught
by Calvin and most of the Puritans? Quite the contrary. The evidence is that
when the doctrine of grace -- i.e., the doctrine of God's total power but also his
total love -- when this doctrine is held with complete consistency and seriousness, as in the case of someone like Karl Barth, then this consistency and
seriousness leads to far more optimistic and positive theological conclusions
than apparently the Puritans or Calvin ever came to. "I am a Calvinist but not
a gloomy one," Barth has said. Grace, when taken seriously and consistently,
leaves no room for gloom:

> The election of grace is the sum of the Gospel—we must put
> it as pointedly as that. But more, the election of grace is the whole
> of the Gospel, the Gospel *in nuce*. It is the very essence of all good
> news ....

> We cannot be too soon, or too radical, in the opposition which
> we must offer to the classical tradition .... And we introduce the first
> and most radical point with our thesis that the doctrine of election
> must be understood quite definitely and unequivocally as Gospel..that

it is not No but Yes; that it is not Yes and No, but in its substance, in the origin and scope of its utterance, it is altogether Yes.[25]

But is this is what could happen to _faith_ if faith were faithful to grace, what would happen to _science_ if faith once again began to take the doctrine of _Sola Gratia_ in this utterly consistent and serious way? Well, the most obvious answer to this question is that this more optimistic understanding of Christian faith certainly wouldn't produce as many atheistic scientists as the traditionally "gloomy" understanding has in the past. All you have to do is take a quick look at the history of the relations between these two—between science and Christianity—to see a very clear pattern emerging in why so many scientists have rejected Christianity. They reject it because it lacks grace. Instead of God's love and power, which is the meaning of grace, they only see Christianity's more traditional emphasis on God's damnation of people who have chosen the wrong path by their own power. Talk about a "turn off"! This view of Christianity has always turned people off. I submit it's the number one reason why so many people reject Christianity: and at this point scientists are no different from anyone else.

Charles Darwin, who began his career as a committed Christian, talks about his increasing difficulties in accepting, as he put it, "God the ... revengeful tyrant."

> Thus disbelief crept over me at a very slow rate, but was at least complete ... and [I] have never since doubted even for a single second that my conclusion was correct. I can indeed hardly see how anyone ought to wish Christianity to be true; for if so ... the men who do not believe, and this would include my Father, Brother and almost all my best friends, will be everlastingly punished.

> And this is a damnable doctrine[26]

Albert Einstein, in the following statements, takes us up to the present time:

> Nobody, certainly, will deny that the idea of the existence of an omnipotent, just, and omnibeneficent personal God is able to accord man solace, help, and guidance; also, by virtue of its simplicity it is accessible to the most undeveloped mind. But on the other hand, there are decisive weaknesses attached to this idea itself, which have been painfully felt since the beginning of history. That is, if this being is omnipotent, then every occurrence, including every human action, every human thought, and every human feeling and aspiration is also his work; how is it possible to think of

holding men responsible for their deeds and thoughts before such an almighty Being? In giving out punishments and rewards He would to a certain extent be passing judgment on Himself. How can this be combined with the goodness and righteousness ascribed to him?

Science has therefore been charged with undermining morality, but the charge is unjust .... Man would indeed be in a poor way if he had to be restrained by fear of punishment and hope of reward after death.

The main source of the present-day conflicts between the spheres of religion and of science lies in this concept of ... God.[27]

In other words, the concept of a God without grace. A God of unconditional power and unconditional love, the God of grace, has been replaced by a weak, peevish little human-like god who rewards or punishes people on the basis of their own power to love and obey. And there's no doubt that both Freud and Marx also thought this angry little god was the God of Christian faith, and therefore rejected Christianity for the same reasons as Darwin and Einstein.

These, then, are some of the ways that science can help Christian faith by cleaning the crap off practically everything, including off its concept of God.

But now how can science be more helpful to Christian faith in a more positive way? Well, Jesus has told us that faith would be known by its "fruits" or its results. Science can't investigate faith itself, since "faith is the ... conviction of things not seen" (Heb. 11:1). But it can investigate observable results. It can observe where Christian faith and other religions would seem to be making good on their promises to decrease both the physical and spiritual suffering in this world. Science can check to see where it finds "no pain" as a result of religious belief. For the most part, this will be the job of the "social sciences" -- of history, psychology, sociology, political science and anthropology. Far more seriously than they have in the past, these sciences should be carefully aware of the various faiths that people live by and the far-reaching consequences of these different faiths. Nor is it scientifically permissible to lump all of these different groups into something called "religion," as the supposedly ultra-scientific Marxists have tended to do. Science, the "great observer," should be keenly analytical in attempting to understand why one religious faith will seem to deliver one set of results, and another faith another set -- or no results at all. And so science can help Christian faith by asking to see this faith in the form of its works. And again Christian faith has only to gain from such an investigation. For what sort of faith would we have if this good tree didn't produce good fruit?

But on the other side of the ledger Christian faith can also be helpful to science. Faith can likewise assume a negative stance toward science and play the prophet's part by attempting to clean the shit off practically everything— including off science. Scientists, just as easily as anyone else, can "fall victim to an ideology of science," to use Barth's words. And this is no small problem. In recent years, for instance, we've all witnessed the grief that can be produced by such "ideologies of science" as Nazi racial theories or the so-called "scientific socialism" of communist tyranny. In different ways this kind of thing can keep happening again and again. So it's an important prophetic function that faith is called to play here in delivering a strong "No!" to all science-sponsored ideologies or false gods.

But of course there would be little need for such ideologies or false gods if faith were to do a better job in its positive function of being more true to itself and truly witnessing to the true God. Says John Baillie --

When nature is believed to have no preordained meaning or purpose in itself ... the remaining concern is only to subdue its inherent purposelessness to our own chosen ends. Yet if, in their turn, these ends ... are not themselves informed by faith ... if they represent only human preferences dictated by interest instead of solemn obligations emanating from a source beyond ourselves, then science becomes a desperately dangerous tool to put in men's hands.[28]

We have seen how science itself rose, grew strong and gained its independence precisely out of a rich soil of faith-sponsored meaning and hope. "On the other hand," says Baillie,

I am equally convinced that, if faith should languish, the scientific impulse would in the end languish no less. For science does not possess in itself the necessary nourishment of its own vitality....I am sure that if I believed nature to have no meaning, to be leading nowhere and accomplishing nothing, I should lose all speculative interest in the manner of its preceding ....

Science itself produces no outlook on life. The outlook which it is made to serve is always determined for it by some judgment of value such as cannot by any magic be spirited out of its own observation of facts, some apprehension of quality which ... has nothing to do with quantity or measure.[29]

Einstein was pointing to this problem when he could say in 1950: "Perfection of means and confusion of goals seem -- in my opinion -- to characterize our age."[30]

Or, as one *New Yorker* cartoon puts it:

"They have the know-how, but do they have the know-why?"

Drawing by J. Mirachi; ©1972. The New Yorker Magazine, Inc.

Or, to put it still another way: "They have the means, but do they have the meaning?"

So then it's true today just as it was at the beginnings of modern science: science needs Christian faith not only to give it a strong context of <u>meaning</u>, but also to prevent it from becoming <u>demonic</u>, For this reason, Herbert Butterfield's famous dictum, which no doubt is a good one for all of us, is especially made to order for scientists to carry around in their mental pockets. Butterfield said: "We can do worse than remember a principle which both gives us a firm Rock and leaves us the maximum elasticity for our minds: The principle: Hold to Christ, and for the rest be totally uncommitted."[31]

Science also needs the social-political context of <u>freedom</u> to work in. And there are plenty of good indications in this world that modern political freedom, just like modern science, came into being and is nourished by a strong context of Christian faith and meaning. It's no accident that most of the early Puritan champions of science were also strong champions of political liberty. Faith in Christ not only effectively drove out the demons of superstition, but it also began the modern demand for freedom in order that faith in Christ could truly be people's own faith and not something forced on them by others, in which case of course it wouldn't really be faith at all.

And anytime science and freedom think they forget their background in Christian faith, they are unconsciously sawing off the limb on which both are sitting. As far as I'm concerned it was actually Bonhoeffer who really said it best to the modern age: that Christian faith can best serve science—and best serve freedom and all the rest—by being true to itself and its own Lord. Bonhoeffer said:

> In devoting herself to her proper task...the Church strikes a blow at the spirit of destruction. The "restrainer," the force of order, sees in the Church an ally, and, whatever other elements of order may remain, will seek a place at her side. Justice, truth, science, art, culture, humanity, liberty, patriotism, all at last, after long straying from the path, are once more finding their way back to their fountain-head. The more central the message of the Church, the greater now will be her effectiveness.[32]

NOTES

1.   John Baillie, *Natural Science and the Spiritual Life* (New York: Scribner's Sons, 1952), p. 20.

2.

Carl-Friedrich von Weizsäcker, *The Relevance of Science* (London: Collins, 1964), p. 163.

3.   Baillie, *op. cit.*, p. 20.

4.   Ian G. Barbour, *Issues in Science and Religion* (New York: Harper & Row, 1966), p. 48.

5.   *The Westminster Confession of Faith*, 1647, Chapter I, No. 1.

6.   Weizsäcker, *op. cit.*, p. 112.

7.   Nicolas Berdyaev, *The Meaning of History* (Cleveland: World Publishing Co., 1962), p. 106.

8.   Dewey D. Wallace, Jr., *Puritans and Predestination* (Chapel Hill: University of North Carolina Press, 1982), p. 6.

9.   Robert K. Merton, *Science, Technology and Society in Seventeenth-Century England* (New York: Harper & Row, 1970), p. 108.

10.   Barbour, *op. cit.*, pp. 48-49

384   Robert Short

11. Baillie, *op. cit.*, p. 16.
12. Albert Einstein, *Ideas and Opinions* (New York: Crown Publishers, 1954), p. 41.
13. Kurt Vonnegut, *Welcome to the Monkey House* (New York: Delacorte, 1968), pp. ix-x.
14. Kendrick Frazier, "UFOs, horoscopes, Big foot, psychics and other nonsense," *Smithsonian*, March 1978, p. 56.
15. William Raspberry, "Where have all the scientists gone?," *Chicago Tribune*, 28 November 1987.
16. Karl Barth, *Fragments Grave and Gay*, Martin Rumscheidt, ed. (Glasgow: Wm. Collins & Co., 1971), p. 56.
17. *Selected Short Stories of Franz Kafka*, tr. Willa and Edwin Muir (New York: The Modern Library, 1952), p. 173.
18. Albert Einstein, *op. cit.*, p. 39.
19. *Ibid.*, p. 8.
20. *A Compend of Luther's Theology*, Hugh Thoreson Kerr, Jr., ed. (Philadelphia: Westminster Press, 1943), p. 90.
21. John Updike, *Roger's Version* (New York: Fawcett Crest, 1986), p. 180.
22. *Ibid.*, p. 84.
23. John Dillenberger, *Protestant Thought and Natural Science* (Nashville: Abingdon Press, 1960), p. 288.
24. *Ibid.*, pp. 286, 288-9.
25. Karl Barth, *Church Dogmatics*, II/2 Authorised Translation (Edinburgh: T. & T. Clark, 1957), pp. 13-14.
26. *The Autobiography of Charles Darwin*, Nora Barlow, ed. (New York: W.W. Norton & Co., 1958), p. 87.
27. Einstein, *op. cit.*, pp. 46-47.
28. Baillie, *op. cit.*, pp. 35-6.
29. *Ibid.*, p. 34.
30. Albert Einstein, *Out of My Later Years* (New York: Philosophical Library, 1950), p. 113.
31. Herbert Butterfield, *Christianity and History* (New York: Chas. Scribner's Sons, 1950), p. 146.
32. Dietrich Bonhoeffer, *Ethics*, tr. N. H. Smith (New York: Macmillan Co., 1965), p. 20.

Appendix I

Final Report and Recommendations
to the
Advisory Council on Church and Society
from the
Task Force on Theology and Cosmology

Referral:

A Study of the Role of Cosmology
Mackinac Presbytery Overture

To initiate a study of the role of cosmology in the Bible and in the traditional doctrinal formulations of the church, the changes in cosmology as the result of the rise of science, and the theological significance of contemporary cosmological positions for traditional doctrinal affirmations.

... Request the Advisory Council on Church and Society to develop a process for initiating such a study and for communicating its contents to the church ... (and) to communicate a report of the process it develops to the 195th General Assembly (1983). (Minutes, UPCUSA, 1982, Part I, pp. 101 and 487.)

Response:

The Advisory Council on Church and Society authorized Rev. Kenneth McCall to chair a task force of five persons, chosen because of their particular expertise and interest.

The focus of the study was to be "directed to the theological and intellectual framework within which our understanding of society, history and social policy is developed."

Membership:

The Task Force Members were: Dr. Kenneth McCall, Chairperson, Pastor, First Presbyterian Church, Bend, OR; Dr. Ian Barbour, Bean Professor of

Science, Technology and Society, and Professor of Religion, Carleton College, Northfield, MN; Dr. Eric Juengst, Research Associate, Division of Medical Ethics, University of California Medical School, San Francisco, CA; Dr. James Miller, Campus Minister, United Campus Ministry of Pittsburgh, Pittsburgh, PA; Dr. Harold Nebelsick, Professor of Theology, Louisville Theological Seminary, Louisville, KY; and Dr. Robert Russell, Associate Professor of Theology and Science, Graduate Theological Union, Berkeley, CA. Dr. Edward Daub and Dr. Dean Fowler served on the Task Force for brief periods. Rev. Daniel Little, Pastor, First Presbyterian Church, Ithaca, NY, assisted the Task Force in developing a proposal for a network on theology and science concerns. Dr. Terry Bunde, member of the Advisory Council, and Dean Lewis, Director of the Advisory Council, served as liaison members.

Responsibilities:

1. Plan and implement a design for studies: define an overall concept and approach; describe specific subjects to be addressed; identify and commission persons or groups to prepare papers; edit and compile the products for publication.

2. Seek ways for identifying persons, both clergy and lay, in the United Presbyterian Church and the Presbyterian Church in the United States as the nucleus for a potential network on religion and science issues,

    beginning with those who will contribute to the studies because of interest and expertise. The formation of a limited number of pastors' response groups on an experimental basis is encouraged.

3. Establish relationships with such groups as:

    a. The Center for Theology and the Natural Sciences, The Graduate Theological Union, Berkeley, California.

    b. The Institute on Religion in an Age of Science, Chicago, Illinois.

    c. The Center for Theological Inquiry, Princeton, New Jersey.

        The task group should seek ways to mediate the resources available from such groups to the churches and also ways to achieve greater church involvement in their work.

    d. Seek the greatest possible awareness and use in the United Presbyterian Church of the report of the Presbyterian Church in the United

States, entitled "The Dialogue Between Theology and Science," received by the 122nd PCUS General Assembly in 1982.

e. Seek to foster United Presbyterian Church participation in the project sponsored by the Education in Society Division of the National Council of Churches, designed to bring together persons engaged in the faith, science, and technology dialogue.

Meetings:

The Task Force me September 16-17, 1983, Berkeley, CA; May 24-27, 1984, New York, NY; October 4-7, 1984, Macinaw City, MI; November 21-24, 1985, Anaheim, CA; December 4-7, 1986, Berkeley, CA; April 24-27, 1987, Louisville, KY; and December 9-12, 1987, Burlingame, CA.

Accomplishments:

The work of the Task Force has been previously reported to the General Assembly. The following are brief highlights.

1984 — Sponsored a session at the annual American Association for the Advancement of Science meeting. The AAAS session was entitled "Science and Religion: Renewed Dialogue in a Post-Modern, Post-Critical Culture." Approximately 200 persons attended the three-hour session. Two papers were presented by Task Force members, James Miller and Robert Russell. Other papers were presented by the Reverend Ernan McMullin of Notre Dame, the Reverend Matthew Lamb of Marquette, and Professor Stephen Toulmin of the University of Chicago.

1985 — Sponsored a seminar at Ghost Ranch led by Dr. Robert Russell and Dr. Harold Nebelsick. Prepared a questionnaire for the Presbyterian Panel on "The Relationship of Religious Beliefs and Understandings of Science."

The work of the Task Force culminated in "The Consultation on the Church and Contemporary Cosmology: Implications of Science for Christian Life and Thought," held at Mercy Center, Burlingame, California, December 9-12, 1987.

Fourteen papers were prepared and presented along with extensive discussion in small groups. Over 90 laypersons and pastors from across the church, including many scientists, joined in the discussion of the papers and their implications.

The purpose of the Consultation was defined in the following terms:

"To help initiate dialogue and discussion in the Church concerning the significance of contemporary science for theological expression and moral life. In addition to surveying the history of the impact of cosmological ideas on the Christian heritage, the consultation will review the major developments in the physical and biological sciences which are forming the contemporary cosmological vision. The significance of this vision for Christian theology will be considered along with implications for ethics, social and economic policy, literature and the arts, personal faith, and education."

The preparation and convening of this Consultation has helped to identify many scientists and theologians as well as laypersons, pastors and campus ministers who wish to continue and expand discussion and exploration of the issues concerning faith and contemporary science.

Therefore:

The 200th General Assembly (1988)

1. Commends the Advisory Council on Church and Society for convening the Consultation on the Church and Contemporary Cosmology, for arranging for the findings to be published and expresses appreciation to those who planned the Consultation and prepared papers for it as well as all who participated in it.

2. Urges members of the Presbyterian Church (U.S.A.) to read the reported findings of the Consultation and particularly urges congregations and presbyteries to explore use of the materials in educational events and continuing dialogues, drawing on the scientific and theological knowledge of members and pastors of the churches.

3. Requests the adoption of the following recommendations from the Task Force.

    "It was the sense of the Consultation on the Church and Contemporary Cosmology that:

    WHEREAS, the very existence of our church is threatened today by its inability to speak intelligibly to a scientific and technological world; and

WHEREAS, all the church's ongoing concerns for proclamation, mission, pastoral care, and social action are dependent on the continued existence and credibility of the church and its message; and

WHEREAS, the church in its theology and ministry need to understand the world of science and technology which shapes to way its members think and live and without such understanding is unable to adequately express the relation of God to this world and to humanity as it develops its ministry; and

WHEREAS, the profound changes in our understanding of the world in the 20th century, emerging from the continuing exploration and discoveries of science concerning the nature of life and the universe, have enormous potential implications for the forms in which Christians express their faith in a creating, redeeming and sustaining God and for human life and society; and

WHEREAS, both the continuing search of science and the intentional exploration of its theological implications are hallmarks of the Reformed Christian faith which values all human faculties as gifts of a providential God and seeks to bring their exercise to the service of God in the world; and

WHEREAS, this crisis will continue to deepen as we approach the 21st century in a global human community and global Christian community;

THEREFORE, we call upon the 200th General Assembly to recognize the urgent need to develop a major program to address these concerns and to initiate this program through the following recommendations.

1. Calls upon the church through its General Assembly Units and governing bodies to support and encourage continued research, discussion and action related to the above concerns by:

    a. Urging the Theology and Worship Unit to give priority consideration to implementing their responsibility as stated in the Mission Design to "encourage theological reflection on new developments in science and technology."

    b. Requesting the Theology and Worship Unit to establish a work group or task force to continue the work begun by the Task Force on Theology and Cosmology, with the intent to maintain an ongoing interaction between the development of theology and the developing body of scientific knowledge.

c.   Urging the General Assembly Council and the Theology and Worship Unit to provide adequate budget and staff resources to implement this work.

d.   Urging the Social Justice and Peacemaking Unit to give careful attention to the issues of science and technology, especially as they impact our understanding of the human being as a part of the natural order and the web of life and how our theological understanding of science and technology impact the overall direction, strategy and advocacy of public policies and actions.

2.   Calls upon the church through the General Assembly Units, educational institutions and educational activities to develop resources and educational programs related to the above concerns by:

a.   Urging our theological seminaries to insure that students are thoroughly familiar with contemporary cosmologies that have emerged through the natural sciences and provide instruction to help students understand the significance of contemporary science and technology for systematic theology and Christian ethics.

b.   Encouraging our church-related colleges and ministries in higher education to consider ways to help students understand and relate the contemporary cosmologies to their religious perspectives and understandings.

c.   Requesting that the Educational and Congregational Nurture Unit include the above concerns in the churchwide strategy for church education and these concerns be addressed in curriculum and resources for all age groups.

d.   Urging that seminaries, church-related colleges, and ministries in higher education include these concerns in programs of continuing education for pastors and laity and develop specific courses that address science, technology and the Christian faith.

3.   Calls upon the church through the General Assembly Units and its governing bodies to give careful attention to ways of relating to and being involved with the scientific and technological community by:

a.   Encouraging congregations to identify scientists and persons working in various technological fields to help in educating the congregation about the above concerns and to assist persons to gain an understanding of the theological and ethical issues.

b. Encouraging the Theology and Worship Unit to discover effective means of building a liaison with the scientific community.

c. Calling on all governing bodies to help in identifying persons in the scientific community and encouraging them to contribute their knowledge and experience in the church.

d. Creating relationships with centers working on the concerns of theology and science, and working with other churches, ecumenical bodies, and international communities concerned with these issues."

Appendix II

Actions of the 200th General Assembly

The General Assembly of the Presbyterian Church, U.S.A., met in its 200th annual session in June 1988 at St. Louis, Missouri. Included among the items on its agenda were the report and resolution of its Advisory Council on Church and Society dealing with the work of the Task Force on Theology and Cosmology. (See Document 1.) In addition, there were overtures to the General Assembly from three Presbyteries calling upon the Presbyterian Church to initiate an ongoing effort to attend to developments in the science and technologies and to assess the significance of these developments for the thought and work of the Church: from the Presbyteries of Riverside, Genesee Valley and Pittsburgh. (See Documents 2, 3 and 4.) All of these items had been influenced by the Consultation on the Church and Contemporary Cosmology whose papers constitute this volume.

After due deliberation in sub-committees and standing committees, the General Assembly as a body acted to adopt the report and resolution of the Advisory Council on Church and Society and to approve the three overtures. This action was taken acknowledging that implementation would involve an estimated annual cost of $24,550 to cover meetings of an advisory committee, leadership for seminary based consultations, publications of occasional papers-sermons-prayers-liturgical materials, and consultations with seminary representatives.

Document 1

Report of the Advisory Council on Church and Society

Referral: A Study of the Role of Cosmology

... initiate a study of the role of cosmology in the Bible and the traditional doctrinal formulations of the church, the changes in cosmology as the result of the rise of science, and the theological significance of contemporary cosmological positions for the traditional doctrinal affirmations.
    ... Request the Advisory Council on Church and Society to develop a process for initiating such a study and for communicating its contents to the church ... [and] to communicate a report of the process that it develops to the

195th General Assembly (1983). (Minutes, UPCUSA, 1982, Part I, pp. 101, 487.)

Response:

The work of the Advisory Council on this referral has been reported annually to the General Assembly. The exploration has been conducted by a task group composed of: Kenneth McCall, chairperson, pastor, First Presbyterian Church, Bend, Oregon; Ian Barbour, dean, professor of Science, Technology and Society and professor of Religion, Carleton College, Northfield, Minnesota; Eric Jeungst, research associate, Division of Medical Ethics, University of California School of Medicine, San Francisco, California; James Miller, campus minister, United Campus Ministries of Pittsburgh, Pittsburgh, Pennsylvania; Harold Nebelsick, professor of Theology, Louisville Theological Seminary, Louisville, Kentucky; and Robert Russell, associate professor of Theology and Science, the Graduate Theological Union, Berkeley, California. Dan Little, pastor, First Presbyterian Church, Ithaca, New York, assisted the task group in developing a proposal for a network on theology and science concerns. Terry Bunde, member of the Advisory Council, and Dean Lewis, director of the Advisory Council served as liaison members.

The work of the task force has included: sponsorship of a session at the 1984 meeting of the American Association for the Advancement of Science, entitled "Science and Religion: Renewed Dialogue in a Post-Modern, Post-Critical Culture"; sponsorship of a 1985 Ghost ranch Seminar; sponsorship of a questionnaire to the Presbyterian Panel on "The Relationship of Religious Belief and Understandings of Science"; an initial attempt to identify lay persons and clergy in the Presbyterian Church (USA) working in science or particularly interested in relations between faith and science; and the planning of a major consultation on Christian faith and contemporary cosmology.

The work of the task group culminated in the Consultation on the Church and Contemporary Cosmology: Implications of Science for Christian Life and Thought, held at the Mercy Center, Burlingame, California, December 9-12, 1987.

Fourteen papers were prepared and presented along with extensive discussion in small groups. Over ninety lay persons and pastors from across the church, including many scientists, joined in the discussion of the papers and their implications.

The purpose of the consultation was defined in the following terms:

- To help initiate dialogue and discussion in the church concerning the significance of contemporary science for theological expression and moral life. In addition to surveying the history of the impact of cosmological ideas in the Christian heritage, the consultation will review major developments in the physical and biological sciences which are forming the contemporary and cosmological vision. The significance of this vision for Christian theology will be considered along with implications for ethics, social and economic policy, literature and the arts, personal faith, and education.

The preparation and convening of this consultation have helped to identify many scientists and theologians as well as lay persons, pastors and campus ministers who wish to continue and expand the discussion and exploration of issues concerning faith and contemporary science. Several participants agreed to found a Presbyterian Association on Religion and Science and seek recognition by the General Assembly under Chapter IX of the Book of Order. Plans have also been made to publish the papers from the consultation, and the resulting volume should be a significant resource for continuing study and exploration.

The Advisory Council on Church and Society has not attempted to formulate event tentative conclusions concerning "the theological significance of contemporary cosmological positions for traditional doctrinal affirmations." It is far too early in the season of required dialogue and discussion for that. Such reformulation is a necessary task for the church. The power and presence of the creating, redeeming God is as real in a cosmology or quasars and quarks as in a cosmology of a firmament gathered in the midst of the waters — and our theology, preaching and nurture must be a credible witness to that reality. The papers from the consultation promise a place to begin, and their publication will communicate the contents of the study to the church as requested by the 194th General Assembly (1982). Part Two of the report of the Advisory Council to the 200th General Assembly (1988) contains a general resolution intended to provide continuing impetus to the study and exploration.

****

Resolution on Cosmology and Christian Faith

The Advisory Council on Church and Society submits the following resolution on Cosmology and Christian Faith to the 200th General Assembly (1988) are recommends that the resolution be adopted.

Whereas the 194th general Assembly (1982) requested the Advisory Council on Church and Society to "initiate a study of the role of cosmology in the Bible and in the traditional doctrinal formulations of the church, the changes in cosmology as the result of the rise of science, and the theological significance of contemporary cosmological positions for traditional doctrinal affirmations"; and

Whereas the Advisory Council on Church and Society held a Consultation on the Church and Contemporary Cosmology: Implications of Science for Christian Life and Thought at the Mercy Center in Burlingame, California, on December 9-12, 1987, in which fourteen scientists and theologians presented papers whose findings and implications were discussed by more than ninety laypersons and clergy from across the church; and

Whereas the papers and findings of the consultation will be published and made available for study and discussion beyond the circle of participants in the consultation; and

Whereas, the preparation and convening of the consultation identified a number of scientists and theologians, as well as other lay persons and pastors, who wish to continue and expand discussion and exploration of the issues concerning faith and contemporary science, both within the Presbyterian Church (U.S.A.) and in ecumenical circles as well as in dialogue with societal groups and institutions; and

Whereas the continuing exploration and discoveries of science concerning the nature of life and the universe have great potential implications for the forms in which Christian express their faith in the creating, redeeming and sustaining God, and for human and societal understanding and structure in general; and

Whereas both the continuing search of science and the intentional exploration of its theological implications are hallmarks of Reformed Christian faith which values all human faculties as gifts of a providential God and seeks to bring their exercise to the service of God in the world:

Therefore, the 200th General Assembly (1988) of the Presbyterian Church (U.S.A.):

1. Commends the Advisory Council on Church and Society for convening the Consultation on the Church and Contemporary Cosmology and arranging for its findings to be published; and expresses appreciation to those who planned the consultation and prepared papers for it as well as all those who participated in it.

2.   Urges members of the Presbyterian Church (U.S.A.) to read the report and findings of the consultation; and particularly urges congregations and presbyteries to explore use of the book in educational events and continuing dialogues, drawing on the scientific and theological knowledge and experience of members and pastors of the church.

3.   Requests the Unit on Theology and Worship, which is charged to "encourage theological reflection on new developments in science and technology," in consultation with other appropriate units and governing bodies, to

a.   consider ways to continue and enlarge within the church the study and discussion of the implications of scientific knowledge and discoveries for the faith and witness of the church and for the life of the society.

b.   encourage greater attention to these issues and developments in the educational programs of the church and in the colleges and seminaries related to the church.

c.   foster and participate in discussions and dialogue between scientists and theologians, within the life of the Presbyterian Church (U.S.A.), in ecumenical circles, and in academic settings.

d.   seek to identify Presbyterian scientists and theologians in Presbyterian and other academic institutions to assist the church at all levels in educational programs and events.

e.   consider the establishment of an advisory group or task force with Presbyterian scientists and theologians interested in these matters in its membership, to assist the unit in the development and implementation of the activities noted above.

4.   Requests the Committee on Social Witness Policy, as it designs its agenda for future work, to consider giving attention to the impact of science and technology on our understanding of human beings as a part of the natural order, and how our theological understanding of science and technology impact the overall direction, strategy and advocacy of public policies and actions.

(Financial Implications: No implementing action is mandated for any agency of the General Assembly. The initiatives agencies are requested to consider are within areas of responsibility now assigned to them and for which budget exists. Possible use of those budgets for the purposes suggested here thus becomes a matter of the planning and priority processes already in existence.)

Document 2

Overture 35-88 from the Presbytery of Riverside

Whereas, the impact of discoveries in the natural sciences and of the technological developments stemming from these discoveries have had a profound effect on the economic, social, and life of modern society, and

Whereas, serious ethical and moral questions have been raised as a result of this impact; and

Whereas, the consultation organized by the Task Force on Theology and Cosmology (December 1987) produced A great sense of urgency to develop theological responses to such questions; and

Whereas, the majority of the population, including Christians (pastors and laity alike) are without sufficient understanding of our technological environment to be able to do much more than react to popular, equally uninformed, wisdom on such issues; it is urgent that steps be taken to continue the work begun by the Task Force on Theology and Cosmology, extended to include technology, and prepare the church to act rather than react to modern issues in this area; and

Whereas, the Structural Design for Mission assigned the responsibility to the Theology and Worship Ministry Unit to "encourage theological reflection on new developments in science and technology" (assigned Function No. 10); therefore, be it

Resolved, That the Presbytery of Riverside respectfully overtures the 200th General Assembly (1988) of the Presbyterian Church (U.S.A.)

A.   To direct the Theology and Worship Ministry Unit to establish a working group or task force to continue the work begun by the Task Force on Theology and Cosmology, extended to include technology, and to provide an adequate budget, staff time, and technical resource assistance necessary to implement this work, and to work in consultation with the Committee on Theological Education and the Education and Congregational Nurture Ministry Unit to facilitate the preparation of appropriate educational curricula for possible use in seminaries and appropriate educational materials for parish use; and

B.   To direct the Committee on Theological Education to work with our theological seminaries to insure that students are sufficiently familiar with the contemporary cosmological outlook and with the contemporary technological situation to prepare them for effective teaching and counseling congregations in our modern society.

Document 3

Overture 89-88 from the Presbytery of Genesee Valley

Whereas, the impact of discoveries in the natural sciences and of the technological developments stemming from these discoveries have had a profound effect on the economic, social, and life of modern society, and

Whereas, serious ethical and moral questions have been raised as a result of this impact; and

Whereas, theological reflection and understanding of such issues are essential to proper pastoral teaching and counseling; and

Whereas, it is often perceived that the majority of the population, including Christians (pastors and laity alike), are without sufficient understanding of our technological environment to be able to do much more than react to popular, equally uninformed, wisdom on such issues; and

Whereas, the Structural Design for Mission assigned the responsibility to the Theology and Worship Ministry Unit to "Encourage theological reflection on new developments in science and technology (Function 10)"; and

Whereas, the Theology and Worship Unit, in response, formed the Task Force on Theology and Cosmology which held a consultation in December 1987 as their final act; and

Whereas, this consultation generated a great sense of urgency that steps be taken to continue the work begun by the Task Force on Theology and Cosmology, extended to include technology, and prepare the church to act rather than react to modern ethical and moral issues; therefore, be it

Resolved, That the Presbytery of Genesee Valley respectfully overture the 200th General Assembly (1988) of the Presbyterian Church (U.S.A.)

A.   To direct the Theology and Worship Ministry Unit to establish a working group or task force to continue the work begun by the Task Force on Theology and Cosmology, extended to include technology, and to provide an adequate budget, staff time, and technical resource assistance necessary to implement this work, and to work in consultation with the Committee on Theological Education and the Education and Congregational Nurture Ministry Unit to facilitate the preparation of appropriate educational curricula for possible use in seminaries and appropriate educational materials for parish use; and

B. To direct the Committee on Theological Education to work with our theological seminaries to insure that students are sufficiently familiar with the contemporary cosmological outlook and with the contemporary technological situation to prepare them for effective teaching and counseling congregations in our modern society.

Document 4

Overture 142-88 from the Presbytery of Pittsburgh

Whereas, we proclaim that "the heavens declare the glory of God, and the earth shows forth God's handiwork"; and

Whereas, we are called to love God with the mind as well as the heart and body; and

Whereas, developments in the sciences and related technologies over the past 400 years have not only substantially reshaped the surface of the earth and human society but also profoundly influenced our understanding of the nature and place of human beings in the cosmos; and

Whereas, churches in the Reformed tradition, as confessional, are always conscious of the historical and cultural context within which they seek to proclaim and live out the gospel; and

Whereas, there is widespread innocence in the church among both clergy and laity concerning a scientific description of the world and technological possibilities which are immediately before humanity; and

whereas, participants in the Consultation on the Church and Contemporary Cosmology, called by the Task Force on Theology and Cosmology of the Advisory Council on Church and Society of the General Assembly, expressed a great sense of urgency for the church to give more deliberate, consistent, and coherent attention to the implications of scientific and technological development for the thought, life, and mission of the church; and therefore, be it

Resolved, That the Presbytery of Pittsburgh respectfully overture the 200th General Assembly (1988) of the Presbyterian Church (U.S.A.) to:

1. Direct the Theology and Worship Unit to establish a working group on science, technology, and the church to build upon the work begun by the Advisory Council on Church and Society through its Task Force on Theology and Cosmology and to that end provide adequate budget, staff time, and technical resources for the functioning of this working group;

2. Direct the Education and Congregational Nurture Unit in consultation with the Theology and Worship Unit to develop appropriate liturgical and educational materials for congregational use which celebrate the gospel of Christ who is also the Logos of the world and which explore the relationships between our knowledge about the history and structure of the universe and our understanding and expression of the Christian faith and between emerging technological possibilities and Christian moral commitments;

3. Direct the Committee on Theological Education to explore with our theological seminaries ways to insure that those preparing for careers of professional ministry are scientifically and technologically literate so that they can be adequately prepared for effective theological reflection, preaching, teaching, pastoral care, and leadership in our congregations in the contemporary global scientific and technological society.